# CONTEMPORARY

# READINGS

# IN

# LOGICAL

# THEORY

Irving M. Copi
*The University of Michigan*

James A. Gould
*The University of South Florida*

The Macmillan Company, New York
Collier-Macmillan Limited, London

Library of Congress catalog card number: 67–15535

THE MACMILLAN COMPANY, NEW YORK
COLLIER-MACMILLAN CANADA, LTD., TORONTO, ONTARIO

PRINTED IN THE UNITED STATES OF AMERICA

*This book is dedicated to*

MARGARET RUTH COPI
LESLIE WAREHAM GOULD
FRANCESCA JEAN GOULD
STEPHANIE SCENNA GOULD

# Preface

Textbooks of modern logic tend to devote most of their space to the development of logical techniques and the construction of systems of logic. Consequently, they can pay little attention to the history of their subject, to problems of logical theory, or to the newest directions logic is taking. But fruitful classroom discussion must deal with the theory or philosophy of logic rather than with its techniques—which, as techniques, are scarcely debatable. This book of readings is designed to serve as a supplementary textbook in a course in symbolic logic. Its intended function is to furnish the bases and stimulation for classroom discussion of logical issues.

Not every question of logical theory can be considered in a single volume. Our principle of selection was to include those topics that have aroused the greatest interest among modern logicians, provided that readable essays were available for their presentation. Each part contains essays by distinguished logicians. In some parts the various essays serve to supplement each other—the two historical essays in Part 1, the three essays on the purposes and limitations of formalization in Part 2, and the three essays on deontic logic in Part 8. In all the other parts the essays set forth alternative analyses or theories, often in vigorously polemical language. These essays should help to kindle the dialogue so essential to real learning.

The editors wish to thank many friends for helpful suggestions. They are particularly indebted to Professor Henry W. Johnstone, Jr., of The Pennsylvania State University and to Professor Ruth Barcan Marcus of the University of Illinois at Chicago Circle, who read an early version of the manuscript and made very useful comments. Warm thanks are also due to Mr. John D. Moore and Mr. Ronald C. Harris of The Macmillan Company for their wise counsel and expert professional advice. Finally, appreciation must be expressed to Amelia Copi and Margaret Ruth Copi for their help in the labor of reading proof.

I. M. C.
J. A. G.

# Contents

# *Part*
# 1 THE HISTORY OF LOGIC

## *Introduction*

Kant said that logic would have no history, but the advances in logical studies over the past one hundred and twenty years have proved him wrong. These began in the 1840's with the work of De Morgan and Boole. The latter, we are told by Lewis and Langford, "was really the second founder of symbolic logic" (the first having been Leibniz). Boole's algebra of logic "is the basis of the whole development since." The most significant advance in modern logic was made by Frege in 1879 with the publication of his *Begriffsschrift*, a rigorously formalized predicate calculus. Frege's use of quantifiers to bind variables is perhaps the most important single contribution to symbolic logic. The first selection does not sufficiently emphasize Frege's achievements.

Peano developed a much superior notation in his logico-mathematical studies. Whitehead and Russell combined Peano's improved notation with the deeper insights of Frege to produce the three volumes of their *Principia Mathematica*, which is the high point of the classical period of symbolic logic. After its publication logic's growth accelerated so rapidly and in so many different directions as to defy summary. Some of these new directions are reported in other parts of this anthology.

Logic is defined by Lewis and Langford as "the principles which govern the validity of inference." The Kneales write that logic "is best defined as the pure theory of involution . . . a relation that holds between two sets of propositions when it is impossible that all of the first should be true and all of the second false." It is

1

worth noting that these two definitions agree with each other and also with those offered by Boole and Frege. Gödel's theorem, the theory of logical types, and problems of identity, briefly touched on by the Kneales, are discussed at greater length in Parts 2, 4, and 7, respectively.

# THE DEVELOPMENT
# OF SYMBOLIC LOGIC*

CLARENCE IRVING LEWIS (1883–1964) made major contributions
to the development of logic, epistemology, and value theory.
His books include *Survey of Symbolic Logic*; *Symbolic Logic*
(with C. H. Langford); *Mind and the World Order*; and
*An Analysis of Knowledge and Valuation*.

COOPER HAROLD LANGFORD (1895–1965) made significant
contributions to logic and philosophical analysis in frequent
journal articles, reviews, and his book (with C. I. Lewis),
*Symbolic Logic*.

The study with which we are concerned in this book has not yet
acquired any single and well-understood name. It is called 'mathematical
logic' as often as 'symbolic logic,' and the designations 'exact logic,' 'formal
logic,' and 'logistic' are also used. None of these is completely satisfactory;
all of them attempt to convey a certain difference of this subject from the
logic which comes down to us from Aristotle and was given its traditional
form by the medieval scholastics. This difference, however, is not one of
intent: so far as it exists, it is accidental or is due to the relative incompleteness and inexactness of the Aristotelian logic. The use of symbols has
characterized logic from the beginning—for example, in the use of letters
to represent the terms of the syllogism. Symbolic logic merely extends this
use in ways which are required by, or conducive to, clarity and precision.
Thus the subject matter of symbolic logic is merely *logic*—the principles
which govern the validity of inference.

It is true, however, that the extended use of symbolic procedures opens
up so much which is both new and important that symbolic logic becomes
an immensely deeper and wider study than the logic of tradition. New
implications of accepted logical principles come to light; subtle ambiguities
and errors which have previously passed unnoticed are now detected and
removed; new generalizations can be made which would be impossible of
clear statement without a compact and precise symbolism: the subject of
logic becomes broader in its scope, and enters into new relationships with
other exact sciences, such as mathematics.

That such changes should come about as a result of a more auspicious
mode of representation, will not be surprising if we consider a little the

parallel case of mathematics. Arithmetic, at first, lacked any more appropriate medium than that of ordinary language. Ancient Greek mathematicians had no symbol for zero, and used letters of the alphabet for other numbers. As a result, it was impossible to state any general rule for division —to give only one example. Operations which any fourth-grade child can accomplish in the modern notation, taxed the finest mathematical minds of the Age of Pericles. Had it not been for the adoption of the new and more versatile ideographic symbols, many branches of mathematics could never have been developed, because no human mind could grasp the essence of their operations in terms of the phonograms of ordinary language.

Thus while the subject-matter which symbolic logic studies is merely that of logic in any form, it does not follow that there will be no important results of it which are not possible in the older terms. Quite the contrary. As a result of improved methods of notation, we find ourselves in a lively period of new discoveries: an old subject, which has been comparatively stagnant for centuries, has taken on new life. We stand to-day, with respect to logic, where the age of Leibnitz and Newton stood with respect to what can be accomplished in terms of number; or where Riemann and Lobatchevsky stood with respect to geometry. A wealth of new facts dawn upon us, the significance of which we are only beginning to explore. The manner in which the forms and principles characterizing inference admit of extension and generalization, and the connection between such general principles and the more special procedures of other exact sciences —these are matters concerning which the last four decades have produced more light than any preceding four centuries since Aristotle. It is probable that the near future will see further results of equal or greater importance.

As might be expected, it is difficult to mark any historical beginning of the distinctively symbolic method in logic. It is of the essence of the subject that its laws hold for all terms—or all propositions, or all syllogisms, or all conditional arguments, and so on. Thus it is natural that, in the expression of its laws, some indifferent terms or 'variables' should be used to designate those elements of any piece of reasoning which are irrelevant to the validity of it. Even the traditional logic, recognizing that only the *form* of the syllogism (its mood and figure) need be considered in determining its validity, most frequently used letters—A, B, C, or S, M, and P—for the terms of the propositions composing the syllogistic argument. Frequently, also, it was recognized that, in a hypothetical argument, validity did not depend upon the particularity or content of the statements connected by the 'if-then' relation. This recognition was exhibited by throwing the argument into such form as,

If A, then B.
But A is true.
Hence B is true.

Here symbols are used for propositions, which is a step beyond the use of them for substantive terms.

However, the advances which the symbolic procedure makes upon traditional methods hardly begin to appear until symbols are used not only for terms, or for propositions, but for the relations between them. Here and there, through the history of logic in the middle ages, one finds such symbols for the logical relations, used as a kind of shorthand. But it is not until the time of Leibnitz that this use of symbolism begins to be studied with a view to the correction and extension of traditional logic.

Leibnitz may be said to be the first serious student of symbolic logic, though he recognized the *Ars Magna* of Raymond Lull and certain other studies as preceding him in the field. Leibnitz projected an extended and Utopian scheme for the reform of all science by the use of two instruments, a universal scientific language (*characteristica universalis*) and a calculus of reasoning (*calculus ratiocinator*) for the manipulation of it. The universal language was to achieve two ends; first, by being common to all workers in the sciences, it was to break down the barriers of alien speech, achieving community of thought and accelerating the circulation of new scientific ideas. Second, and more important, it was to facilitate the process of logical analysis and synthesis by the substitution of compact and appropriate ideograms for the phonograms of ordinary language.

In part, this second point of Leibnitz's scheme was thoroughly sound: the superiority of ideograms to phonograms in mathematics is an example; and science since Leibnitz's time has made continuously increasing use of ideograms devised for its particular purposes. But in part his program was based upon more dubious conceptions. He believed that all scientific concepts were capable of analysis into a relatively few, so that with a small number of original or undefined ideas, all the concepts that figure in science could be defined. The manner of such definition would, then, exhibit the component simple ideas used in framing a complex notion, somewhat as the algebraic symbolization of a product may exhibit its factors, or the formula of a chemical substance will exhibit its component elements and their relation. Finally, he conceived that the reasoning of science could then be carried out simply by that analysis and synthesis of concepts to which such ideographic symbolisms would supply the clue.

To criticize and evaluate these conceptions of Leibnitz would be a complicated business which is impossible here. Briefly, we may note that the kind of development which he here envisages for science in general coincides to a remarkable extent with the logistic analysis now achieved in mathematics and beginning to be made in other exact sciences. On the other hand, the notion that such development is the major business of science reflects that exaggeration of the role of deduction, as against induction, which is characteristic of Leibnitz's rationalistic point of view. And the conception that the primitive or simple concepts which would be disclosed by a just analysis of scientific ideas are uniquely determinable is not supported by developments since his time. Instead, we find that a plurality of possible analyses, and of primitive concepts, is the rule.

Leibnitz himself is more important for his prophetic insight, and for his stimulation of interest in the possibilities of logistic, than for any positive contribution. Though the projects above referred to were formulated before he was twenty years old,[1] and though he made innumerable studies looking toward the furtherance of them, the results are, without exception, fragmentary. The reformation of all science was, as he well understood, an affair which no man could accomplish single-handed. Throughout his life he besought the coöperation of learned societies to this end, but of course without success.

The *calculus ratiocinator* was a more restricted project. If this had been accomplished, it would have coincided with what we now know as symbolic logic. That is, it would have been an organon of reasoning in general, developed in ideographic symbols and enabling the logical operations to be performed according to precise rules. Here Leibnitz achieved some degree of success; and it would be interesting to examine some of his results if space permitted. He did not, however, lay a foundation which could be later built upon, because he was never able to free himself from certain traditional prepossessions or to resolve the difficulties which arose from them.[2]

Other scholars on the Continent were stimulated by these studies of Leibnitz to attempt a calculus of logic. The best of such attempts are those of Lambert and Holland.[3] But all of them are inferior to Leibnitz's own work.

The foundations from which symbolic logic has had continuous development were laid in Great Britain between 1825 and 1850. The signally important contribution was that of the mathematician George Boole; but this was preceded by, and in part resulted from, a renewed interest in logic the main instigators of which were Sir William Hamilton and Augustus De Morgan. Hamilton's "quantification of the predicate" is familiar to most students of logic. "All A is B" may mean "All A is *all* B" or "All A is *some* B." The other traditional forms of propositions may be similarly dealt with so as to render the 'quantity' of the predicate term unambiguous. The idea is a simple one, and really of little importance for exact logic: no use has been made of it in recent studies. It was not even new: Leibnitz, Holland, and others had previously quantified the predicate. But often the

---

[1] They constitute the subject of his first published work, the intent of which is set forth on the title page as follows: "Dissertatio de Arte Combinatoria; In qua ex Arithmeticæ fundamentis Complicationum ac Transpositionum Doctrina novis præceptis exstruitur, & usus ambarum per universum scientiarum orbem ostenditur; nova etiam Artis Meditandi, seu Logicæ Inventionis femina sparguntur." This book was published in Leipzig, in 1656.

[2] For example, the conception that every universal proposition implies the corresponding particular; and the conception that the relations of terms in extension are always inversely parallel to their relations in intension.

[3] See Bibliography at the end of the chapter.

historical importance of an idea depends less upon its intrinsic merit than upon the stimulus exercised upon other minds; and this is a case in point. The sole significance of quantification of the predicate for exact logic is that it suggests a manner in which propositions can be treated as equations of terms; and the mere representation of propositions as equations keeps the thought of an analogy between logic and mathematics before the mind. This single fact, together with Hamilton's confident assumption that now at last logic was entering upon a new period of development, seems to have been a considerable factor in the renewal of logical studies in Great Britain.

Augustus De Morgan brought to the subject of logic a more versatile mind than Hamilton's, and one trained in mathematics. He, too, quantified the predicate, and he gives an elaborate table of the thirty-two different forms of propositions which then arise, with rules of transformation and statement of equivalents. His contributions are, in fact, literally too numerous to mention: one can only select the most important for brief notice. One of the most prophetic is his observation that the traditional restriction to propositions in which the terms are related by some form of the verb 'to be,' is artificial and is not dictated by any logical consideration. He wrote, "The copula performs certain functions; it is competent to those functions . . . because it has certain properties which validate its use. Every transitive and convertible relation is as fit to validate the syllogism as the copula '*is*,' and by the same proof in every case. Some forms are valid when the relation is only transitive and not convertible; as in 'give.' Thus if X — Y represent X and Y connected by a transitive copula, *Camestres* in the second figure is valid, as in

'Every Z — Y, No X — Y, therefore No X — Z.' " [4]

He also investigated many other non-traditional modes of inference, suggested new classifications, and indicated novel principles which govern these. In so doing, he provided the first clear demonstration that logical validity is not confined to the traditional modes and traditional principles.

De Morgan also made numerous and extended studies of the hitherto neglected logic of relations and relative terms. These investigations dropped from sight in the next twenty-five years—that is until they were renewed by Charles S. Peirce. But as we now know, this study of relations in general is that extension of logic which is most important for the analysis of mathematics. De Morgan was first in this field, and he correctly judged the significance of it. In the concluding paper of one series of studies, he remarks:

"And here the general idea of relation emerges, and for the first time in the history of knowledge, the notion of relation and *relation* of *relation*

[4] *Transactions of the Cambridge Philosophical Society*, X, 177.

are symbolized. And here again is seen the scale of graduation of forms, the manner in which what is difference of form at one step of the ascent is difference of *matter* at the next. But the relation of algebra to the higher developments of logic is a subject of far too great extent to be treated here. It will hereafter be acknowledged that, though the geometer did not think it necessary to throw his ever-recurring *principium et exemplum* into imitation of *Omnis homo est animal, Sortes est homo*, etc., yet the algebraist was living in the higher atmosphere of syllogism, the unceasing composition of relation, before it was admitted that such an atmosphere existed." [5]

To-day we can observe how accurately this trenchant prophecy has been fulfilled.

George Boole was really the second founder of symbolic logic. His algebra, first presented in 1847, is the basis of the whole development since. Intrinsically it may be of no greater importance than the work of De Morgan; and Leibnitz's studies exhibit at least an equal grasp of the logical problems to be met. But it is here for the first time that a complete and workable calculus is achieved, and that operations of the mathematical type are systematically and successfully applied to logic.

Three fundamental ideas govern the structure of Boole's system: (1) the conception of the operation of "election" and of "elective symbols"; (2) the "laws of thought" expressible as rules of operation upon these symbols; and (3) the observation that these rules of operation are the same which would hold in an algebra of the numbers 0 and 1.

The elective symbol $x$ represents the result of electing all the $x$'s in the universe: that is, $x$, $y$, $z$, etc., are symbols for classes, conceived as resulting from an operation of selection.

This operation of electing can be treated as analogous to algebraic multiplication. If we first select (from the world of existing things) the $x$'s, and then from the result of that select the $y$'s, the result of these two operations in succession, represented by $x \times y$, or $x\,y$, will be the class of things which are both $x$'s and $y$'s.

It is obvious that the order of operations of election does not affect the result: whether we first select the $x$'s and then from the result of that select the $y$'s; or first select the $y$'s and from the result of that select the $x$'s; in either case we have the class 'both $x$ and $y$.' That is, 'both $x$ and $y$' is the same as 'both $y$ and $x$':

$$x\,y = y\,x.$$

The law that if $x = y$, then $z\,x = z\,y$, will also hold: if $x$ and $y$ are identical classes, or consist of the same members, then 'both $z$ and $x$' will be the same class as 'both $z$ and $y$.'

Repetition of the same operation of election does not alter the result:

[5] *Loc. cit.*, p. 358.

selecting the $x$'s and then from the result of that selecting again all the $x$'s merely gives the class of $x$'s. Thus

$$x\,x = x, \quad \text{or} \quad x^2 = x.$$

This is the one fundamental law peculiar to this algebra, which distinguishes it from the usual numerical algebra.

Boole uses the symbol $+$ as the sign of the operation of aggregation, expressible in language by "Either . . . or . . . ." The class of things which are either $x$'s or $y$'s (but not both) is represented by $x + y$. This operation is commutative:

$$x + y = y + x.$$

The class of things which are either $x$ or $y$ coincides with the class which are either $y$ or $x$.

The operation of election, or 'multiplication,' is associative with respect to aggregation, or 'addition':

$$z(x + y) = z\,x + z\,y.$$

That is, if we select from the class $z$ those things which are either $x$ or $y$, the result is the same as if we select what is 'either both $z$ and $x$ or both $z$ and $y$.'

The operation of 'exception' is represented by the sign of subtraction: if $x$ is 'men' and $y$ is 'Asiatics,' $x - y$ will be 'all men except Asiatics' or 'all men not Asiatics.'

Multiplication is associative with respect to subtraction: that is,

$$z(x - y) = z\,x - z\,y.$$

'White (men not Asiatics)' are the class 'white men except white Asiatics.'

Boole accepts the general algebraic principle that

$$- y + x = x - y,$$

regarding it as a convention that these two are to be equivalent in meaning.

The number 1 is taken to represent 'the universe' or 'everything,' and 0 to represent 'nothing,' or the class which has no members. These interpretations accord with the behavior of 0 and 1 in the algebra:

$$1 \cdot x = x.$$

Selecting the $x$'s from the universe gives the class $x$.

$$0 \cdot x = 0.$$

Selecting the $x$'s from the class 'nothing' gives 'nothing.'

The negative of any class $x$ is expressible as $1 - x$; the 'not-$x$'s' are 'everything except the $x$'s.' Thus what is '$x$ but not $y$' is $x(1-y)$. And the law holds that

$$x(1-y) = x \cdot 1 - xy = x - xy.$$

What is '$x$ but not $y$' coincides with the class '$x$ excepting what is both $x$ and $y$.'

The aggregate or sum of any class and its negative is 'everything':

$$x + (1-x) = x + 1 - x = 1.$$

Everything is either $x$ or not-$x$. The product of a class and its negative is 'nothing':

$$x(1-x) = x - x^2 = x - x = 0$$

Nothing is both $x$ and not-$x$. This equation holds because of the previous law, $x^2 = x$.

An important consequence of the law, $x + (1-x) = 1$, is that, for any class $z$,

$$z = z \cdot 1 = z[x + (1-x)] = zx + z(1-x).$$

That is, the class $z$ coincides with 'either both $z$ and $x$ or both $z$ and not-$x$.' This law allows any class symbol $x$ to be introduced into any expression which does not originally contain it—a procedure of great importance in manipulating this algebra, and one which accords with a fundamental logical fact.

It will be evident from the foregoing that at least a considerable number of the operations of ordinary algebra will be valid in this system. The results will be logically interpretable and logically valid. Leibnitz and his Continental successors had all of them tried to make use of the mathematical operations of addition and subtraction; and most of them had tried to use multiplication and division. Always they ran into insuperable difficulties—though they did not always recognize that fact. Boole's better success rests upon four features of his procedure: (1) he thinks of logical relations in extension exclusively, paying no regard to relations of intension; (2) he restricts 'sums,' $x + y$, to the adjunction of classes *having no members in common*; (3) in the law $xx = x$, he finds, at one and the same time, the distinctive principle of his algebra and the representation of a fundamental law of logic; (4) in hitting on the analogy of 1 to 'everything' and 0 to 'nothing,' he is able to express such basic logical principles as the laws of Contradiction and of the Excluded Middle Term in terms of the algebra.

The second of these features was later eliminated from his system—to its advantage—but for the time being it contributed to his success by avoiding certain difficulties which otherwise arise with respect to addition. These difficulties had been the principal reason for the failure of previous attempts at a mathematical calculus of logic. In good part, Boole's better success is due to superior ingenuity rather than greater logical acumen. This ingenuity is particularly evident in his meeting of certain difficulties which have, perhaps, already occurred to the reader:

(1)   What will be the meaning of an expression such as $1 + x$? Recognizing that terms of a sum must represent classes having no members in common, and that no class $x$ can be related in that manner to the class 'everything' except the class $0$, we might say that $1 + x$ has no meaning unless $x = 0$. But in the manipulation of equations, expressions of this form can occur where $x = 0$ is false.

(2)   What about $x + x$? Since the terms of this sum violate the requirement that they have no common members, such an expression will not be logically interpretable. But expressions of this form are bound to occur in the algebra. How are they to be dealt with?

(3)   If the operations of ordinary algebra are to be used, then division will appear, as the inverse of multiplication. But if $xy = z$, and hence $x = z/y$, can the 'fraction' $z/y$ be interpreted; and is the operation logically valid?

Boole surmounts these difficulties, and many others which are similar, by clever devices which depend upon recognizing that his system is completely interpretable as an algebra in which the "elective symbols" are restricted to the numbers 0 and 1. The distinctive law of the system is $xx = x$. This holds of 0 and 1, and of no other numbers. Suppose, then, we forget about the logical interpretation of the system, and treat it simply as a numerical algebra in which the variables, or literal symbols, are restricted to 0 or 1. All the ordinary laws and operations of algebra may then be allowed. As Boole says,

> "But as the formal processes of reasoning depend only upon the laws of the symbols, and not upon the nature of their interpretation, we are permitted to treat the above symbols, $x$, $y$, $z$, as if they were quantitative symbols of the kind described. We may in fact lay aside the logical interpretation of the symbols in the given equation; convert them into quantitative symbols, susceptible only of the values 0 and 1; perform upon them as such all the requisite processes of solution; and finally restore them to their logical interpretation. . . .
>
> "Now the above system of processes would conduct us to no intelligible result, unless the final equations resulting therefrom were in a form which should render their interpretation, after restoring to the symbols their logical significance, possible. There exists, however, a general method of reducing equations to such a form." [6]

With the devices which make up this general method we need not trouble ourselves. It is, as a matter of fact, always possible to secure a finally interpretable result, even though the intermediate stages of manip-

[6] *Laws of Thought*, pp. 69–70.

ulation involve expressions which are not interpretable; and such results are always in accord with the logical significance of the original data, representing a valid inference. It is not, of course, satisfactory that a logical calculus should involve expressions and operations which are not logically interpretable; and all such features of Boole's Algebra were eventually eliminated by his successors. But even in its original form, it is an entirely workable calculus.

The main steps of the transition from Boole's own system to the current form of Boolean Algebra may be briefly summarized.

W. S. Jevons did not make use of the algebraic methods, but formulated a procedure for solving logical problems by manipulations of the "logical alphabet," which represents what we shall later come to know as 'the expansion of 1'; that is, all possible combinations of the terms involved in any problem. Since this method of Jevons's, though entirely workable and valid, is less simple than the algebraic, and is no longer in use, our chief interest is in two differences of Jevons from Boole which were adopted later as modifications of Boole's algebra.

Jevons interprets $a + b$ to mean 'either $a$ or $b$ or both.' Logically it is merely a matter of convention whether we choose to symbolize by $a + b$ Boole's meaning of 'either-or' as mutually exclusive, or this non-exclusive meaning of Jevons. But adoption of the wider, non-exclusive meaning has three important consequences which are advantageous: it removes any difficulty about expressions of the form $a + a$; it leads to the law $a + a = a$, and it introduces the possibility of a very interesting symmetry between the relation of logical product, $a\,b$, and the logical sum, $a + b$. As we have seen, Boole's interpretation of the relation $+$ has the consequence that $a + a$ is logically uninterpretable.. When such expressions occur in his system, they are treated by ordinary algebraic laws, which means that $a + a = 2a$; and such numerical coefficients must be got rid of by devices. If the other meaning be chosen, $a + a$ has meaning, and $a + a = a$ states an obvious principle. With this principle in the system, numerical coefficients do not occur. Thus the two laws, $a\,a = a$ and $a + a = a$, together result in the elimination of all notion of number or quantity from the algebra. Also, when $a + b$ means 'either $a$ or $b$ or both,' the negative of $a\,b$, 'both $a$ and $b$,' is 'either not-$a$ or not-$b$,' $(1 - a) + (1 - b)$, or as it would be written in the current notation, $-a + -b$. This law had already been stated by De Morgan, and, as we shall see, is a very important principle of the revised Boolean algebra.

John Venn and Charles S. Peirce both followed the practice of Jevons in this matter; and no important contributor since that time has returned to Boole's narrower meaning of $a + b$, or failed to recognize the law $a + a = a$.

Also, Boole's system was modified by eliminating the operations of subtraction and division. Peirce included these in certain of his early papers, but distinguished a relation of "logical subtraction" and "logical division" from "arithmetical subtraction" and "arithmetical division" (within a Boolean system). Later he discarded these operations altogether, and they have not been made use of since. As Peirce points out, $a/b$ is uninterpretable unless the class $b$ is contained in the class $a$. Even when this is the case, $a/b$ is an ambiguous function of $a$ and $b$, which can have any value between the 'limits' $a\,b$ and $a + (1 - b)$, or $a + -b$. When $a + b$ is given the wider meaning 'either $a$ or $b$ or both,' $a - b$, defined as the value of $x$ such that $a = b + x$, is also an ambiguous function. Nothing is lost in the discarding of these two operations: anything expressible by means of them can likewise be expressed—and better expressed—in terms of the relations of logical product and logical sum alone. The only remaining use of either is in the function 'negative of.' The negative of $a$, which Boole expressed by $1 - a$, is now written $-a$; and it does not behave, in the algebra, like a minus quantity.

Peirce added a new relation, the inclusion of one class in another; "All $a$ is $b$," now symbolized by $a \subset b$. This is not a mathematical alteration of the algebra, since the same relation is expressible in Boole's terms as $a(1 - b) = 0$. But it is an obvious advantage that this simplest and most frequent of logical relations should be simply represented.

These changes, then, mark the development from Boole's own system to the algebra of logic as we now know it: (1) substitution of the meaning 'either $a$ or $b$ or both' for 'either $a$ or $b$ but not both' as the relation symbolized by $a + b$; (2) addition of the law, $a + a = a$, eliminating numerical coefficients; (3) as a result of the two preceding, the systematic connection of sums and products, according to De Morgan's Theorem; (4) elimination of the operations of subtraction and division; (5) addition of Peirce's relation, $a \subset b$. The changes (1), (2), and (4) together result in the disappearance from the algebra of all expressions and operations which are not logically interpretable. Other and less fundamental changes, consisting mostly of further developments which do not affect the mathematical character of the system, had also been introduced, principally by Peirce and Schröder. . . .

The next stage in the development of the subject is the bringing together of symbolic logic and the methodology of rigorous deduction, as exhibited in pure mathematics. This turns principally upon development of the logic of propositions and propositional functions, and the logic of relations. Two lines of research, more or less independent, lead up to this. Starting from beginnings made by Boole himself, Peirce and Schröder developed the logic of propositions, propositional functions, and relations, up to the point where these approximate to a calculus which is adequate to the actual deductive procedures exemplified by mathematics. Peano and his collaborators, in the *Formulaire de mathématiques*, began at the other end. They took mathematics in its ordinary deductive form and rigorously analyzed the processes of proof which they found in such deductions. By symbolizing the logical relations upon which proof depends, they gave mathematics the 'logistic' form, in which the principles of logic actually become the vehicles of the demonstration. These general logical principles, set forth in the earlier sections of the *Formulaire*, coincide, to a degree, with the logical formulæ resulting from the work of Peirce and Schröder; but it was found necessary to make certain important additions. (Frege also had developed arithmetic in the logistic form, at an earlier date, and had made most penetrating analyses of the logic of mathematics. But Frege's work passed unnoticed until 1901, when attention was called to it by Mr. Bertrand Russell.)

Boole had indicated a second interpretation of his algebra. In this second interpretation, any term *a* is taken to represent the times when (or cases in which) the proposition *a* is true. The negative $1 - a$ or $-a$, will then represent the times, or cases, when the proposition *a* is false; $a \times b$, or *a b*, will represent the cases in which *a* and *b* are both true; and $a + b$, the cases in which one of the two, *a* and *b*, is true. The entire algebra will then hold for the logical relations of propositions. This will be true whether we take the system in its original form, or as modified by Schröder; with the sole fundamental difference that, in the former case, $a + b$ must be interpreted as the times when *a* or *b* *but not* both are true, whereas in the latter case it represents the times when *a* or *b* *or* both are true.

However, we should recognize to-day that a statement which is sometimes true and sometimes false is not a proposition but a 'propositional function.' Thus the interpretation of the algebra made by Boole is in reality for propositional functions rather than propositions; or more accurately, Boole makes both applications, not distinguishing them, but providing a discussion which strictly applies only to functions. Peirce and Schröder distinguished these two. The entire algebra applies to *both*. But it is a distinguishing feature of a proposition, as against a propositional function, that if it is ever true, it is always true, and if it is ever false, then it is always false. In other words, a proposition is either definitely true or definitely false; while a propositional function may be sometimes true and sometimes false. Since in the algebra, $a = 1$ will mean "The class of cases in which *a* is true is *all* cases" and $a = 0$ will mean "*a* is true in *no* case," $a = 1$ represents "*a* is true," and $a = 0$ represents "*a* is false." Thus when the distinction is made between propositions and propositional functions, the whole of the algebra holds of both, but there is an *additional* law holding of propositions, but not of propositional functions: "If $a \neq 0$, then $a = 1$."

Peirce and Schröder made the distinction in question. They developed the calculus of propositions, incorporating this additional principle. And they developed the calculus of propositional functions, incorporating the ideas "*a* is sometimes true," "*a* is always true," "*a* is sometimes false," and "*a* is always false." The result of symbolizing these conceptions, and developing the laws which hold of them, is a considerable expansion of the calculus of propositional functions beyond what can be symbolized in terms of the Boolean algebra. . . . Though the calculuses . . . given [later in *Symbolic Logic*] are not precisely those of Peirce and Schröder, and though the method is not quite the same, these differences are not fundamental. We shall, therefore, omit further discussion of the subject here. What is important for understanding the development of symbolic logic is to remember that substantially such calculuses as are given [later] were at hand in the period when Peano and his collaborators began their work.

The aim of the *Formulaire de mathématiques* is stated in the opening sentence of the Preface: "Le Formulaire de Mathématiques a pour but de publier les propositions connues sur plusiers sujets des sciences mathématiques. Ces propositions sont exprimées en formules par les notations de la Logique mathématique, expliquées dans l'Introduction au Formulaire."

The authors had before them, on the one hand, mathematics in the ordinary but non-logistic deductive form. It was by this time (1895) generally recognized as the ideal of mathematical form that each branch of the subject should be derived from a small number of assumptions, by a rigorous deduction. It was also recognized that pure mathematics is abstract; that is, that its development is independent of the nature of any concrete empirical things to which it may apply. If, for example, Euclidean geometry is true of our space, and Riemannian geometry is false of space, this fact of material truth or falsity is irrelevant to the mathematical development of Euclid's system or of Riemann's. As it became customary to say, the only truth with which pure mathematics is concerned is the truth that certain postulates imply certain theorems. The emphasis which this conception throws upon the *logic* of mathematics, is obvious: the logic of it is the *truth* of it; no other kind of truth is claimed for pure mathematics.

On the other hand, Peano and his collaborators had before them the developed logic of Peirce and Schröder, which had now become a sufficiently flexible and extended system to be capable (almost) of representing all those relations which hold amongst the assumed entities of mathematical systems, by virtue of which postulates deductively give rise to theorems. It becomes, therefore, an obvious step to use the notations of symbolic logic for representing those relations, and those steps of reasoning, which, in the usual deductive but non-logistic form, are expressed in ordinary language.

Let us take a sample of mathematics as exhibited in the *Formulaire*.[7] For the development of arithmetic, the following undefined ideas are assumed:

"No signifies 'number,' and is the common name of 0, 1, 2, etc.

"0 signifies 'zero.'

[7] See V, 27–32. The successive volumes of this work do not represent a continuous development but are, to an extent, different redactions or editions.

"+ signifies 'plus.' If $a$ is a number, $a+$ signifies 'the number succeeding $a$.' "

In terms of these ideas, the following postulates are assumed:

"1·0   No $\epsilon$ Cls
"1·1   0 $\epsilon$ No
"1·2   $a \epsilon$ No. $\supset$ . $a+ \epsilon$ No
"1·3   $s \epsilon$ Cls. $0 \epsilon s$ . $a \epsilon s$ . $\supset_a a + \epsilon s : \supset$ . No $\epsilon s$
"1·4   $a, b \epsilon$ No . $a+ = b+ : \supset$ . $a = b$
"1·5   $a \epsilon$ No . $\supset$ . $a+ - = 0$"

Let us translate these into English, thus giving the meaning of the symbolism:

1·0   No is a class, or 'number' is a common name.

1·1   0 is a number.

1·2   If $a$ is a number, then the successor of $a$ is a number; that is, every number has a next successor.

1·3   If $s$ is a class, and 0 is a member of $s$; and if, for all values of $a$, "$a$ is an $s$" implies "The successor of $a$ is an $s$," then 'number' belongs to the class $s$. In other words, every class $s$ which is such that 0 belongs to it, and that if $a$ belongs to it, the successor of $a$ belongs to it, is such that every number belongs to it.

1·4   If $a$ and $b$ are numbers, and the successor of $a$ is identical with the successor of $b$, then $a$ is identical with $b$. That is, no two distinct numbers have the same successor.

1·5   If $a$ is a number, then the successor of $a$ is not identical with 0.

The ideas of 'zero,' 0, and 'successor of $a$,' $a+$, being assumed, the other numbers are defined in the obvious way: $1 = 0+$, $2 = 1+$, etc.

Further ideas which are necessary to arithmetic are defined as they are introduced. Sometimes such definitions take a form in which they are distinguished from postulates only by convention. For example, the sum of two numbers, represented by the relation $+$ (which must be distinguished from the idea "successor of $a$," $a+$) is defined by the two assumptions:

$$a \epsilon \text{No.} \supset . a + 0 = a$$
$$a, b \epsilon \text{No} . \supset . a + (b+) = (a+b)+$$

These are read: (1) If $a$ is a number, then $a + 0 = a$. (2) If $a$ and $b$ are numbers, then $a$ plus the successor of $b$, is the successor of $(a$ plus $b)$.

The product of two numbers is defined by:

$$a, b \epsilon \text{No} . \supset . a \times 0 = 0$$
$$a \times (b+1) = (a \times b) + a$$

It will be fairly obvious how, from these assumptions, the laws governing the sums and products of numbers in general may be deduced.

With the detail of this first development of mathematics in the logistic form we cannot deal here. But several important facts which stand out may be noted. First, in translating the logical relations and operations actually exhibited in mathematical deductions from ordinary language to precise symbols, the authors of the *Formulaire* were obliged to note logical relations and to make distinctions which had previously passed unnoticed. One example of this occurs in the above: they had to distinguish the relation of a member of a class to the class itself (symbolized by $\epsilon$) from the relation of a subclass to the class including it—the relation of $a$ to $b$ when all $a$ is $b$. Another example is the fact that they had very frequently to make use of the idea of a singular subject, '*the* so-and-so,' distinguishing statements about such a subject from those about '*some* so-and-so' or about '*every* so-and-so.' The greater precision of the logistic method revealed the necessity for such distinctions, and for such additions to logical principles, through the fact that, in the absence of them, fallacious mathematical consequences would follow from perfectly good assumptions, or valid mathematical consequences, which should be capable of being proved, could not actually be deduced. Thus, starting with the aim to take mathematics as already developed, and to express the logical relations and operations of proof in an exact and terse symbolism, the authors found that they must first expand logic beyond any previously developed form. The head and front of mathematical logic is found in the calculus of propositional functions, as developed by Peirce and Schröder; but even this logic is not completely adequate to the task in hand.

A second result which stands out in the *Formulaire* is one which was already implicit in the recognition of pure mathematics as abstract and independent of any concrete subject-matter to which it may apply. One of two things must be true of mathematics: either (1) it will be impossible to express the logic of it completely in terms of principles which are universally true—laws of logic which are true of every subject-matter, and not simply of deductions in geometry or in arithmetic—or (2) mathematics must consist of purely analytic statements. If the essential truth asserted by mathematics is that certain assumptions imply certain theorems, and if every such implication in mathematics is an instance of some universally valid principle of deduction (principle of logic), then there can be no step in a proof in mathematics which depends, for example, upon the particular character of our space, or the empirical properties of countable collections. That is to say, Kant's famous dictum that mathematical judgments are *synthetic a priori* truths, must be false. Such mathematical truths will be *a priori*, since they can be certified by logic alone. But they will be *a priori* precisely because they are *not synthetic*, but are merely instances of general logical principles.

As has been said, this is implicit in the previously recognized ideal of mathematics as at once deductive and abstract; for example, in the recognition that non-Euclidean geometry has the same mathematical validity as

Euclid. The importance of the logistic development, in this connection, is that the possibility of achieving the logistic form depends upon the elimination from mathematics of any deductive step which is not simply an instance of some universal logical principle; and that symbolic representation is a very reliable check upon this purely analytic character of the demonstration. Thus the actual achievement of the logistic form is a concrete demonstration that it *is a priori* and that it is *not*, in any least detail, *synthetic*. Since this result is of immense importance for our understanding of mathematics, it constitutes one significant consequence of modern logistic.

This bearing of their work is one with which the authors of the *Formulaire* are not explicitly concerned. It had, however, been noted by Frege as a central point of his logistic development of arithmetic, and it was again recognized by the authors of *Principia Mathematica* as an essential bearing of their work.

The *Principia* may, in good part, be taken as identical in its aim with the *Formulaire*. So far as this is the case, the difference between the two works is much as might be expected between a first attempt at the realization of certain aims and a later work having the advantage of the earlier results. Peano had taken mathematics as he found it and translated it completely into precise symbols, and in so doing achieved a degree of explicit analysis and explicit formulation of principles which was not attained in the non-logistic form. The *Principia* goes further in the same direction: the analysis of mathematics is here more extended and more meticulous; the logical connections are more firmly made; the demonstrations achieve rigor in a higher degree.

However, there is also a shift of emphasis. The purpose is no longer that of a compendious presentation of mathematics in the neatest form; it is, rather, the demonstration of the nature of mathematics and its relation to logic. On this point, moreover, the authors of the *Principia* found it possible to go far beyond Peano in the derivation of mathematical truth from logical truth. In the *Formulaire*, as we have seen, the development of arithmetic requires, in addition to the general principles of logic, (1) the undefined ideas, 'number,' 'zero,' and 'the successor of (any given number)'; (2) five postulates in terms of these; (3) definitions of arithmetical relations or operations, such as $+$ and $\times$, in a fashion which is hardly distinguishable from additional postulates. By contrast, in the *Principia*, the development of arithmetic is achieved in a fashion such that: (1) *All* ideas of arithmetic are defined; the only undefined ideas in the whole work being those of logic itself. 'Number,' 'zero,' 'the successor of,' the relations $+$ and $\times$, and all other ideas of arithmetic are defined in terms of the *logical* ideas assumed, such as 'proposition,' 'negation,' and 'either-or.' This achievement is so extraordinary that one hardly credits it without examining the actual development in the *Principia* itself. (2) *Postulates of arithmetic are eliminated*. There are some exceptions to this, but exceptions which affect only a certain class of theorems concerning transfinite numbers. These exceptions are made explicit by stating the assumption made (there are two such) as an hypothesis to the theorem in question. With these somewhat esoteric exceptions, the propositions of mathematics are proved to be merely *logical consequences of the truths of logic itself.* When mathematical ideas have been defined—defined in terms of logical ideas—the postulates previously thought necessary for mathematics, such as Peano's postulates for arithmetic, which we have given, can all be deduced.[8]

Logic itself, in a form sufficient for all further demonstrations, is developed in the early sections. And it is developed in the same deductive fashion, from a small number of undefined ideas and a few postulates in terms of these. Thus it is proved that these primitive ideas and postulates for logic are the only assumptions required for the whole of mathematics.[9]

It is difficult or impossible to convey briefly the significance of this achievement. It will be increasingly appreciated, as time goes on, that the publication of *Principia Mathematica* is a landmark in the history of mathematics and of philosophy, if not of human thought in general. Speculation and plausible theories of the nature and basis of mathematical knowledge have been put forward time out of mind, and have been confronted by opposed conceptions, equally plausible. Here, in a manner peculiarly final, the nature and basis of mathematical truth is definitely determined, and demonstrated *in extenso.* It follows logically from the truths of logic alone, and has whatever characters belong to logic itself.

Although contributions to logic and to mathematics in the logistic form have been more numerous in the period since *Principia Mathematica* than in any other equal period of time, it is hardly possible as yet to have perspective upon these. Three outstanding items may be mentioned. First, by the work of Sheffer and Nicod, considerably greater economy of assumption for any such development as that of the *Principia* has been achieved: two undefined ideas and five symbolic postulates of logic (as in the first edition of the *Principia*) have been replaced by one undefined idea and a single postulate. Second, the nature of logical truth itself has become more definitely understood, largely through the discussions of Wittgenstein. It is 'tautological'—such that any law of logic is equivalent to some statement which exhausts the possibilities; whatever is affirmed in logic is a truth to which no alternative is conceivable. From the relation of mathematics to logic, it follows that mathematical truth is similarly tautological.[10] Third,

---

[8] The steps by which all Peano's five postulates are rendered unnecessary is clearly and interestingly explained in the first three chapters of Russell's *Introduction to Mathematical Philosophy.* This book is written without symbols, and is intelligible to any reader having an elementary knowledge of mathematics.

[9] Various fundamental ideas of geometry are developed in the later portion of Volume III of the *Principia*; but Volume IV, intended to complete that subject, has not appeared.

[10] With the further detail of Wittgenstein's conceptions the present authors would not completely agree.

we are just beginning to see that logical truth has a variety and a multiform character hardly to be suspected from the restricted conceptions in terms of which, up till now, it has always been discussed. The work of Lukasiewicz, Tarski, and their school demonstrates that an unlimited variety of systems share that same tautological and undeniable character which we recognize in the logic of our familiar deductions. The logic which we readily recognize as such has been restricted to those forms which we have found useful in application—somewhat as geometry was restricted up to the time of Riemann and Lobatchevsky. The field of logical truth, we begin to understand, is as much wider than its previously recognized forms as modern geometry is wider than the system of Euclid. . . .

The relation of logic to other sciences than mathematics is an obvious subject for future investigation. The extent to which, and the sense in which, other sciences are, or may be, deductive, is a complex question. That as they become exact, they may also achieve deductive form, is rendered plausible by recent developments in physics, and by the studies of Carnap. Whether if they can thus become deductive, their basic ideas and principles can be analytically derived from logic, like those of mathematics, is a further and even more doubtful question. But we may be sure that the not too distant future will see developments bearing upon these questions.

## Bibliography

LEIBNITZ, G. W., *Philosophische Schriften* (hrsg. v. C. I. Gerhardt, Berlin, 1887), Bd. VII; see esp. fragments XX and XXI.

COUTURAT, L., *La logique de Leibniz, d'après des documents inédits* (Paris, 1901).

LAMBERT, J. H., *Deutscher Gelehrter Briefwechsel*, 4 vols. (hrsg. v. Bernouilli, Berlin, 1781–1784).

——, *Logische und philosophische Abhandlungen*, 2 vols. (hrsg. v. Bernouilli, Berlin, 1872–1887).

HAMILTON, SIR W., *Lectures on Logic* (Edinburgh, 1860).

DE MORGAN, A., *Formal Logic; or, the Calculus of Inference, Necessary and Probable* (London, 1847).

——, "On the Syllogism," etc., five papers, *Transactions of the Cambridge Philosophical Society*, Vols. VIII, IX, X (1846–1863).

——, *Syllabus of a Proposed System of Logic* (London, 1860).

BOOLE, G., *The Mathematical Analysis of Logic* (Cambridge, 1847).

——, *An Investigation of the Laws of Thought* (London, 1854; reprinted, Chicago, 1916).

JEVONS, W. S., *Pure Logic, or the Logic of Quality Apart from Quantity* (London, 1864).

VENN, J., "Boole's Logical System," *Mind*, I (1876), 479–491.

——, *Symbolic Logic*, 2d ed. (London, 1894).

# THE PLACE OF LOGIC
# AMONG THE SCIENCES*

WILLIAM CALVERT KNEALE (1906–    ) is White's Professor of
Moral Philosophy at Oxford University.

MARTHA HURST KNEALE (1909–    ) is a Fellow of Lady Margaret
Hall, Oxford University.

It was a question much debated in antiquity whether logic
should be accounted a branch of philosophy, as the Stoics said, or merely
a preliminary to philosophical studies, as the Peripatetics maintained. But
the dispute was little more than a quarrel about words. Both sides agreed
that logic should come first in the education of a philosopher; and if the
Stoics, unlike Aristotle, called it a part of philosophy, that was merely
because they came later and were self-conscious in the presentation of
their doctrines as a system. What most men in later centuries have called
logic is the study of questions such as Aristotle discussed in the works of
his *Organon:* and the novelty of the Stoic contribution, as we see it in
retrospect, is not any new demarcation of subject-matter, but an emphasis
on relations of propositions as distinct from relations of universals or
concepts. But Aristotle gave no clear account of the province of logic, and
for this reason important questions about its relation to other sciences
have remained for discussion in modern times.

In the syllogistic doctrine of his *Prior Analytics* he enunciates a number
of general principles about a relation between classes which he calls *inclusion in a whole* (ἐν ὅλῳ τῷ A εἶναι) or a relation between universals which
he calls *belonging* (ὑπάρχειν) or *being predicated* (κατηγορεῖσθαι), e.g. the
principle *If A belongs to all B and B belongs to all Γ then A belongs
to all Γ.* But it is clear that he thinks of these principles as important
because they guarantee the validity of certain patterns of argument for all
possible subject-matters to which they may be applied. And he is interested
in such patterns of argument primarily because he thinks they are required
for the elaboration of science as he explains it in his *Posterior Analytics*. It
is therefore not surprising that his successors have often connected logic
with the theory of knowledge and the psychology of reasoning. In other
parts of the *Organon* Aristotle deals with the ways in which terms can
have meanings and the sorts of entities to which they can be applied.
Among the preliminaries of his syllogistic also there is a good deal about

* From Kneale and Kneale, *The Development of Logic* (1964), pp. 737–742 and
541. Reprinted by permission of the authors and of the Clarendon Press, Oxford.

21

the analysis of discourse and classification of statements. Again, therefore, it is not surprising that in later centuries logic has sometimes been classed with grammar and rhetoric as an *ars sermocinalis*. So long as men were content to take Aristotle's own works as their chief sources of logic, these differences of conception did not produce any great intellectual discomfort; by shifting their attention according to the part of the *Organon* with which they were concerned logicians could still think of logic as concerned alike with words, thoughts, and things. But the developments of the last century have made it impossible for us to remain content with a merely traditional grouping of themes. Following analogies suggested by the work of Aristotle and his successors, mathematicians and philosophers have used the word 'logic' in contexts of which older logicians never thought. The result is a confusion in which some usages of the word are so far removed from others that it no longer serves for clear communication between thinkers of diverse tendencies. In this situation we must first consider what is most central in our tradition and then try, if we can, to establish conventions which will make it easy for men to appreciate how this central core is related to all the matters with which it has been connected in the thought of various thinkers.

Although Boole called his most ambitious work on logic *The Laws of Thought* and sometimes wrote as though he supposed himself to be investigating the constitution of the human intellect, it is clear that his algebra has nothing to do with thought processes. In each of the interpretations which we call logical it is concerned with relations between entities that are entirely non-mental. In Frege's works there is even less possibility of confusion between logic and psychology, since the author makes an explicit contrast on many occasions. It is true that he called his concept-script 'a symbolic language of pure thought' (*eine Formelsprache des reinen Denkens*), but his explanations show that he does not mean by this phrase a language designed for talking about a special kind of thinking. On the contrary, when he asserts that arithmetic is identical with logic, he makes clear that he thinks of arithmetical statements as concerned with objects, namely numbers, which are not constructed by human thinking or in any way dependent upon human minds. The concept-script is a language of pure thought only in the sense that it is designed for expressing truths which we think when we abstract entirely from the special contents of our various experiences. This description is not precise enough to indicate that it is a language which provides only for the formulation of principles of logic. So far as the title goes, Frege's first book might be about a new symbolism for metaphysics; but there can be no doubt that he thinks of it as an aid to the development of the science which Aristotle began in his *Prior Analytics*. In his view arithmetic, which he identifies with logic, is the most fundamental of all sciences. But it is not about what philosophers commonly call the external world, i.e. the world of things in space. Nor, on the other hand, is it about minds. It is indeed about inferences which are made by minds, but only because it is concerned with connexions between think-ables. Its laws are not laws of nature, but laws of the laws of nature.[1]

We shall argue presently that this last remark, which Frege offers as an epigram rather than as a definition, may be taken seriously as a delimita-tion of the province of logic. But for the moment our chief purpose is to draw attention to the fact that Boole and Frege, like Leibniz before them, presented logic as a system of principles which allow for valid inference in all kinds of subject-matter, i.e. as the theory of relations such as Aristotle had considered in his doctrine of syllogisms and Chrysippus in his many books about derivative patterns of inference. There are, as we have seen, other elements in the tradition of logical teaching, but the greatest logicians of modern times have taken this as the central theme, and it seems reasonable to say that everything else in the corpus has its place there because of its connexion with the main enterprise of classifying and articulating the principles of formally valid inference. So much is clear; but two developments of the present century have produced some uncer-tainty and made it necessary to strive for greater precision in the charac-terization of logic.

The first of these is the discovery of paradoxes within the field which Cantor and Frege assigned to logic. This is disturbing because it shows that convictions which philosophers have sometimes dignified with the name of 'logical intuitions' may be misleading. To Brouwer it has even suggested that we ought to deny the general validity of the principle of excluded middle. But, apart from that, it has introduced doubts about the correctness of trying to identify arithmetic with logic. Hilbert, as we have seen, prefers to think of arithmetic as derived from a set of special axioms which he adds to the apparatus of quantification theory. And although Whitehead and Russell continue to maintain the thesis of Frege, the expedients to which they are driven reveal the peculiarity of their usage of the word 'logic.' Russell's theory of logical types seems plausible to many philosophers, but even those who favour it have sometimes remarked that it looks more like metaphysics than like logic in the traditional sense, and there can be little doubt that the axioms of reducibility and infinity which he finds it necessary to introduce together with his theory of types are not what would ordinarily be called principles of logic.

The second event of the present century which has made it seem nec-essary to consider afresh the scope of logic is the debate about necessity and language which we noticed in our chapter on the philosophy of logic after Frege. Some of those who adopt a conventionalist view of logic wish to include under the title all *a priori* truths, thinking that these are all alike made true by linguistic rules. If their usage became general, it would be useless to ask whether Frege was right or wrong in thinking arithmetic a continuation of logic, since arithmetic would undoubtedly be the logic

[1] *Grundlagen der Arithmetik*, §§ 87 and 93.

of numerals, just as geometry would be the logic of shape words, mechanics the logic of 'force,' analytical economics the logic of 'price,' philosophical theology (if such a science exists) the logic of 'God,' and so forth. Such an enormous extension of the meaning of a technical term makes it useless for any but the coarsest classification, and it is therefore fortunate that the fashion is still confined to a relatively small school. But it is easy to see that the extension has been suggested by some elements in the old tradition. From the time of Aristotle onwards logicians have discussed the semantic rules or customs for the use of words such as 'all,' 'if,' 'or,' 'possible.' When it is supposed that all principles of traditional logic such as those for the various syllogistic moods have been made true by semantic rules for the use of the words in which they are expressed, it is natural to remark that many other statements are made true in the same way, and it may even seem illuminating for a while to say that they all belong to logic. Already before this theory had been fully developed the word 'logical' was sometimes used in discussions of necessity to make a contrast with 'causal,' as though between them the two covered the whole field.

When the word 'logic' has no agreed definition, the question whether the theory of sets or any other branch of *a priori* knowledge should be accounted part of logic is one that can be settled only by linguistic legislation. But such legislation may be well- or ill-advised. For it is desirable that any new rules we adopt deliberately for old words should depart little, if at all, from previously established customs, and that the distinctions on which they depend should be distinctions important in the organization of knowledge. Thus, if we think that the logic of tradition has been concerned primarily with principles of inference valid for all possible subject-matters, we must reject as unprofitable an extension of usage which allows such phrases as 'the logic of "God." ' And if we think that the theory of sets is closely connected with some topics of traditional logic but are nevertheless puzzled by the devices needed to free it from paradox, we must consider carefully the structure of the science of logic as it is presented by those who wish to make it include the theory of sets. In this connexion the discoveries recorded in the present chapter are obviously relevant.

The distinction between theories which admit a decision procedure and those which do not is very interesting philosophically, and it may have great practical importance in an age of computers; but we can scarcely use it to delimit the province of logic. For it would be contrary to long-established tradition to decide that the name 'logic' should be reserved for the calculus of propositions, which we have called in this book primary logic, and there is no clear line to be drawn within the restricted (or first-order) calculus of propositional functions. We know that there can be no decision procedure for the whole calculus, but we cannot give a satisfactory general characterization of all that part for which a decision procedure may be constructed. On the other hand, it is easy to distinguish the restricted calculus of propositional functions which is known to be deductively complete from the theory of sets (or the corresponding higher-order functional calculus) which has been shown to be not only incomplete but incompletable, and it seems reasonable to say that the former should be called logic but not the latter. For the word 'logic' is connected traditionally with discussion of rules of inference; and while it is strange to apply it to any axiomatic system such as that of Frege, it is even more strange to apply it to a system in which the consequences of the axioms are not all accessible by inference from the axioms. Yet that, as we can now see in the light of Gödel's theorem, is what Frege did when he undertook to reduce arithmetic to logic. Where he noticed only a difference of levels, there is in reality a gulf that may properly be taken as the boundary of logic.

We might perhaps include the theory of identity within logic, since its basic notion is one of very high generality and its axioms can be added to quantification theory without loss of completeness for the resulting complex. But when once the theory of sets has been distinguished from the rest of Frege's system and based on axioms for membership, it seems most natural to present quantification theory in rules of inference like those of Gentzen or rules of development like those we have offered in an earlier section, and this technique cannot be extended to the theory of identity. We can, of course, replace axioms of identity by additional rules of inference; for that purpose we need only say that each axiom is a formula which may be inferred from the null class of premises. But we cannot replace Frege's axioms of identity by paired rules of inference (or development) which provide between them for the introduction and the elimination of the identity sign. Nor can we define identity by means of a $\gamma$-rule within the system of higher-order rules which we have put forward in our section on modal logic. This implies that the notion of identity is not connected with the notion of entailment, or the more general notion of involution,[2] in the same intimate way as the notions of conjunction, negation, universality, &c., which are commonly accounted logical. We therefore conclude that the theory of identity may be conveniently excluded from the scope of logic, and that our science is best defined as the pure theory of involution, that is to say, the theory of the general form of principles of involution without regard to the special natures of the propositions contained in the classes between which the relation holds. This account of the science agrees, as we have seen, very closely with an epigrammatic pronouncement of Frege about the way in which the laws of logic are related to the laws of other sciences, and it may be regarded also as a very strict interpretation

---

[2] *Earlier (p. 541) "involution" had been explained as follows:* "Just as a derivation is said to be valid if the premises entail the conclusion, so a development may be said to be valid if the premises *involve* the limits to which the development leads. Here we follow Carnap, who in his *Formalization of Logic* introduced the name 'logical involution' for the relation that holds between two sets of propositions when it is impossible that all of the first should be true and all of the second false. Entailment is then to be regarded as involution of a set containing only one member." [*The editors.*]

of Bolzano's suggestion that logic is the science of sciences. No doubt in practice logic as we define it will always be studied together with other subjects which are relevant to the organization of knowledge, and in particular with those with which it has been associated by Aristotle, Chrysippus, Leibniz, Bolzano, and Frege. For we have seen that logic in our narrow sense is not even co-extensive with the theory of deductive systems which has been developed by mathematicians out of Hilbert's suggestions. But however it may be named or described, this relatively simple study is central in the great tradition of European thought about science.

## SUGGESTIONS FOR FURTHER READING IN THE HISTORY OF LOGIC

BETH, E. W.    "Hundred Years of Symbolic Logic. A Retrospect on the Occasion of the Boole De Morgan Centenary," *Dialectica*, Vol. I (1947), pp. 331–346.

BOCHÉNSKI, I. M.    A History of Formal Logic. Translated and edited by Ivo Thomas. Notre Dame, Ind. University of Notre Dame Press, 1961.

BOEHNER, P, A. CHURCH, D. H. H. INGALLS, and B. MATES.    "Logic, History of," *Encyclopaedia Britannica*, Vol. 14, 1961.

JØRGENSEN, J.    A Treatise of Formal Logic. 3 Volumes. New York. Russell and Russell, Inc., 1962.

KNEALE, W. C., and M. H. KNEALE.    The Development of Logic. Oxford. Oxford University Press, 1962.

LEWIS, C. I.    A Survey of Symbolic Logic. New York. Dover Publications, Inc., 1960.

MOSTOWSKI, A.    Thirty Years of Foundational Studies, Acta Philosophica Fennica, Fasc. XVII. Helsinki, 1965.

NIDDITCH, P. H.    The Development of Mathematical Logic.   New York. The Free Press, 1962.

QUINE, W. V. O.    "Whitehead and the Rise of Modern Logic," *The Philosophy of Alfred North Whitehead*, P. A. S. Schilpp ed. Evanston, Ill. Northwestern University Press, 1941.

SCHOLZ, H.    Geschichte der Logik. Berlin. Junker und Dünnhaupt, 1931.

# Part
## 2 THE FORMAL APPROACH

## *Introduction*

Modern logic and modern mathematics are most often presented today as formal deductive systems. The degree of formalism involved may vary, but the value of formalization in these areas is quite generally accepted. To question this method is to raise doubts about the very foundations of mathematics and logic. Yet the formal approach has led to such surprising results that serious logicians have begun to entertain second thoughts about that method. It is not that the method is regarded as erroneous in any way. It is rather that the aims of the method, and its proper scope and limits, must be reconsidered, and new decisions reached in the light of conclusions that have been arrived at by its means.

In the first selection in this part, Hao Wang raises a number of these questions. Does formalization render a theory or a proof easier to understand? Does formalization help us "to analyze and to clarify concepts"? Can we formalize without residue our intuitions about logic and mathematics? What is the utility of formalization, and what are its limits? These are some of the questions considered by Wang—questions that must be faced sooner or later by every serious student of logic and mathematics.

Myhill's essay explores some philosophical implications of the Löwenheim-Skolem Theorem. "The theorem states that every formal system expressed in the first order functional calculus has a denumerable model. In particular, the general theory of sets . . . has a denumerable model; yet this theory was designed in part in order to formalize in a consistent and rigorous manner the arguments of Cantor's theory of infinite cardinals, one of the main results of which is that the continuum is more than denumerably infinite." It would seem, then, "that the attempt to formalize the notion of a non-denumerable infinity is forever doomed to failure, and that this is an essential and unanticipated limitation of formalism." Following his brilliantly lucid exposition of the theorem in question, Myhill considers with great sensitivity and insight some of the difficulties and perplexities involved in it.

Even more surprising is Gödel's conclusion that arithmetic itself cannot be completely formalized. As Nagel and Newman put it, "there is at least one arithmetical truth which cannot be derived from the arithmetical axioms and yet can be established by a meta-mathematical argument outside the system." It had been the "grand object of *Principia* . . . to demonstrate that mathematics was only a chapter in logic," that is, to prove that from a group of logical axioms one could derive a consistent and complete system of arithmetical statements. Gödel ingeniously proved this goal impossible to reach.

# ON FORMALIZATION[*]

Hao Wang (1921–     ) of Harvard University has contributed
many important articles to mathematical, logical, and
philosophical journals. He is the author of A Survey of
Mathematical Logic.

## 1. SYSTEMATIZATION

The most striking results of formalization occur in logic and
mathematics.

Here formalization provides at least one kind of systematization. We
are led to believe that there is a fairly simple axiom system from which it
is possible to derive almost all mathematical theorems and truths mechan-
ically. This is at present merely a theoretical possibility, for no serious
attempts seem to have been made to prove, for instance, all the theorems
of an elementary textbook of calculus. Nevertheless, we seem to get a feeling of grandeur from the realization that a simple axiom system which we
can quite easily memorize by heart embodies, in a sense, practically all the
mathematical truths. It is not very hard to get to know the axiom system
so well that people would say you understood the system. Unfortunately
just to be able thus to understand the system neither gives you very deep
insight into the nature of mathematics nor makes you a very good mathematician.

To say that physics uses the experimental method is not to say much
about physics. To say that all theorems of mathematics can be proved
from certain axioms by chains of syllogism (or modus ponens) is to say
just as little about mathematics. Merely knowing the experimental method
is not knowing the whole of physics; merely knowing an axiom system
adequate for developing mathematics is not knowing the whole of
mathematics.

There is another kind of systematization which is less superficial than
learning the axiom system. It is an intuitive grasp of the whole field, a
vivid picture of the whole structure in your mind such as a good chess
player would have of the game of chess. This second kind of systematization is something that formalization (or at least formalization alone)
would not provide us.

If we had never used logistic systems at all, the many interesting results
about logistic systems (such as those of Skolem, Herbrand, and Gödel)
would, of course, never have been expressed in the specific form in which

* Reprinted by kind permission of the author and publisher, from Hao Wang, A
Survey of Mathematical Logic, The North-Holland Publishing Co., 1962, pp. 57–67.
This article appeared originally in Mind, Vol. 64, 1955, pp. 226–238.

they are now being expressed. But it is not certain that essentially the same results might not have been attained, though in other contexts and as the results about other things. Nevertheless, axiomatics or the axiomatic method has a strong appeal in that here we seem to be able to prove sweeping conclusions about whole fields. For many of us a significant theorem about a whole field appears more important than particular theorems in the field. In generating systems, formalization serves the function of enabling us to talk precisely about whole fields of learning.

## 2.  COMMUNICATION

It is hard to say whether in general formalization renders a theory or a proof easier to understand.

Consider, for example, an oral sketch of a newly discovered proof, an abstract designed to communicate just the basic idea of the proof, an article presenting the proof to people working on related problems, a textbook formulation of the same, and a presentation of it after the manner of *Principia Mathematica*. The proof gets more and more thoroughly formalized as we go from an earlier version to a later. It is, however, questionable whether in general a more completely formalized version is clearer or serves better as a means of communication. Each step of it should be easier to follow since it involves no jumps. But even this is not certain, for there are many jumps which we are so used to making that we find it more natural to make the jumps than not to. Or alternatively, we may say that the step actually does not involve jumps and that our formal proof suggests that it does only because our formal system is defective as a map of our intuitive logic.

Who finds which proof easier to follow or who understands which proof in a shorter while depends pretty much on what background the man happens to have. In general, the better acquainted one is with the problem, the easier he finds the use of a more sketchy proof. But there is also a certain limit beyond which even the expert in the matter can no longer supply for himself the missing details. Moreover, there is always the possibility that the presentation would be much shorter if it were not so short. It seems safe, however, to say that a more thoroughly formalized proof is generally longer, provided that we do not appeal to abbreviations in its presentation and the less formalized version does not waste words.

We are all familiar with requests to explain a physical theory without using mathematics, to convey the basic idea of a proof without using symbols. Therefore, it would seem that in general the plain words or the less technical language provide a more efficient means of communication. Actually, however, we can easily think of examples which would indicate that this is not quite true.

To put thoughts on physics into mathematical symbols is one way of formalization. Through accumulation and tradition this way of formalization has also become a powerful way of communication: for those who understand the language, a short formula may express more precisely thought which could only be explained by many pages of ordinary words, and much less satisfactorily. Sometimes it becomes practically impossible to avoid the mathematical language in communicating with others. An elderly English political figure complains that none of the many eminent physicists with whom he has corresponded is courageous enough to pass any definite judgment on his proposed new theory of ether. Then he stresses the similarity between his theory and the concluding paragraph of a recent article by Dirac, and proceeds to discard as non-essential the accompanying mathematical passages in Dirac's article. It may be presumed that if he had also included comparable non-essential mathematical passages in his theory, he would have received more definite responses.

## 3. CLARITY AND CONSOLIDATION

Does formalization help us to analyse and clarify concepts?

Often in formalizing ordinary concepts, we appear to have platitudes restated in pedantic obscurity; for instance, the mathematical definition of the continuity of a curve or the technical definition of the notion of effective computability. Moreover, the exact formalizations almost always distort our ordinary language at one place or another. For example, it has been pointed out that Russell's theory of descriptions does not apply to sentences such as "the whale is a mammal," and that sometimes in ordinary use the sentence "the king of France is bald" is neither taken as true nor taken as false.

In scientific investigations, we often recognize the advantage and even necessity of paying the price of considerable deviation from ordinary use of words in order to reach fairly precise terminology and notation. But, in what sense is, for instance, the technical notion of effective computability clearer than the corresponding common sense concept? Ordinarily, we would tend to say that the technical notion is *less* clear because it is more difficult to learn and a concept is clearer if and only if it is easier. We might speak of different kinds of clarity just as Mill speaks of different kinds of pleasure. Then we can also speak of a principle of preference: Only those who have experienced the feeling of clarity both of the ordinary notion and of the technical one are qualified to judge which is really clearer. And then, we hope, they will find the formalized notion clearer.

Perhaps we should also say that which definition of a term is clearer depends partly on the purposes we want the term to serve, and partly on our familiarity with the notions involved in each definition. The main advantage of the more articulate definition of a notion is, presumably, that it is sharper: for example, there are many cases where we can give a definite answer to the question whether certain given functions are effectively computable, only after we have made use of the technical notion of computability.

There are many cases where we could neither ask a univocal question nor obtain a univocal answer until we possessed the formalized notion. For example, we needed an exact definition of continuous curves before we could ask and answer the question whether there are space-filling continuous curves. And it was necessary first to formalize the notions of completeness and decidability before a negative answer could be given to the question whether number theory is complete or decidable.

Significant formalization of a concept involves analysis of the concept, not so much in the sense of analysis when we say that being a bachelor entails being unmarried, but more in the sense that an analysis of the problem of squaring the circle is provided by the proof of its unsolvability. When formalization is performed at such a level, it does serve to clarify and explicate concepts.

Another function of formalization is the clarification and consolidation of arguments or proofs. Sometimes we are not quite sure whether we have understood a certain given proof, sometimes we understand a proof once but fail to understand it again when reading it a few days later. Then there often comes the desire to work over the proof thoroughly, to make explicit all the implicit steps involved, and to write down the expanded result once and for all. With some people this desire to formalize and expand proofs may become a habit and a handicap to studying certain branches of mathematics. Yet occasional indulgence in this kind of thoroughness need not be a harmful thing.

In certain cases, there is no sharp line between formalizing and discovering a proof. There are many cases where essentially incomplete sketches, sometimes containing errors as well, get expanded and made into more exact proofs. Sometimes it is not until we have the thoroughly worked out proof on hand that we begin to perceive a connexion between it and the existing hint or sketch. Sometimes it seems hard to decide whether to consider the sketcher or the formalizer the true discoverer of the proof.

## 4.   RIGOUR

In a sense, to formalize is to make rigorous.

There was Berkeley's attack on the mathematicians of his day entitled: "The analyst: or, a discourse addressed to an infidel mathematician. Wherein it is examined whether the object, principles, and inferences of the modern analysis are more distinctly conceived, or more evidently deduced, than religious mysteries and points of faith." There is the long story of how Lagrange, Cauchy, Weierstrass, and others strove to formalize exactly the basic notions of limits, continuity, derivatives, etc., providing thereby rigorous (though not necessarily reliable) foundations for mathematical analysis.

In the contemporary scene, we have logicians deploring how carelessly ordinary mathematicians use their words and symbols. Some logicians are puzzled that so many apparent confusions in mathematics do not lead more often to serious errors. On the other hand, mathematicians in turn complain about the inaccuracy of alleged proofs of mathematical theorems by physicists and engineers.

In the other direction, physicists consider that mathematicians are wasting their time when they worry about "foundational crisis"; mathematicians consider that logicians are indulging in learned hair-splitting when they devote pages and volumes to discussing the meanings of meaning or the use of quotation marks and brackets.

The right course is to be as rigorous and detailed as the occasion or the purpose requires. But this is more easily said than done. For example, certain authors seem to dwell tirelessly on the obvious, while skipping the crucial and more difficult steps.

The matter of distinguishing expressions from that which is expressed may serve to illustrate some of the questions about rigour. There were occasions when failure to be careful about the distinction actually hindered greatly the advance of logic. It is now customary in logic and philosophy to stress the difference, usually using quotation marks to separate, for example, the city Peking from the word "Peking." At present, even those who do not want to spend much time on using the quotation marks rigorously, often find it necessary to declare, for example, "quotation marks are omitted in most cases since we believe that no confusion will arise from this negligence." Every now and then, we run into certain articles in which the authors are so meticulous about using quotation marks that it becomes very difficult to read and understand what is being said.

One might even distinguish logicians into two groups depending on whether or not they always try to use quotation marks consistently and exactly. It may be a matter of temperament. Or it may also be a question of whether one happens to be either too lazy or too busy.

## 5.  APPROXIMATION TO INTUITION

To put thoughts in words or to describe a particular experience involves formalization of intuition. It has been contended that no finite number of propositions could describe exhaustively all that is involved in a particular experience. In other words, it is impossible to formalize without residue the complete intuition at the moment.

The matter of approximating intuition by formalization is clearer with regard to mathematics. For example, we know intuitively many things about integers. If we are asked to characterize our notion of integers, one way of answering is to say that integers form a group with respect to addition, they form an ordered set with regard to the ordinary relation of being greater than, and so on. The notions of group, ordered set, etc., are more exactly defined or more formalized than the notion of integers. Consequently, such answers tend to clarify somewhat our notion of integers, but they are usually inadequate because they fail to characterize unambiguously the integers.

We may compare the place of abstract structures such as group, field, ordered set, etc., in mathematics with the place of general concepts in ordinary life. They all can be considered as results of formalization or abstraction which serve as tools of thinking and research. As tools they help to economize our thought, as is often remarked. For example, not only integers, but transformations in space, etc., all form groups; anything that we prove about groups in general, of course, applies also to the special groups which may differ from one another in many respects. Similarly, there are many different chairs which can all be employed to support buttocks. In this way formalization, closely tied up with abstraction, produces useful tools.

On the other hand, it is often hard to characterize adequately our intuition through the use of formal structures. For example, it is not easy to describe exactly the colour, shape, etc., of a particular chair. Peano's axioms are thought to be capable of characterizing completely our notion of positive integers. Yet, as Russell observed long ago, Peano's axioms are satisfied by all progressions such as the odd positive integers, the negative integers. Russell thought that only by calling in a set theory could we make a univocal characterization. More recent advances in logic show that he was wrong even in believing this.

In fact, as we know, there are important results which indicate unmistakably that we can formalize without residue neither the fundamental intuitive notion of positive integers nor the basic notion of sets or classes.

Thus, there is Gödel's famous theorem according to which, for any fairly rich system, we can find some property expressible in the system such that we can prove for each of the integers 1, 2, . . . that it has the property, but we cannot prove the general statement that all positive integers have the property in question. In other words, although intuitively if $P(1)$ (*i.e.*, 1 has the property P), $P(2)$, $P(3)$, . . . are all true, then it must be the case that all positive integers have the property P; yet in no fairly strong logistic system can we formalize adequately this intuition so as to guarantee the performability of such an inference for all the properties P expressible in the system. It also follows that no ordinary axiom system can preclude the interpretation that besides the ordinary 1, 2, . . . the set of positive integers also contains certain other queer things; there is no way to formalize in an ordinary logistic system our intuition that 1, 2, . . . are the only integers.

On the other hand, there is no axiom system in which we can get *all* the real numbers or the classes of positive integers. This follows easily from Cantor's famous argument for non-denumerability. Thus, given any axiom system, we can enumerate all the classes of positive integers which can be proved to exist in the system, either by applying Löwenheim's theorem or by reflecting on the fact that the theorems of existence in the system can be enumerated. Hence, if we define with Cantor a class K of positive integers such that for each $n$, $n$ belongs to K if and only if $n$ does not belong to the $n$th class in the enumeration, then the existence of K cannot be proved in the system. In other words, although in the system we can also speak of all the classes of positive integers, we cannot really formalize without residue the intuitive notion of "all" with regard to classes of positive integers; in each formalized axiom system, there is always some class of positive integers that is left out.

## 6. APPLICATION TO PHILOSOPHY

The application of mathematical logic to the treatment of philosophical problems may also be viewed as an attempt to formalize. Such applications often give the impression that a formidable technical book expresses in tiresome exactitude more or less commonplace ideas which could be conveyed more easily and more directly in a few sentences of plain language. Yet, undoubtedly, there are cases where the appeal to formalization is of more than pedantic interest. For instance, Heyting's formalization of the intuitionistic view of logic and mathematics helps quite a bit in conveying Brouwer's ideas to those people who have a radically different orientation. Another example is the gradual formalization of the notion of being a definite property, employed for defining sets in Zermelo's axiomatic treatment of set theory.

Perhaps we can compare many of the attempts to formalize with the use of an airplane to visit a friend living in the same town. Unless you simply love the airplane ride and want to use the visit as an excuse for having a good time in the air, the procedure would be quite pointless and extremely inconvenient. Or we may compare the matter with constructing or using a huge computer solely to calculate the result of multiplying seven by eleven. When the problems are so simple, even the task of translating them into a language which, so to speak, the machine can understand would already take longer than if we were to calculate the results by memory or with a pencil and a sheet of paper.

It is a practical problem to decide what means of transportation to use in making a certain particular trip, or to decide whether it is feasible to build a computer to handle a certain given type of question. As we know, there are many different factors which are ordinarily taken into consideration before making the decision. Similarly, it is also a practical problem to decide in each particular case whether it is profitable to apply mathematical logic in handling a definite kind of problem. The only difference is that the factors which have to be considered here are often more involved and less determinate.

Take the principle of verification. Various attempts at giving an exact definition of the notion of verifiability have failed. And systematic use of the logistic method has been recommended as the only way to a satisfactory solution. On the other hand, there is also the view that the important thing is a general attitude expressed vaguely in the rough principle of verification, rather than an exact definition of verifiability. Underlying this dispute, perhaps, are the varying attitudes toward the general desirability of crystallization of ideas.

This raises larger problems. Why should we want such crystallization in philosophy? What is the function and business of philosophy? Fortunately, general observations can be made without going into such hard questions.

## 7.  TOO MANY DIGITS

After sketching an axiom system for his theory of probability, F. P. Ramsey goes on to say, "I have not worked out the mathematical logic of this in detail, because this would, I think, be rather like working out to seven places of decimals a result only valid to two." There are several disadvantages in working out a result to too many places. It uses up time which might be spent otherwise. It also makes the result harder to memorize or to include in future calculations, if anybody should want to make use of it. And pointless problems would arise regarding the last five places: do they exhibit any interesting pattern which would indicate the lawfulness of nature? Do they coincide with the five digits starting with the 101st in the decimal expansion of $\pi$? and so on.

How do we decide whether a result is valid only to two places? If the same experiment is repeated under different but, so far as we know, equally favourable circumstances, with results which agree satisfactorily only to the first two places, then we tend to conclude that the places after the second are not quite reliable. If most people refuse to calculate up to many places and a single person has an irresistible itch for reporting every result to at least seven places, it might be rather hard to decide whether his result is right.

The matter of constructing an exact theory of (say) probability contains an additional factor. Since ordinary language is not exact, new words are coined or ordinary words are given technical usage. In order to evaluate the theory, you have first to understand it. In order to understand it, you have first to learn a new language. Since it is usually impossible to explain clearly and exactly even the technical usages, a formal or exact theory can almost always be defended against charges that it does not conform to fact. As long as there is a sufficiently complicated system and a fairly big and energetic group of people who, for one reason or another, enjoy elaborating the system, we have a powerful school of learning, be it the theory of meaning, the sociology of knowledge, or the logic of induction. There is always the hope that further development of the theory will yield keys to old puzzles or fertilise the spirit of new invention. In any case, since there is mutual support between different parts of a given system, there is little danger that the discrepancy between one part and the facts should discredit the system. And of course if we are interested in the "foundations," there is no need to fear any immediate tests. The worst that can happen to such theories is not refutation but neglect.

## 8. IDEAL LANGUAGE

Language is employed for expression and communication of thoughts. Failure in communication may either be caused by inadequate mastery of the language, or by internal deficiencies of the language: that is, if there is thought to be conveyed at all. Language is also sometimes used for talking nonsense. Here again, certain languages just seem to offer stronger temptations for doing so. And sometimes the language user is not careful enough, or he merely parrots others. In such cases he does not have thoughts or feelings to express, and there is, of course, no question of correct communication. A less serious disease is confused thinking, often involving internal inconsistency. This again is sometimes the fault of the language, such as the ambiguity of words and a misleading grammar.

The creation of an ideal language would yield a solution of these difficulties once and for all. Such a language should be so rich, clear, and exact as to be sufficient both for expressing all thoughts and feelings with unmisunderstandable clarity, and for precluding nonsense. Given such a language, many problems now known as philosophical would be dissolved. Disagreement about what is to be taken as nonsense would lead to the construction of different ideal languages. There would be then the problem of understanding each other's ideal language.

An alternative to the ideal language is to handle each individual case separately and thoroughly. To explain at great length what we intend to say, to give concrete examples when possible, to invite questions and discussions. And to reflect carefully and ask what we really want to say, whether we do have something to say, whether we are not misled by false analogies or naive syntax.

The task of constructing a comprehensive ideal language is in many ways similar to that of finding a mechanical procedure to decide answers to all problems of mathematics. They are equally impossible. If and when these two tasks are clearly formulated, the impossibility can be proved definitely in both cases. In certain simple areas of logic and mathematics, we do possess decision procedures. Similarly in mathematical logic and theoretical physics we have more exact languages. But there is no mechanical method for finding decision procedures, and each significant mathematical problem calls for a special treatment. It is demonstrably impossible to reduce all mathematics to its decidable portion. It seems equally impossible to fit everything we say into the language of logic and physics. Moreover, these languages are more exact in their abstract setup than in their actual use. It is a familiar experience that mathematicians who know the language of mathematics very well often offer fallacious proofs.

The quest for an ideal language is probably futile. The problem of formalization is rather to construct suitable artificial languages to meet individual problems.

## 9.  HOW ARTIFICIAL A LANGUAGE?

The contrast between natural and artificial languages suggests a sharp distinction. Russian is natural, while Esperanto is artificial. But is the language of the biologists or that of the philosophers natural or artificial? Is Mr. Woodger's proposed language for biology natural or artificial? Hilbert's language for the Euclidean geometry is more exact and artificial than that of Euclid's *Elements*. So far as the development of human scientific activities is concerned, the creation of the language of the classical mechanics or of the axiomatic set theory was rather natural.

We might speak of degrees of artificiality, as perhaps measured by the amount of deviation from the natural course. The Chinese language spoken today differs to a rather great extent from that used two thousand years ago, although the changes have been mostly natural. If we had attempted two thousand years ago to bring about the same changes in one year's time, we would have had to create at that time a language quite artificial. To introduce an artificial language is to make a revolution. Unless there are compelling natural needs, the resistance will be strong and the proposal will fail. On the other hand, when an artificial language meets existing urgent problems, it will soon get generally accepted and be no longer considered artificial. Hence, it may be more to the point if we compare artificial languages with Utopian projects.

Attempts to formalize the theory of probability are sometimes criticized on the ground that the efforts fail to make contact with the crucial and burning problems of physical science. One ready reply is that the situation is the same with many interesting investigations in branches of mathematics such as abstract algebra, set theory, and topology. One may argue, however, that more new ideas and methods are introduced through such studies than through the researches on foundations of probability theory. Or maybe there is more substance behind the new languages of algebra and set theory and results obtained there are not as easily discredited by slight shifts of emphasis or subtle mistakes in the original analysis.

Mrs. Joan Robinson somewhere remarks that economists are usually behind their time. An urgent practical problem often ceases to be urgent or practical long before the discovery of a theoretically satisfactory solution. Whether it is worthwhile to continue the search for the solution of a problem which is no longer urgent depends to a large extent on whether the particular problem is intimately connected with larger issues, whether it is sufficiently intriguing intellectually, and whether it is likely to recur in the near future. Similarly, the value of an artificial language has to be decided in accordance with its elegance and its usefulness either in its direct applications or as a model to be followed in future constructions. In a certain sense, an interesting artificial language must not be excessively artificial.

## 10. THE PARADOXES

Much time and space has been devoted to the discussion of the logical paradoxes or contradictions. Sometimes it is said that these paradoxes bring to light the self-contradictory character of our logical intuition. Indeed, as we know, the formalization of logic and set theory was largely motivated by a desire to avoid the paradoxes and yet obtain what we ordinarily want.

It has been suggested that we take the paradoxes too seriously, largely because of our preoccupation with formalization and our lack of flexibility.

What is proposed instead seems to be this. Suppose we find a contradiction by a seemingly plausible argument. Since we get a contradiction, we see that the argument is really not correct and indeed must be faulty. So let us remember never to use the argument again. And that is the end of the matter.

However, when we say that the argument looks plausible, we mean, among other things, that each step of the argument also looks plausible. It seems necessary not only to reject the whole argument as a unit but to pin down exactly which step or steps in the argument caused the trouble. Hence, there are the various attempts to reject one or another of the steps as unwarranted. But why can we not say that although each step is in itself all right, they must not be combined in the particular way that leads to the contradiction? Indeed, we may even use this possibility to justify the attitude of indifference, on the part of many working mathematicians, toward the paradoxes.

It is only when we come to constructing a formal system to embody our arguments that this procedure proves awkward. In a logistic system, we break up proofs and arguments into isolated steps so that if a step is valid at all, it is valid no matter where it occurs. In other words, certain combinations of shapes are taken as axioms so that they can be asserted as valid no matter where they occur; and certain (finite) sequences of combinations of shapes are taken as justified by the rules of inference so that any such sequence, wherever it occurs, is taken as determining valid steps. For instance, if we agree to take as an axiom, for two specific sets named $a$ and $b$, the assertion "Either $a$ belongs to $b$ or $a$ does not belong to $b$," we can no longer reject the same statement as an unwarranted step when it occurs in an argument that leads to a contradiction.

Two alternatives to the customary logistic method are: (1) not to attempt any exact characterization of all the valid arguments of any important branch of mathematics; (2) to list either all or samples of all the warranted and unwarranted whole specific arguments as inseparable units, instead of trying to break up all warranted arguments into a small number of basic atomic steps. The alternative (2) will either produce quite messy results or lead to something which is hardly distinguishable from a logistic system. . . .

# ON THE ONTOLOGICAL
# SIGNIFICANCE OF THE
# LÖWENHEIM-SKOLEM THEOREM*

John R. Myhill (1923–    ) of the State University of New
   York at Buffalo has contributed many important articles to
   mathematical, logical, and philosophical journals.

. . . I share the conviction that the Löwenheim-Skolem theorem has no direct philosophical implications. This phrase should be clarified. What is implied is a proposition and to say there are philosophical implications implies that there are philosophical propositions. This runs counter to the idea that philosophy is an activity rather than a doctrine, an idea to which with reservations I subscribe. However part if not all of this activity consists in the assertion of propositions, which are not however philosophical propositions in themselves, but become philosophical in virtue of being asserted in the course of philosophical activity. Hence no proposition has philosophical implications in the strict sense, but perhaps every proposition may with propriety be asserted in the course of philosophical activity. Almost any proposition may I suppose initiate philosophical activity, and I take the invitation to contribute the present paper as a request to perform a philosophical activity initiated (after those introductory remarks) by the assertion of the Löwenheim-Skolem theorem. The assertions made by me subsequently to this assertion I shall call indirect implications of the Löwenheim-Skolem theorem, using the word 'implication' in its colloquial rather than its technical sense. My initial remark that the theorem has no direct philosophical implications is therefore a direct consequence of my view that philosophy is an activity rather than a doctrine.

* From *Academic Freedom, Logic, and Religion*, ed. M. White, 1951, pp. 57–70. Reprinted by permission of The University of Pennsylvania Press.

I do not maintain that philosophy is wholly or primarily an activity of clarification. In particular I cannot see that clarification is the principal goal of ethics, though it might be an important instrument in achieving that goal. None the less clarification is part of philosophy, or at least the clarification of certain issues is. Much of the activity which I will perform in this paper will be clarificatory, that is, it will be devoted to stating in non-technical terms what the Löwenheim-Skolem theorem is. Why is this a philosophical activity? Would a clarification of say the binomial theorem be philosophical? Clearly not; more exactly, it seems highly dubious that the assertion of the binomial theorem could profitably initiate a philosophical discourse, except perhaps by way of illustration of some general aspect of mathematics for which purpose a good many other theorems would have served equally well. The reason why the Löwenheim-Skolem theorem seems a fruitful proposition with which to begin a philosophical discourse, while the binomial theorem does not, is that we are inclined to ask "What does the Löwenheim-Skolem theorem really mean?" while we are not inclined to ask "What does the binomial theorem really mean?"

I take such questions seriously. A question is an expression of intellectual anxiety and an answer is an attempt at resolution of that anxiety. I distinguish formal from informal questions, and within the latter I distinguish subjective and objective. A formal question carries with it the form of its answer, that is, the social context is such that the criterion of acceptability for the answer is known and agreed upon by both questioner and answerer in abstraction from the answer itself. The purest kind of formal question is the question of the truth or falsity of a mathematical theorem within a known system. For the criteria of being a proof or not being a proof within that system are capable of exact specification and are in the ideal case specifically agreed upon by questioner and answerer. Questions in the empirical sciences are a less pure kind of formal question, since the criteria of confirmation are less exactly specifiable than those of mathematical proof.

An informal question is one the form of whose answer is not known either by questioner or answerer in abstraction from the answer itself. The dictum that the meaning of a proposition is the method of its verification does not apply to propositions which answer informal questions, for part of the meaning of such a question is to question what the form of its answer would be. Thus part of the meaning of the question "How shall I face the prospect of my death?" is "What form of answer (psychoanalytic, theological, semantical) would resolve the anxiety expressed by the question 'How shall I face the prospect of my death?'?" More simply; if and in proportion as a question is formal, the questioner is prepared to state precisely what kind of evidence would convince him of the truth of any proposed answer. A formal question asks for the matter of its answer but provides the form; an informal question asks for both.

Any question, therefore, which asks after the general features of formalism, must be itself informal, for if the form of the answer were known to the questioner, he would already presuppose or regard as unquestioned a certain form as appropriate to answering his question, and so in questioning the nature of formalism would already be operating in the framework of a formalism which was unquestioned. Hence metamathematics must be in the final analysis informal; for the process of discussing formalisms by means of other formalisms must either terminate in a formalism which is not discussed, or be informal. But in the first case we would be doing mathematics and not in the strict sense metamathematics. Anyone familiar with the writings of Hilbert can provide illustrations for himself of this phenomenon. I shall try to show that anxiety concerning the Löwenheim-Skolem theorem originates partly in a desire to consider formal objects outside of the formalism in which they are imbedded, and so presents in a specifically acute way the informality characteristic of metamathematical anxiety. The opinions that this anxiety results from a confusion of different formalisms or from a confusion between internal and external questions, or from a self-contradictory desire that an object be at once formal and non-formal, I dismiss because of my contention that anxiety can frequently be resolved by verbal answer even when it does not provide the form of that answer. A question does not have to be precise in order to express a genuine anxiety and thus be a genuine question.

I distinguish within informal questions between objective and subjective, according as there is or is not agreement as to the effectiveness of the answer in resolving the anxiety which prompted the question. Hence there is no way of knowing whether an informal question is objective or subjective until the question is answered. Even in that case, there is usually the possibility that a subjectively satisfying answer may later be replaced by an objectively satisfying one. Evidently the distinction between subjective and objective informal questions is relative, dependent on social conditions. A question which is informal, but close to objectivity is "What is the meaning of the definite article?" At the other extreme are questions expressive of neurotic anxiety which can be resolved only by special treatment in each case.

Philosophical activity is the activity of resolving anxiety expressed by objective informal questions. Because what is at one time informal may later become formal, the philosophical area shrinks progressively, yielding place to science. Because few if any informal questions are entirely objective, there is diversity of philosophical systems. I repeat that the anxiety expressed in feeling the Löwenheim-Skolem theorem as a paradox results in part from the desire to grasp a formal object apart from its setting in a formal system; thus this anxiety concerns formalism in general and so can be resolved only informally. On the other hand, I am optimistic enough to hope that at least part of my comments will provoke agreement; hence the clarificatory part of them and a certain amount of the motivational analysis may claim to be philosophical in the sense I have explained.

I shall now state the theorem roughly and exhibit the proximate grounds for anxiety concerning its 'real meaning.' The theory states that every formal system expressed in the first order functional calculus has a denumerable model. In particular the general theory of sets as axiomatized e.g., by von Neumann and Gödel has a denumerable model; yet this theory was designed in part in order to formalize in a consistent and rigorous manner the arguments of Cantor's theory of infinite cardinals, one of the main results of which is that the continuum is more than denumerably infinite. One can state the perplexity arising from this circumstance in various ways; e.g., that the attempt to formalize the notion of a non-denumerable infinity is forever doomed to failure, and that this is an essential and unanticipated limitation of formalism. This perplexity we shall resolve incidentally later. Simpler to handle now and nearer the spirit of the foregoing discussion is the following statement: the continuum is according to formalized set-theory non-denumerable; i.e., its non-denumerability is a thesis of that theory. This thesis however asserts that no one-to-one correlation between the continuum and the integers exists; for in this way is non-denumerability defined. On the other hand, since formalized set-theory possesses a denumerable model, it possesses a model in the integers; and so there is a one-to-one correlation between all the sets of formalized set-theory and the integers, namely the correlation which correlates each set with the integer representing it in the model. A fortiori there is a correlation between those particular sets in the formal system which constitute the continuum and a subset of the integers. It appears to follow that the continuum dealt with in formal set-theory is denumerable, hence not a true continuum; moreover, that the thesis of formal set-theory to the effect that (this) 'continuum' is non-denumerable actually asserts merely that it is not capable of enumeration by any correlation appearing amongst the objects of that theory, i.e., appearing as a value of its variables. For the thesis asserts "there is no R which is a one-to-one correlation between (this) continuum and the integers"; and since there does appear in the light of the Löwenheim-Skolem theorem to be such a correlation, we seem forced to conclude that this correlation is not amongst the range of values of the variable R, i.e. not amongst the objects of formal set-theory. Hence we infer that we cannot adequately express the notion of indenumerability and of the continuum within formalized set-theory, in the sense that all we can assert is the absence of a correlation *within the set-theory itself* between the continuum and the integers, whereas to do justice to our intuitive idea of a non-denumerable continuum we would wish to assert the absence of *any correlation whatsoever*. Here 'any correlation whatsoever' is an informal notion, for as soon as it is formalized we have once more only those correlations which one represented in a particular formal system, and the whole argument could be repeated concerning this system. Hence we suspect the existence of a non-formalizable notion, and that on a very low level of mathematics. The 'paradox' thus concerns the inadequacy of formalism to its supposed informally conceived object, and is therefore, in line with our previous discussion, a paradigm of the eventually informal and philosophical character of metamathematical anxiety. Naturally this whole argument is unprecisely formulated and probably contains outright fallacies; this is unimportant if it has served its purpose of directing attention to the proximate grounds of anxiety surrounding the Löwenheim-Skolem theorem. The exhibition of the fallacies would in any case not resolve the anxiety.

As a first step to this resolution we state the theorem again with pedantic lucidity; we use this to pass to a discussion of the relation between formalism and its object. The theorem deals in its usually stated form only with systems framed in the notation of the first-order functional calculus: recent extensions to higher-order calculi by Henkin offer no essential further problem from our present point of view. We now explain what the first-order functional calculus is.

By an atomic matrix will be meant a property of or a relation between a finite number of variables, e.g. 'x is a woman,' 'x hates y,' 'x takes z from y.' Here the variables 'x,' 'y,' 'z' are without meaning, hence the matrix as a whole is without meaning. The English words 'woman,' 'hates,' 'takes,' etc. however retain their ordinary meanings. The variables are not to be regarded as names or abbreviations. We can abbreviate the English words denoting properties or relations by so-called predicate letters; thus 'x is a woman' might be 'Wx,' 'x hates y' might be 'Hxy' and so forth. As abbreviations of English words these letters have a meaning: we repeat that the variables, as mere place-holders for meanings, have in themselves no meaning, and so the entire matrix has no meaning.

From atomic matrices we form other matrices by the following two operations. (1) *Quantification.* The variables occurring in atomic matrices, along with certain other variables to be explained presently, are called free (i.e., meaningless) variables. We consider a certain domain of objects U which we call the universe of discourse; it may be any non-empty domain whatever. In order to specify the interpretation of a system in which quantifiers are used we have to state not only the interpretation of the predicate letters (e.g. that 'W' means woman, 'H' means hate and so forth) but also the universe of discourse U. Now take any matrix containing a free variable (it may or may not be atomic). Take for example the matrix 'Wx' read 'x is a woman.' We take the free variable and place it in parentheses before the matrix, thus (x) Wx. The variable then becomes so-called bound or meaningful, and the meaning is that when the variable x in the matrix is interpreted as any element whatever of U, the result is true. Thus (x)Wx means that every element of U is a woman. Suppose now that the matrix contains other free variables besides x and that we prefix the quantifier (x). For example, consider the matrix (x) Hxy. This 'means' that every element of U hates y; but y is still meaningless and free, whereas the x has become meaningful and bound. Hxy needs either interpretation or quantification of both its variables to make it meaningful; (x)Hxy only needs interpretation or quantification of the y. If we further quantify the y we get (y) (x) Hxy which means in view of the interpretation of the quantifiers and of H that every element of U hates every element of U (including incidentally itself; distinct variables do not have to refer to distinct elements of U).

If free variables occur in a matrix it is meaningless pending interpretation or quantification of those variables. As soon as and not before all the variables have been bound it becomes a meaningful assertion, true or false provided that the interpretation of the quantifiers (i.e., the universe of discourse) and that of the letters 'H,' 'W,' etc., have been specified, as we assume they have.

I must apologize for boring you with this somewhat pedantic explanation of the first-order functional calculus. I claim, however, that it is necessary for my purpose to do this, and that even those who are familiar with the technique of proof in that calculus may perhaps profit from the semantical remarks made in the course of this exposition. The aim of the exposition is to clarify the notion of 'model,' which plays such an important role in the Löwenheim-Skolem theorem. Confused ideas about 'non-standard' models are rife today, and the lay reader is not entirely to blame. If this paper explains what models and non-standard models are, it will perhaps forestall confusion in philosophical circles.

(2) The other means by which complex matrices are built up from simpler and ultimately from atomic matrices is *truth-functional composition*. Given two matrices like 'x hates z' and '(y) (y is a woman)' we can form their conjunction, disjunction, implication, and so on: and given a single matrix we can form its negation. The variables which are free and meaningless in an element of a truth-functional compound are still free and meaningless, awaiting quantification, in the compound itself; similarly for the bound variables. Thus in 'x hates z or (y) (y is a woman)' x and z are free while y is bound; the matrix is meaningless until the x and z become bound also.

A matrix in which all variables are bound is the only meaningful kind of matrix. We shall speak of it as a (formal) sentence. Thus (supposing U specified e.g. as the class of people) the matrix 'not (x) (x hates x)' is equivalent to the English sentence 'not every person hates himself,' and this is true. Formal properties of relations and properties (in this case the non-reflexivity of hate) are expressed by matrices without free variables, otherwise called (formal) sentences or closed matrices.

By a system framed within the first order functional calculus is meant a set of sentences (not necessarily finite or even axiomatizable, though it will aid understanding to concentrate for the nonce on the case of axiomatizability). We give an example of a system:

1.   (x) (y) (if x hates y, then y does not hate x).
2.   (x) (y) (z) (if x hates y and y hates z, then x hates z).

These two statements together (we could have conjoined them into a single statement) assert (falsely if U means all people) that U is partially ordered by hatred. Now let us make the notational change of writing Hxy for 'x hates y.' We get

1′.  (x) (y) (if Hxy, then not Hyx).
2′.  (x) (y) (z) (if Hxy and Hyz, then Hxz).

Let us now consider the system consisting of these two sentences in abstraction from our interpretation of U as all people and H as hatred. We now have an uninterpreted formal system; it 'means' that the (unspecified) relation H is a partial ordering of U. Pending specification of H and U, it has no real meaning; it is *true of* some choices of H and U, *false of* others. That is, some relations are partial orderings of some classes, some not.

Hence we define an uninterpreted formal system framed within the first order functional calculus as a set of sentences exactly like those of an interpreted formal system except that U is unspecified and so are the predicate letters (as H in the present instance). To any such uninterpreted system we may assign a vastly infinite number of interpretations. An interpretation consists of a specification of U (i.e., a [partial] interpretation of the quantifiers) together with an interpretation of each predicate letter appearing. Thus a possible interpretation of the uninterpreted formal system (1′, 2′) is: U (i.e., the range of the variables) is people, H is hatred. This interpretation makes false each of 1′, 2′ and a fortiori their conjunction. On the other hand if we specify U as integers and H as 'less than' we get a true interpretation; we get the truism that the relation 'less than' partially orders the integers.

A true interpretation of a system is called a model of that system. Thus the relation 'less than' and the universe of discourse consisting of the integers forms a model of the uninterpreted system (1′, 2′) and in a derivative sense a model (this time a *re*interpretation) of the interpreted system (1, 2). A system is called syntactically inconsistent if a contradiction is formally derivable from it; semantically inconsistent if it has no model. It is a fundamental theorem of (classical) metamathematics that these two notions and hence the corresponding notions of consistency are equivalent. I take this opportunity of criticizing a remark of the previous speaker that for the conceptualist the Löwenheim-Skolem theorem was a trivial consequence of his conceptualism. There are four propositions to be considered:

A.  Every syntactically consistent system possesses a model.
B.  Every system which possesses a model possesses a denumerable model.
C.  Every model is denumerable.
D.  Every syntactically consistent system possesses a denumerable model.

The previous speaker maintained correctly that for the conceptualist the Löwenheim-Skolem theorem B was a trivial consequence of the conceptualistic dogma C. D is also a form of the theorem, which from the classical standpoint (which is expressed in A) is equivalent to B. But unless the conceptualist accepts A, he cannot get D out of B. But the only grounds that he can have for accepting A are the grounds on which we usually believe the Löwenheim-Skolem theorem itself. Hence only an uninteresting form of the Löwenheim-Skolem theorem is a trivial consequence of conceptualism; no reason has been offered by the speaker why the conceptualist should accept the interesting form D. But this is a digression.

The Löwenheim-Skolem theorem may now be stated precisely as follows. Let 'system' here and henceforth mean interpreted or uninterpreted formal system framed within the first order functional calculus. *If a system has a model it has a denumerable model, hence* (for a platonist) *if a system is syntactically consistent it has a denumerable model.* Uneasiness concerning this result may now be expressed more precisely than before: it seems that we cannot ensure by means of any formal system that any of the sets, or the fields of any of the relations, referred to in the (interpreted) system are non-denumerable. For there will always exist relations satisfying all the theorems of such systems, whose fields are included in a denumerable universe of discourse U. Hence there is an elementary mathematical notion which escapes formalization within the first order functional calculus. (Notice that the sense of 'escapes formalization' is here much more far-reaching than that in which, according to Gödel's theorem, the arithmetic of natural numbers escapes formalization. For here we place no restriction on the system from the point of view of axiomatizability or recursive enumerability.)

In order to understand the reasons why this is felt to be paradoxical, it will be illuminating to reflect on just what properties of relations *are* formalizable within the first order functional calculus. First we define this phrase more precisely.

A property of relations is said to be formalizable within the first order functional calculus if there exists a consistent system framed in that calculus and a predicate letter, say 'R,' appearing in that system, such that in every model of that system the relation assigned as interpretation to 'R' has the given property. Thus the property of being a partial ordering of its field is formalizable in the first-order functional calculus while the property of having a non-denumerable field is not.

The problem of characterizing in a simple fashion the set of all properties of relations which are in this sense formalizable within the first order functional calculus is one which the literature barely touches upon in its generality. For our present purposes we concentrate upon those properties of relations which involve only the cardinality of their fields. As an example of a system restricting this cardinality consider the system having as its sole member the following sentence:

Not (y) (x) not (Hxy and Gx and not Gy)

This says that H relates a G to a non-G; hence its field must contain at least two members. Similarly we can put any desired finite lower bound on the cardinality of the field of a relation. Also by means with which you must be familiar,[1] we can compel H to have a field (at least denumerably) infinite. Finally, we can trivially by means of the axiom:

$$(x) \ (y) \ \text{not } Hxy$$

assure that H has an empty field.

The following conditions upon the cardinality of the field of a relation are thus expressible within the first order functional calculus:

A.  The condition of being void.
B.  For each finite integer n, the condition of having at least n members.
C.  The condition of being infinite.

It can be shown that no conditions other than these can be imposed by systems formalized within the first order functional calculus upon the cardinality of the field of a relation. In particular we cannot impose in this manner the restriction of having an indenumerably infinite field, nor the condition of having a field of *at most* n elements for any positive integer n.

The same holds for restrictions on the cardinality of the universe U, except that for trivial technical reasons we cannot compel it to be void. For every consistent system S there exists a number n less than or equal to A (the number sometimes designated by the first letter of the Hebrew alphabet with an inferior 'o') such that S has models in all sizes greater than or equal to n. Thus we may place any desired finite or denumerably infinite *lower* bound on the size of U by means of an axiomatization in the first order functional calculus, but we cannot impose any upper bound nor a non-denumerable lower one.

It will bear on our problem if we now consider how we would "naturally" impose an upper bound on the size of U. Clearly the sentence:

4.  Not $(x) \ (y)$ not $(z) \ (z$ is $x$ or $z$ is $y)$

where 'is' is taken in the sense of identity imposes the upper bound 2 on the size of U. Yet is not this couched within the first order functional calculus? For surely we could just as easily write it:

4'.  Not $(x) \ (y)$ and $(z) \ (Izx$ or $Izy)$

But in this form, *where we do not insist on any particular interpretation of I*, we no longer impose any upper bound whatever on the size of U. It is only when we interpret I as identity that the intended effect is achieved. For instance 4' has an infinite model, if we take U for example as the set of integers and I as congruence *modulo 2*.

---

[1] $(x)$ not $Hxx \ (x)$ not $(y)$ not $Hxy$. [*The editors.*]

We therefore see that if certain interpretations are specified in advance, we can say more about an unspecified relation H than we can if no interpretation is specified in advance. For instance if 4' appears in some formal system along with other sentences containing 'H,' and if I is interpreted as identity, then neither U nor a fortiori the field of H can contain more than two elements; but in the light of our previous discussion this restriction could not have been put upon H if the interpretation of I had been left free.

We are thus led to the conception of a *standard model*, which we define as follows. Let there be given a system S formalized within the first-order functional calculus, and let there be given preassigned interpretations to certain of the predicate letters appearing therein, and possibly also to U. Then by an (arbitrary) model will be meant any interpretation of U and of the predicate letters appearing in S which makes all the sentences in S come out true, regardless of whether or not the interpretations coincide with the preassigned ones. Those models which accord with the preassigned interpretation are called standard (relative to that preassigned interpretation); the others non-standard. Thus we can say that, relative to the interpretation of I as identity, no standard model of a system containing 4' has more than two elements in its U, but that non-standard models of arbitrarily great cardinality exist.

We can now deal formally with the so-called 'Skolem paradox.' Let the interpretation 'x is a member of y' be given to the Greek letter epsilon. Then by the Löwenheim-Skolem theorem, denumerable models for set-theory exist; that is, there exist relations having all the formal properties assigned to class-membership by the axioms of (any consistent) set-theory, and also having denumerable fields. But *none of these relations is class-membership*; for class-membership certainly has a vastly non-denumerable field. Hence all the Skolem-Löwenheim models of set-theory are non-standard, relative to the given interpretation. Indeed there is evidently only one standard model of set-theory, because the predicate-letter epsilon, the only one which appears, is already preassigned on interpretation.

The insight we get into the relation between formalism and its object is therefore as follows: Formalism can determine its object with varying degrees of specificity. The more determination we bring to the interpretation of the formalism, the more formalism will determine its object. Thus any finite relation can be determined to within an isomorphism by a system in which a symbol I for identity occurs, provided this symbol is antecedently given a standard interpretation: but if the interpretation of I is left free, the other relations of the system are determined only to within a 'homomorphism.'

This remark sounds trivial, however, if we take the limiting case that *all* the symbols have been preassigned on interpretation, as is in particular the case with the set-theoretic situation which prompted the original anxiety. For then it seems to say only that if we fix the interpretation of epsilon, the set-theory has but one model, namely the one which interprets epsilon in the way we fixed it, and U as the field of epsilon thus interpreted; and that this model is indenumerable. But then it seems after all that the indenumerability arose in the (informal, external) interpretation and not in the formalism itself; so that after all there is a good sense in which formalism is inadequate to express indenumerability.

This difficulty can I think be resolved by distinguishing a private and a public aspect of formalism. Formalism in its private aspect is a computational device for avoiding 'raw thought'—we operate with symbols which keep their shape rather than with ideas which fly away from us. All real mathematics is made with ideas, but formalism is always ready in case we grow afraid of the shifting vastness of our creations. Ultimately formalism in its private aspect is an expression of fear. But fear can lend us wings and armor, and formalism can penetrate where intuition falters, leading her to places where she can again come into her own. The Skolem 'paradox' thus proclaims our need never to forget completely our intuitions. We could shift to a formalism indistinguishable from set-theory and it could be something other than set-theory. It only remains set-theory as long as the intuition of membership has not slipped away from us. It could be formally the same and have a grotesquely different meaning. The astonishing thing is perhaps less the Skolem "paradox" that formalism apart from prior interpretation does not completely determine its object, than the fact that an uninterpreted formalism can determine its object at all. At least, even if our intuition of membership perishes entirely, we can rely on set-theory not to turn overnight into the theory of some finite group, even though we cannot guarantee that it will not turn into a theory about some complicated arithmetical relation.

If it did it would look the same in print, though the motivation would puzzle the reader. This brings us to the public aspect of formalism. In those cases (e.g., the setting of a lower bound on the cardinality of the universe) where formalism adequately delimits its object, we may consider that communication has been established. (But really even this is a matter of degree; for we presuppose a standard interpretation of truth-functional connectives even in arbitrary models, and perhaps a good deal more.) But (ignoring this point) there seem to be no *formal* means of assuring that our conception of membership any more than our perception of a particular sense-quality is the same as another person's. For no finite or even infinite number of formal assertions agreed on by us both could be evidence that his set-theory was not in my sense denumerable. Of course it would not be denumerable in his sense, but I would not know if he meant by 'denumerable' what I meant by 'denumerable' unless I knew that he meant the same as I meant by 'membership.' The second philosophical lesson of the Löwenheim-Skolem theorem is that the formal communication of mathematics presupposes an informal community of understanding.

A formalism constrains and limits its objects in certain ways. If we preassign an interpretation to some of these objects, we thereby restrict the interpretation of the rest. A formalism which is *completely* uninterpreted (i.e., even in regard to truth-functional connectives, the part of the meaning of quantifiers which is independent of the specification of U, and the juxtaposition of symbols) imposes *no* restriction on its object. If we fix these three interpretations, there is still room for some latitude. In particular, a formalism interpreted only in these respects cannot force the interpretation of any of its predicate-letters as a relation with a nondenumerable field. Such is the burden of the Löwenheim-Skolem theorem.

The constraint exerted by a formalism on its objects is therefore a resultant of the formalism itself and the preassigned interpretation of its symbols. The theorem places before us in a striking fashion the role of the second factor.

# GÖDEL'S PROOF[*]

ERNEST NAGEL (1901–    ) of Rockefeller University has written extensively in the philosophy of science. His books include *Introduction to Logic and Scientific Method* (with M. R. Cohen); *Principles of The Theory of Probability*; *Logic Without Ontology*; and *The Structure of Science*.

JAMES R. NEWMAN (1907–1966) was a distinguished writer on science and mathematics. He was perhaps best known for having edited the four-volume *World of Mathematics*.

In 1931 a young mathematician of 25 named Kurt Gödel published in a German scientific periodical a paper which was read only by a few mathematicians. It bore the forbidding title: "On Formally Undecidable Propositions of *Principia Mathematica* and Related Systems." It dealt with a subject that has never attracted more than a small group of investigators, and its reasoning was so novel and complex that it was unintelligible even to most mathematicians. But Gödel's paper has become a landmark of science in the 20th century. As "Gödel's proof," its general conclusions have become known to many scientists, and appreciated to be of revolutionary importance. Gödel's achievement has been recognized by many honors; not long after his paper appeared the young man was invited from Vienna to join the Institute for Advanced Study at Princeton, and he has been a permanent member of the Institute since 1938. When Harvard University awarded him an honorary degree in 1952, the citation described his proof as one of the most important advances in logic in modern times.

Gödel attacked a central problem in the foundations of mathematics. The axiomatic method invented by the Greeks has always been regarded as the strongest foundation for erecting systems of mathematical thinking. This method, as every student of logic knows, consists in assuming certain propositions or axioms (e.g., if equals be added to equals, the wholes are equal) and deriving other propositions or theorems from the axioms. Until recent times the only branch of mathematics that was considered by most students to be established on sound axiomatic foundations was geometry. But within the past two centuries powerful and rigorous systems of axioms have been developed for other branches of mathematics, including the familiar arithmetic of whole numbers. Mathematicians came to hope and believe that the whole realm of mathematical reasoning could be brought into order by way of the axiomatic method.

Gödel's paper put an end to this hope. He confronted mathematicians with proof that the axiomatic method has certain inherent limitations which rule out any possibility that even the ordinary arithmetic of whole numbers can ever be fully systematized by its means. What is more, his proofs brought the astounding and melancholy revelation that it is impossible to establish the logical consistency of any complex deductive system except by assuming principles of reasoning whose own internal consistency is as open to question as that of the system itself.

Gödel's paper was not, however, altogether negative. It introduced into the foundations of mathematics a new technique of analysis which is comparable in fertility with René Descartes's historic introduction of the algebraic method into geometry. Gödel's work initiated whole new branches of study in mathematical logic. It provoked a reappraisal of mathematical philosophies, and indeed of philosophies of knowledge in general.

His epoch-making paper is still not widely known, and its detailed demonstrations are too complex to be followed by a nonmathematician, but the main outlines of his argument and conclusions can be understood. This article will recount the background of the problem and the substance of Gödel's findings.

## THE NEW MATHEMATICS

The 19th century witnessed a tremendous surge forward in mathematical research. Many fundamental problems that had long resisted solution were solved; new areas of mathematical study were created; foundations were newly built or rebuilt for various branches of the discipline. The most revolutionary development was the construction of new geometries by replacing certain of Euclid's axioms with different ones. In particular the modification of Euclid's parallel axiom led to immensely fruitful results [see "The Straight Line," by Morris Kline; *Scientific American*, March]. It was this successful departure that stimulated the development of an axiomatic basis for other branches of mathematics which had been cultivated in a more or less intuitive manner. One important conclusion that emerged from this critical examination of the foundations of mathematics was that the traditional conception of mathematics as the "science of quantity" was inadequate and misleading. For it became evident that mathematics was most essentially concerned with drawing necessary conclusions from a given set of axioms (or postulates). It was thus recognized to be much more "abstract" and "formal" than had been traditionally supposed: more "abstract" because mathematical statements can be construed to be about anything whatsoever, not merely about some inherently circumscribed set of objects or traits of objects; more "formal" because the validity of a mathematical demonstration is grounded in the structure of statements rather than in the nature of a particular subject matter. The postulates of any branch of demonstrative mathematics are not inherently about space, quantity, apples, angles or budgets, and any special meaning that may be associated with the postulates' descriptive terms plays no essential role in the process of deriving theorems. The question that confronts a pure mathematician (as distinct from the scientist who employs mathematics in investigating a special subject matter) is not whether the postulates he assumes or the conclusions he deduces from them are true, but only whether the alleged conclusions are in fact the necessary logical consequences of the initial assumptions. This approach recalls Bertrand Russell's famous epigram: Pure mathematics is the subject in which we do not know what we are talking about, nor whether what we are saying is true.

A land of rigorous abstraction, empty of all familiar landmarks, is certainly not easy to get around in. But it offers compensations in the form of a new freedom of movement and fresh vistas. As mathematics became more abstract, men's minds were emancipated from habitual connotations of language and could construct novel systems of postulates. Formalization led in fact to a great variety of systems of considerable mathematical interest and value. Some of these systems, it must be admitted, did not lend themselves to interpretations as obviously intuitive ("common sense") as those of Euclidean geometry or arithmetic, but this fact caused no alarm. Intuition, for one thing, is an elastic faculty. Our children will have no difficulty in accepting as intuitively obvious the paradoxes of relativity, just as we do not boggle at ideas which were regarded as wholly unintuitive a couple of generations ago. Moreover intuition, as we all know, is not a safe guide: it cannot be used safely as a criterion of either truth or fruitfulness in scientific explorations.

However, the increased abstractness of mathematics also raised a more serious problem. When a set of axioms is taken to be about a definite and familiar domain of .objects, it is usually possible to ascertain whether the axioms are indeed true of these objects, and if they are true, they must also be mutually consistent. But the abstract non-Euclidean axioms appeared to be plainly false as descriptions of space, and, for that matter, doubtfully true of anything. Thus the problem of establishing the internal consistency of non-Euclidean systems was formidable. In Riemannian geometry, for example, the famous parallel postulate of Euclid is replaced by the assumption that through a given point outside a line *no* parallel to the line can be drawn in the same plane. Now suppose the question: Is the Riemannian set of postulates consistent? They are apparently not true of the ordinary space of our experience. How then is their consistency to be tested? How can one prove they will not lead to contradictory theorems?

A general method for solving this problem was proposed. The underlying idea was to find a "model" for the postulates so that each postulate was converted into a true statement about the model. The procedure goes something like this. Let us take the word "class" to signify a collection of distinguishable elements, or "members." (For example, the class of prime numbers less than 10 is a collection consisting of 2, 3, 5 and 7 as members.) Suppose now we consider two purely abstract classes, K and L, concerning which these postulates are given:

1.  Any two members of K are contained in just one member of L.
2.  No member of K is contained in more than two members of L.
3.  The members of K are not all contained in a single member of L.
4.  Any two members of L contain just one member of K.
5.  No member of L contains more than two members of K.

From this little set we can derive, by using customary rules of inference, certain theorems. For example, it can be shown that K contains just three members. But is the set a consistent one, so that mutually contradictory theorems can never be derived from it? This is where we invoke the help of a model, or interpretation, of the classes. Let K be the vertices of a triangle, and L its sides. Each of the five abstract postulates is then converted into a true statement: *e.g.*, the first postulate asserts that any two of the vertices are contained on just one side. In this way the set is proved to be consistent.

At first thought such a procedure may seem to suffice to establish the consistency of an abstract system such as plane Riemannian geometry. We may adopt a model embodying the Riemannian postulates in which the expression "plane" signifies the surface of a Euclidean sphere; the expression "point," a point on this surface; the expression "straight line," an arc of a great circle on this surface, and so on. Each Riemannian postulate can then be converted into a theorem of Euclid. For example, on this interpretation the Riemannian parallel postulate reads as follows: Through a point on the surface of a sphere, no arc of a great circle can be drawn parallel to a given arc of a great circle.

All gentlemen are polite.
No bankers are polite.
No gentlemen are bankers.

---

$$g \subset p$$
$$b \subset \overline{p}$$
$$\therefore g \subset \overline{b}$$

- - - - - - - - - - - - - - - - - - - - - - - - - -

$$g\,\overline{p} = 0$$
$$b\,p = 0$$
$$\overline{g\,b = 0}$$

SYMBOLIC LOGIC was invented in the middle of the 19th century by the English mathematician George Boole. In this illustration a syllogism is translated into his notation in two different ways. In the upper group of formulas, the symbol $\subset$ means "is contained in." Thus $g \subset p$ says that the class of gentlemen is included in the class of polite persons. In the equations below two letters together mean the class of things having both characteristics. For example, $bp$ means the class of individuals who are bankers and polite. The second equation in the group says that this class has no members. A line above a letter means "not." (Not-$p$, for example, means impolite.)

Unhappily this method is vulnerable to a serious objection; namely, that it attempts to solve a problem in one domain merely by shifting the problem to another (or, to put it another way, we invoke Euclid to demonstrate the consistency of a system which subverts Euclid). Riemannian geometry is proved to be consistent only if Euclidean geometry is consistent. Query, then: Is Euclidian geometry consistent? If we attempt to answer this question by invoking yet another model, we are no closer to our goal. In short, any proof obtained by this method will be only a "relative" proof of consistency, not an absolute proof.

So long as we can interpret a system by a model containing only a finite number of elements, we have no great difficulty in proving the consistency of its postulates. For example, the triangle model which we used to test the K and L class postulates is finite, and accordingly it is comparatively simple to determine by actual inspection whether the postulates are "true" and hence consistent. Unfortunately most of the postulate systems that constitute the foundations of important branches of mathematics cannot be mirrored in finite models; they can be satisfied only by non-finite ones. In a well-known set of axioms for elementary arithmetic one of the axioms asserts that every integer in the sequence of whole numbers has an immediate successor which differs from any preceding integer. Obviously any model used to test the set of postulates must mirror the infinity of elements postulated by this axiom. It follows that the truth (and so the consistency) of the set cannot be established by inspection and enumeration. Apparently we have reached an impasse.

## RUSSELL'S PARADOX

It may be tempting to suggest at this point that we can be sure that a set of postulates is consistent, *i.e.*, free from contradictions, if the basic notions employed are transparently "clear" and "certain." But the history of thought has not dealt kindly with the doctrine of intuitive knowledge implicit in this suggestion. In certain areas of mathematical research radical contradictions have turned up in spite of the "intuitive" clarity of the notions involved in the assumptions, and despite the seemingly consistent character of the intellectual constructions performed. Such contradictions (technically called "antinomies") have emerged, for example, in the theory of infinite numbers developed by Georg Cantor in the 19th century. His theory was built on the elementary and seemingly "clear" concept of class. Since modern systems in other branches of mathematics, particularly elementary arithmetic, have been built on the foundation of the theory of classes, it is pertinent to ask whether they, too, are not infected with contradictions.

In point of fact, Bertrand Russell constructed a contradiction within the framework of elementary logic itself. It is precisely analogous to the contradiction first developed in the Cantorian theory of infinite classes. Russell's antinomy can be stated as follows: All classes apparently may be divided into two groups: those which do not contain themselves as members, and those which do. An example of the first is the class of mathematicians, for patently the class itself is not a mathematician and is therefore not a member of itself. An example of the second is the class of all thinkable concepts, for the class of all thinkable concepts is itself a thinkable concept, and is therefore a member of itself. We shall call the first type of class "normal," and the second type "non-normal." Now let N stand for the class of all normal classes. We ask whether N itself is a normal class. If so, it is a member of itself. But in that case N is nonnormal, because by definition a class which contains itself is non-normal. Yet if N is non-normal and thus a member of itself, it must be normal, because by definition all the members of N are normal. In short, N is normal if and only if N is non-normal. This fatal contradiction results from an uncritical use of the apparently pellucid notion of class.

Other paradoxes were found later, each of them constructed by means of familiar and seemingly cogent modes of reasoning. Non-finite models by their very nature involve the use of possibly inconsistent sets of postulates. Thus it became clear that, although the model method for establishing the consistency of axioms is an invaluable mathematical tool, that method does not supply a final answer to the problem it was designed to resolve.

## HILBERT'S META-MATHEMATICS

The eminent German mathematician David Hilbert then adopted the opposite approach of eschewing models and draining mathematics of any meaning whatever. In Hilbert's complete formalization, mathematical expressions are regarded simply as empty signs. The postulates and theorems constructed from the system of signs (called a calculus) are simply sequences of meaningless marks which are combined in strict agreement with explicitly stated rules. The derivation of theorems from postulates can be viewed as simply the transformation of one set of such sequences, or "strings," into another set of "strings," in accordance with precise rules of operation. In this manner Hilbert hoped to eliminate the danger of using any unavowed principles of reasoning.

Formalization is a difficult and tricky business, but it serves a valuable purpose. It reveals logical relations in naked clarity, as does a cut-away working model of a machine. One is able to see the structural patterns of various "strings" of signs: how they hang together, how they are combined, how they nest in one another, and so on. A page covered with the "meaningless" marks of such a formalized mathematics does not *assert* anything—it is simply an abstract design or a mosaic possessing a certain structure. But configurations of such a system can be described, and statements can be made about their various relations to one another. One may say that a "string" is pretty, or that it resembles another "string," or that one "string" appears to be made up of three others, and so on. Such statements will evidently be meaningful.

Now it is plain that any meaningful statements about a meaningless system do not themselves belong to that system. Hilbert assigned them to a separate realm which he called "meta-mathematics." Meta-mathematical statements are statements *about* the signs and expressions of a formalized mathematical system: about the kinds and arrangements of such signs when they are combined to form longer strings of marks called "formulas," or about the relations between formulas which may obtain as a consequence of the rules of manipulation that have been specified for them.

A few examples will illustrate Hilbert's distinction between mathematics (a system of meaningless expressions) and meta-mathematics (statements about mathematics). Consider the arithmetical expression $2 + 3 = 5$. This expression belongs to mathematics and is constructed entirely out of elementary arithmetical signs. Now we may make a statement about the displayed expression, *viz.*: "'$2 + 3 = 5$' is an arithmetical formula." The statement does not express an arithmetical fact: it belongs to meta-mathematics, because it characterizes the string of arithmetical signs. Similarly the expression $x = x$ belongs to mathematics, but the statement "'x' is a variable" belongs to meta-mathematics. We may also make the following meta-mathematical statement: "The formula '$0 = 0$' is derivable from the formula 'x = x' by substituting the numeral '0' for the variable 'x.'" This statement specifies in what manner one arithmetical formula can be obtained from another formula, and thereby describes how the two formulas are related to each other. Again, we may make the meta-mathematical statement: " '0 ≠ 0' is not a theorem." It says that the formula in question is not derivable from the axioms of arithmetic, or in other words, that a certain relation does not hold between the specified formulas of the system. Finally, the following statement also belongs to meta-mathematics: "Arithmetic is consistent" (*i.e.*, it is not possible to derive from the axioms of arithmetic both the formula $0 = 0$ and also the formula $0 \neq 0$).

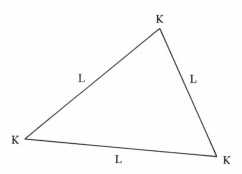

MODEL for a set of postulates about two classes, K and L, is a triangle whose vertices are the members of K and whose sides are the members of L. The geometrical model shows that the postulates are consistent.

Upon this foundation—separation of meta-mathematical descriptions from mathematics itself—Hilbert attempted to build a method of "absolute" proof of the internal consistency of mathematical systems. Specifically, he sought to develop a theory of proof which would yield demonstrations of consistency by an analysis of the purely structural features of expressions in completely formalized (or "uninterpreted") calculi. Such an analysis consists exclusively of noting the kinds and arrangements of signs in formulas and determining whether a given combination of signs can be obtained from others in accordance with the explicitly stated rules of operation. An absolute proof of the consistency of arithmetic, if one could be constructed, would consist in showing by meta-mathematical procedures of a "finitistic" (non-infinite) character that two "contradictory" formulas, such as $(0 = 0)$ and its negation, cannot both be derived from the axioms or initial formulas by valid rules of inference.

It may be useful, by way of illustration, to compare meta-mathematics as a theory of proof with the theory of chess. Chess is played with 32 pieces of specified design on a square board containing 64 square subdivisions, where the pieces may be moved in accordance with fixed rules. Neither the pieces, nor the squares, nor the positions of the pieces on the board signify anything *outside* the game. In this sense the pieces and their configurations on the board are "meaningless." Thus the game is analogous to a formalized mathematical calculus. The pieces and the squares of the board correspond to the elementary signs of the calculus; the initial positions of the pieces correspond to the axioms or initial formulas of the calculus; their subsequent positions correspond to formulas derived from the axioms (*i.e.*, to the theorems), and the rules of the game correspond to the rules of inference for the calculus. Now, though configurations of pieces on the board are "meaningless," statements about these configurations, like meta-mathematical statements about mathematical formulas, are quite meaningful. A "meta-chess" statement may assert that there are 20 possible opening moves for White, or that, given a certain configuration of pieces on the board with White to move, Black is mate in three moves. Moreover, one can prove general "meta-chess" theorems on the basis of the finite number of permissible configurations on the board. The meta-chess theorem about the number of possible opening moves for White can be established in this way, and so can the meta-chess theorem that if White has only two Knights, it is impossible for White to mate Black. These and other "meta-chess" theorems can, in other words, be proved by finitistic methods of reasoning, consisting in the examination of each of a finite number of configurations that can occur under stated conditions. The aim of Hilbert's theory of proof, similarly, was to demonstrate by such finitistic methods the impossibility of deriving certain contradictory formulas in a calculus.

## THE *PRINCIPIA*

It was Hilbert's approach, coupled with the formalization of logic itself in the famous *Principia Mathematica* by Alfred North Whitehead and Bertrand Russell, that led to the crisis to which Gödel supplied a final answer.

The grand object of *Principia*, published in 1910, was to demonstrate that mathematics is only a chapter of logic. But it made two contributions which are of particular interest to us here. First, following up work by the 19th-century pioneer George Boole, it supplied a system of symbols which permitted all statements of pure mathematics to be codified in a standard manner [see "Symbolic Logic," by John E. Pfeiffer; *Scientific American*, December, 1950]. Secondly, it stated in explicit form most of the rules of formal logic that are employed in mathematical proofs. Thus *Principia* provided an essential instrument for investigating the entire system of arithmetic as a system of "meaningless" marks which could be operated upon in accordance with explicitly stated rules.

We turn now to the formalization of a small portion of *Principia*, namely, the elementary logic of propositions. The task is to convert this fragment into a "meaningless" calculus of uninterpreted signs and to demonstrate a method of proving that the calculus is free from contradictions.

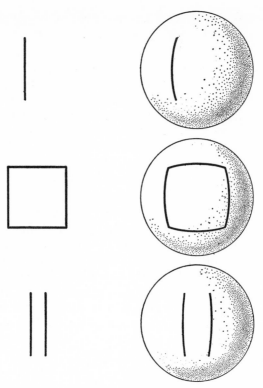

Non-Euclidean Geometry of Bernhard Riemann can be represented by a Euclidean model. The plane becomes the surface of a Euclidean sphere, points on the plane become points on this surface, straight lines become great circles. Thus a portion of the plane bounded by segments of straight lines is depicted as a portion of the sphere bounded by parts of great circles (*center*). Two parallel line segments are two segments of great circles (*bottom*), and these, if extended, indeed intersect, thus contradicting the parallel postulate.

Four steps are involved. First we must specify the complete "vocabulary" of signs to be employed in the calculus. Second, we state the "formation rules" (the rules of "grammar") which indicate the combinations of signs permissible as formulas (or "sentences"). Third, we specify the "transformation rules," which tell how formulas may be derived from others. Finally, we select certain formulas as axioms which serve as foundations for the entire system. The "theorems" of the system are all the formulas, including the axioms, that can be derived from the axioms by applying the transformation rules. A "proof" consists of a finite sequence of legitimate formulas, each of which is either an axiom or is derivable from preceding formulas in the sequence by the transformation rules.

The vocabulary for the elementary logic of propositions (often also called the "sentential calculus") is extremely simple. The "sentential" variables (which correspond to sentences or statements) are certain letters:

*p*, *q*, *r* and so on. Then there are several connectives: ∼, which stands for "not"; v which stands for "or"; ⊃, which stands for "if . . . then," and ·, which stands for "and." Parenthesis marks are used as signs of punctuation.

Each sentential variable counts as a formula, and the signs may be combined according to the formation rules to form other formulas: *e.g.*, *p* ⊃ *q*. If a given sentence (*p* ⊃ *q*) is a formula, so is its negation ∼ (*p* ⊃ *q*). If two sentences, $S_1$ and $S_2$, are formulas, so is the combination ($S_1$) v ($S_2$). Similar conventions apply to the other connectives.

| | |
|---|---|
| 1  (*p* v *p*) ⊃ *p*<br>If either *p* or *p*, then *p* | If either Henry VIII was a boor or Henry VIII was a boor, then Henry VIII was a boor. |
| 2  *p* ⊃ (*p* v *q*)<br>If *p*, then either *p* or *q* | If psychoanalysis is valid then either psychoanalysis is valid or headache powders are better. |
| 3  (*p* v *q*) ⊃ (*q* v *p*)<br>If either *p* or *q*, then<br>either *q* or *p* | If either Immanuel Kant was punctual or Hollywood is sinful then either Hollywood is sinful or Immanuel Kant was punctual. |
| 4  (*p* ⊃ *q*) ⊃ [(*r* v *p*) ⊃ (*r* v *q*)]<br>If *p* implies *q*, then (either<br>*r* or *p*) implies (either *r* or *q*) | If ducks waddle implies that √2 is a number then (either Churchill drinks brandy or ducks waddle) implies (either Churchill drinks brandy or √2 is a number). |

SENTENTIAL CALCULUS, or the elementary logic of propositions, is based on four axioms. The nonsense statements illustrate how general is the "meaning" of the symbols.

For transformations there are just two rules. One, the rule of substitution, says that if a sentence containing sentential variables has been assumed, any formulas may be substituted everywhere for these variables, so that the new sentence will count as a logical consequence of the original one. For example, having accepted *p* ⊃ *p* (if *p*, then *p*), we can always substitute *q* for *p*, obtaining as a theorem the formula *q* ⊃ *q*; or we may substitute (*p* v *q*) for *p*, obtaining (*p* v *q*) ⊃ (*p* v *q*). The other rule, that of detachment, simply says that if the sentences $S_1$ and $S_1$ ⊃ $S_2$ are logically true, we may also accept as logically true the sentence $S_2$.

The calculus has four axioms, essentially those of *Principia*, which are given in the table . . . along with nonsensical English sentences to illustrate their independence of meaning. The clumsiness of the translations, especially in the case of the fourth axiom, will perhaps help the reader to realize the advantages of using a special symbolism.

## SEARCH FOR A PROOF

Each of these axioms may seem "obvious" and trivial. Nevertheless it is possible to derive from them with the help of the stated transformation rules an indefinitely large class of theorems which are far from obvious or trivial. However, at this point we are interested not in deriving theorems from the axioms but in showing that this set of axioms is not contradictory. We wish to prove that, using the transformation rules, it is impossible to derive from the axioms any formula S (*i.e.*, any expression which would normally count as a sentence) together with its negation $\sim$ S.

Now it can be shown that $p \supset (\sim p \supset q)$ (if $p$, then if not-$p$ then $q$) is a theorem in the calculus. Let us suppose, for the sake of demonstration, that a formula S and its contradictory $\sim$ S were both deducible from the axioms, and test the consequences by means of this theorem. By substituting S for $p$ in the theorem, as permitted by the rule of substitution, we first obtain $S \supset (\sim S \supset q)$. From this, assuming S to be demonstrably true, we could next obtain, by the detachment rule, $\sim S \supset q$. Finally, if we assume $\sim$ S also is demonstrable, by the detachment rule we would get $q$. Since we can substitute any formula whatsoever for $q$, this means that any formula whatsoever would be deducible from the axioms. Thus if both S and its contradictory $\sim$ S were deducible from the axioms, then *any* formula would be deducible. We arrive, then, at the conclusion that if the calculus is not consistent (*i.e.*, if both S and $\sim$ S are deducible) any theorem can be derived from the axioms. Accordingly, to prove the consistency of the calculus, our task is reduced to finding at least one formula which cannot be derived from the axioms.

The way this is done is to employ meta-mathematical reasoning upon the system before us. The actual procedure is elegant. It consists in finding a characteristic of formulas which satisfies the three following conditions. (1) it is common to all four axioms; (2) it is "hereditary," that is, any formula derived from the axioms (*i.e.*, any theorem) must also have the property; (3) there must be at least one formula which does not have the characteristic and is therefore not a theorem. If we succeed in this three-fold task, we shall have an absolute proof of the consistency of the axioms. If we can find an array of signs that conforms to the requirements of being a formula but does not possess the specified characteristic, this formula cannot be a theorem. In other words, the finding of a single formula which is not a theorem suffices to establish the consistency of the system.

Let us choose as a characteristic of the required kind the property of being a "tautology." In common parlance a tautology is usually considered

## Connectives and Elementary Signs

| Signs | Gödel Number | Meaning |
|-------|--------------|---------|
| ~ | 1 | not |
| v | 2 | or |
| ⊃ | 3 | If . . . then |
| ⱻ | 4 | There is an . . . |
| = | 5 | equals |
| 0 | 6 | zero |
| S | 7 | The next following number |
| ( | 8 | punctuation mark |
| ) | 9 | punctuation mark |
| , | 10 | punctuation mark |

## Sentential Variables (Each Designated by a Number Greater Than 10 and Divisible by 3)

| Variables | Gödel Number | Sample |
|-----------|--------------|--------|
| $p$ | 12 | Henry VIII was a boor. |
| $q$ | 15 | Headache powders are better. |
| $r$ | 18 | Ducks waddle. |
| etc. | | |

## Individual Variables (Each Designated by a Number Greater Than 10 Which Leaves a Remainder of 1 When Divided by 3)

| Variables | Gödel Number | Meaning |
|-----------|--------------|---------|
| $x$ | 13 | a numerical variable |
| $y$ | 16 | a numerical variable |
| $z$ | 19 | a numerical variable |
| etc. | | |

## Predicate Variables (Each Designated by a Number Greater Than 10 Which Leaves a Remainder of 2 When Divided by 3)

| Variables | Gödel Number | Sample |
|-----------|--------------|--------|
| P | 14 | Being a boor |
| Q | 17 | Being a headache powder |
| R | 20 | Being a duck |
| etc. | | |

Elementary Gödel Numbers are assigned to every symbol used in his system of symbolic logic in accordance with the orderly scheme which is illustrated in the table above.

to be a redundant statement such as: "John is the father of Charles and Charles is a son of John." But in logic a tautology is defined as a statement which excludes no logical possibilities—e.g., "Either it is raining or it is not raining." Another way of putting this is to say that a tautology is "true in all possible worlds." We apply this definition to formulas in the system we are considering. A formula is said to be a tautology if it is invariably true regardless of whether its elementary constituents ($p$, $q$, $r$ and so on) are true or false. Now all four of our axioms plainly possess the property of being tautologous. For example, the first axiom, $(p \lor p) \supset p$, is true regardless of whether $p$ is assumed to be true or is assumed to be false. The axiom says, for instance: "If either Mount Rainier is 20,000 feet high or Mount Rainier is 20,000 feet high, then Mount Rainier is 20,000 feet high." It makes no difference whether Mount Rainier is actually 20,000 feet high or not: the statement is still true in either case. A similar demonstration can be made for the other axioms.

Next it is possible to prove that the property of being a tautology is hereditary under the transformation rules, though we shall not turn aside to give the demonstration. It follows that every formula properly derived from the axioms (i.e., every theorem) must be a tautology. Having performed these two steps, we are ready to look for a formula which does not possess the characteristic of being a tautology. We do not have to look very hard. For example, $p \lor q$ fits the requirements. Clearly it is not a tautology; it is the same as saying: "Either John is a philosopher or Charles reads *Scientific American*." This is patently not a truth of logic; it is not a sentence that is true irrespective of the truth or falsity of its elementary constituents. Thus $p \lor q$, though it purports to be a gosling, is in fact a duckling; it is a formula but it is not a theorem.

We have achieved our goal. We have found at least one formula which is not a theorem, therefore the axioms must be consistent.

## GÖDEL'S ANSWER

The sentential calculus is an example of a mathematical system for which the objectives of Hilbert's theory of proof are fully realized. But this calculus codifies only a fragment of formal logic. The question remains: Can a formalized system embracing the whole of arithmetic be proved consistent in the sense of Hilbert's program?

This was the conundrum that Gödel answered. His paper in 1931 showed that all such efforts to prove arithmetic to be free from contradictions are doomed to failure.

His main conclusions were twofold. In the first place, he showed that it is impossible to establish a meta-mathematical proof of the consistency of a system comprehensive enough to contain the whole of arithmetic—unless, indeed, this proof itself employs rules of inference much more powerful than the transformation rules used in deriving theorems within the system. In short, one dragon is slain only to create another.

Gödel's second main conclusion was even more surprising and revolutionary, for it made evident a fundamental limitation in the power of the axiomatic method itself. Gödel showed that *Principia*, or any other system within which arithmetic can be developed, is essentially incomplete. In other words, given *any* consistent set of arithmetical axioms, there are true arithmetical statements which are not derivable from the set. A classic illustration of a mathematical "theorem" which has thwarted all attempts at proof is that of Christian Goldbach, stating that every even number is the sum of two primes. No even number has ever been found which is not the sum of two primes, yet no one has succeeded in finding a proof that the rule applies without exception to all even numbers. In reply to Gödel it might be suggested that the set of arithmetical axioms could be modified or expanded to make "underivable" statements derivable. But Gödel showed that this approach promises no final cure. That is, even if any finite number of other axioms is added, there will always be further arithmetical truths which are not formally derivable.

How did Gödel prove his conclusions? His paper is difficult. A reader must master 46 preliminary definitions, together with several important preliminary theorems, before he gets to the main results. We shall take a much easier road; nevertheless we hope at least to offer glimpses of the argument.

## GÖDEL NUMBERS

Gödel first devised a method of assigning a number as a label for each elementary sign, each formula and each proof in a formalized system. To the elementary signs he attached as "Gödel numbers" the integers from 1 to 10; to the variables he assigned numbers according to certain rules. . . . To see how a number is given to a formula of the system, let us take this formula: $(\exists x)\ (x = Sy)$, which reads literally "there is an $x$, such that $x$ is the immediate successor of $y$" and in effect says that every number has an immediate successor. The numbers associated with the formula's 10 successive signs are, respectively, 8, 4, 13, 9, 8, 13, 5, 7, 16, 9 [*see table*]. Now these numbers are to be used as exponents, or powers, of the first 10 prime numbers (*i.e.*, 2, 3, 5 and so on). The prime numbers, raised to these powers, are multiplied together. Thus we get the number $2^8 \times 3^4 \times 5^{13} \times 7^9 \times 11^8 \times 13^{13} \times 17^5 \times 19^7 \times 23^{16} \times 29^9$. The product is the Gödel number of the formula. In the same way every formula can be represented by a single unique number.

We can assign a number to a sequence of formulas, such as may occur in some proof, by a similar process. Let us say that we have a sequence of two formulas, the second derived from the first. For example, by substituting 0 for $y$ in the formula given above, we derive $(\exists x) (x = S0)$, which says that 0 has an immediate successor. Now the first and second formulas are identified by Gödel numbers which we shall call $m$ and $n$, respectively. To label this sequence, we use the Gödel numbers $m$ and $n$ as exponents and multiply the first two primes (2 and 3) raised to these powers. That is to say, the Gödel number that identifies the sequence is $2^m \times 3^n$. In like manner we can give a number to any sequence of formulas or any other expression in the system.

| A | 100 |
|---|---|
| B | $4 \times 25$ |
| C | $2^2 \times 5^2$ |
| A | 162 |
| B | $2 \times 81$ |
| C | $2^1 \times 3^4$ |
| D | $\begin{matrix} 1 & 4 \\ \downarrow & \downarrow \\ \sim & \exists \end{matrix}$ |
| E | $\sim \exists$ |

GÖDEL NUMBERS of formulas are constructed by raising the prime numbers, in sequence, to powers which are the Gödel numbers of the symbols involved. Thus 100 is not a Gödel number because its factors skip the prime number 3. On the other hand, 162 is the Gödel number for "there is not."

What has been done so far is to establish a method for completely arithmetizing a formal system. The method is essentially a set of directions for making a one-to-one correspondence between specific numbers and the various elements or combinations of elements of the system. Once an expression is given, it can be uniquely numbered. But more than that, we can retranslate any Gödel number into the expression it represents by factoring it into its component prime numbers, which can be done in only one way, as we know from a famous theorem of arithmetic [see *illustration on p.* 67]. In other words, we can take the number apart as if it were a machine, see how it was constructed and what went into it, and we can dissect an expression or a proof in the same way.

This leads to the next step. It occurred to Gödel that meta-mathematical statements can be translated into arithmetical terms by a process analogous to mapping. In geography the spatial relations between points on the spherical earth can be projected onto a flat map; in mathematical physics relations between the properties of electric currents can be mapped in terms of the flow of fluids; in mathematics itself relations in geometry can be translated into algebra. Gödel saw that if complicated meta-mathematical statements about a system could be translated into, or mirrored by, arithmetical statements within the system itself, an important gain would be achieved in clarity of expression and facility of analysis. Plainly it would be easier to deal with arithmetical counterparts of complex logical relations than with the logical relations themselves. To cite a trivial analogy: If customers in a supermarket are given tickets with numbers determining the order in which they are to be waited on, it is a simple matter to discover, merely by scrutinizing the numbers, how many persons have been served, how many are waiting, who precedes whom and by how many customers, and so on.

| A | 125,000,000 |
|---|---|
| B | $64 \times 125 \times 15,625$ |
| C | $2^6 \times 3^5 \times 5^6$ |
| D | $\begin{matrix} 6 & 5 & 6 \\ \downarrow & \downarrow & \downarrow \\ 0 & = & 0 \end{matrix}$ |
| E | $0 = 0$ |

ARITHMETICAL FORMULA "zero equals zero" has the Gödel number 125 million. Reading down from A to E, the illustration shows how the number is translated into the expression it represents; reading up, how the number for the formula is derived.

What Gödel aimed at was nothing less than the complete arithmetization of meta-mathematics. If each meta-mathematical statement could be uniquely represented in the formal system by a formula expressing a relation between numbers, questions of logical dependence between meta-mathematical statements could be explored by examining the corresponding relations between integers. Gödel did in fact succeed brilliantly in mapping the meta-mathematics of arithmetic upon arithmetic itself. We need cite only one illustration of how a meta-mathematical statement can be made to correspond to a formula in the formal arithmetical system. Let us take the formula $(p \vee p) \supset p$. We may make the meta-mathematical statement that the formula $(p \vee p)$ is the initial part of this formula. Now we can represent this meta-mathematical statement by an arithmetical formula which says in effect that the Gödel number of the initial part is a factor of the Gödel number of the complete formula. Evidently this is so, for the Gödel number of $(p \vee p)$ is $2^8 \times 3^{12} \times 5^2 \times 7^{12} \times 11^9$, while the Gödel number of $(p \vee p) \supset p$ is $2^8 \times 3^{12} \times 5^2 \times 7^{12} \times 11^9 \times 13^3 \times 17^{12}$.

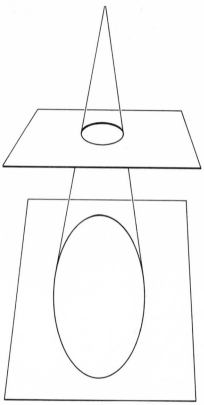

MAPPING of objects from one realm onto another is illustrated above. Points in the upper, horizontal plane can be uniquely mapped onto the lower plane, which slants downward from back to front, by drawing lines from a single point through the points of the upper plane and extending them until they intersect the lower plane. Thus a circle in the upper plane maps as an ellipse in the lower. Gödel mapped statements about arithmetic as expressions in arithmetic.

## THE UNDECIDABLE PROPOSITION

We have now arrived at the very heart of Gödel's analysis. He showed how to construct an arithmetical formula, whose Gödel number we shall suppose is $h$, which corresponds to the meta-mathematical statement, *viz.*: "The formula with Gödel number $h$ is not demonstrable." In other words, this formula (call it G) in effect asserts its own indemonstrability, though it is a legitimate formula belonging to the formal system of arithmetic. Gödel then proceeded to examine the question whether G is or is not a demonstrable formula of arithmetic. He was able to show that G is demonstrable if, and only if, its negation, $\sim$ G, also is demonstrable. But if a formula and its negation are both derivable from a set of axioms, obviously the axioms are not consistent. It follows that if arithmetic is consistent, neither G nor its negation is demonstrable. That is to say, G is an undecidable formula of arithmetic. Now from this Gödel proved the indemonstrability of the proposition that arithmetic is consistent. It can be shown that a meta-mathematical statement of arithmetic's consistency corresponds to a certain arithmetical formula, A, and that the arithmetical formula A ⊃ G (if A, then G) is demonstrable. Thus if A were demonstrable, G would be also. But we have just seen that G is not demonstrable. It follows that A is undecidable. In short, the consistency of arithmetic is undecidable by any meta-mathematical reasoning which can be represented within the formalism of arithmetic.

Gödel's analysis does not exclude a meta-mathematical demonstration of the consistency of arithmetic; indeed, such proofs have been constructed, notably by Gerhard Gentzen, a member of the Hilbert school. But these "proofs" are in a sense pointless, because they employ rules of inference whose own internal consistency is as much open to doubt as is the formal consistency of arithmetic itself. Gentzen's proof employs a rule of inference which in effect permits a formula to be derived from an infinite class of premises. And the employment of this non-finitistic meta-mathematical notion raises once more the difficulty which Hilbert's original program was intended to resolve.

There is another surprise coming. Although the formula G is undecidable, it can be shown by meta-mathematical reasoning that G is nevertheless a *true* arithmetical statement and expresses a property of the arithmetical integers. The argument for this conclusion is quite simple. We need recall only that Gödel mapped meta-mathematical statements upon arithmetical formulas in such a way that every true meta-mathematical statement corresponds to a true arithmetical formula. Now G corresponds to a meta-mathematical statement ("the formula with Gödel number $h$ is not demonstrable") which, as we have seen, is true, unless arithmetic is inconsistent. It follows that G itself must be true. We have thus established an *arithmetical* truth by a *meta-mathematical* argument.

So we come to the finale of Gödel's amazing and profound intellectual symphony. Arithmetic is incomplete, in the transparent sense that there is at least one arithmetical truth which cannot be derived from the arithmetical axioms and yet can be established by a meta-mathematical argument outside the system. Moreover, arithmetic is *essentially* incomplete, for even if the true formula G were taken as an axiom and added to the original axioms, the augmented system would still not suffice to yield formally all the truths of arithmetic: we could still construct a true formula which would not be formally demonstrable within the system. And such would be the case no matter how often we repeated the process of adding axioms to the initial set.

This remarkable conclusion makes evident an inherent limitation in the axiomatic method. Contrary to previous assumptions, the vast "continent" of arithmetical truth cannot be brought into systematic order by way of specifying once for all a fixed set of axioms from which all true arithmetical statements would be formally derivable.

## MEN AND CALCULATING MACHINES

The far-reaching import of Gödel's conclusions has not yet been fully fathomed. They show that the hope of finding an absolute proof of consistency for any deductive system expressing the whole of arithmetic cannot be realized, if such a proof must satisfy the finitistic requirements of Hilbert's original program. They also show that there is an endless number of true arithmetical statements which cannot be formally deduced from any specified set of axioms in accordance with a closed set of rules of inference. It follows that an axiomatic approach to the theory of numbers, for example, cannot exhaust the domain of arithmetic truth. Whether an all-inclusive general definition of mathematical or logical truth can be devised, and whether, as Gödel himself appears to believe, only a thorough-going Platonic realism can supply such a definition, are problems still under debate.

Gödel's conclusions have a bearing on the question whether a calculating machine can be constructed that would equal the human brain in mathematical reasoning. Present calculating machines have a fixed set of directives built into them, and they operate in a step-by-step manner. But in the light of Gödel's incompleteness theorem, there is an endless set of problems in elementary number theory for which such machines are inherently incapable of supplying answers, however complex their built-in mechanisms may be and however rapid their operations. The human brain may, to be sure, have built-in limitations of its own, and there may be mathematical problems which it is incapable of solving. But even so, the human brain appears to embody a structure of rules of operation which is far more powerful than the structure of currently conceived artificial machines. There is no immediate prospect of replacing the human mind by robots.

Gödel's proof should not be construed as an invitation to despair. The discovery that there are arithmetical truths which cannot be demonstrated formally does not mean that there are truths which are forever incapable of becoming known, or that a mystic intuition must replace cogent proof. It does mean that the resources of the human intellect have not been, and cannot be, fully formalized, and that new principles of demonstration forever await invention and discovery. We have seen that mathematical propositions which cannot be established by formal deduction from a given set of axioms may nevertheless be established by "informal" meta-mathematical reasoning.

Nor does the fact that it is impossible to construct a calculating machine equivalent to the human brain necessarily mean that we cannot hope to explain living matter and human reason in physical and chemical terms. The possibility of such explanations is neither precluded nor affirmed by Gödel's incompleteness theorem. The theorem does indicate that the structure and power of the human mind are far more complex and subtle than any non-living machine yet envisaged. Gödel's own work is a remarkable example of such complexity and subtlety. It is an occasion not for discouragement but for a renewed appreciation of the powers of creative reason.

## SUGGESTIONS FOR FURTHER READING
## ON THE FORMAL APPROACH

CARNAP, R. *The Logical Syntax of Language.* London: Routledge and Kegan Paul, New York: Harcourt, Brace and World, Inc.

——. *Formalization of Logic.* Cambridge, Mass.: Harvard University Press, 1943.

FITZPATRICK, P. J. "To Godel via Babel," *Mind,* Vol. 75 (1966), pp. 332–350.

GÖDEL, K. *On Formally Undecidable Propositions of Principia Mathematica and Related Systems.* B. Meltzer, trans. Edinburgh and London: Oliver and Boyd, 1962. [But see corrections in *The Journal of Symbolic Logic,* Vol. 30 (1965), pp. 357–362.]

GÖDEL, K. *On Formally Undecidable Propositions of the Principia Mathematica and Related Systems.* E. Mendelson, trans. in *The Undecidable,* M. Davis, I. Hewlett, ed. New York: Raven Press, 1965.

KLEENE, S. C. *Introduction to Metamathematics,* Princeton, N.J.: Van Nostrand, 1952.

MOSTOWSKI, A. *Sentences Undecidable in Formalized Arithmetic.* New York: Humanities Press, 1952.

NAGEL, E., and J. R. NEWMAN. *Gödel's Proof.* New York: New York University Press, 1959.

ROSSER, J. B. "An Informal Exposition of Proofs of Gödel's Theorems and Church's Theorem," *The Journal of Symbolic Logic,* Vol. 4 (1930), pp. 53–60. Reprinted in *The Undecidable,* M. Davis, I. Hewlett, ed. New York: Raven Press, 1965, pp. 223–230.

WITTGENSTEIN, L. *Remarks on the Foundations of Mathematics.* G. E. M. Anscombe, trans. New York: The Macmillan Company, 1965.

# *Part*
# 3 MEANING AND REFERENCE

## *Introduction*

Questions of meaning have engaged the attention of logicians from the time of Plato and Aristotle. The essays in this section all deal with this important topic. The first three of them have been enormously influential. They cover a considerable range of topics, and are not easily summarized. It may be helpful, however, for us to indicate the main issues with which each writer is concerned.

Frege begins with the well-known puzzle about statements of identity: if it is true that $a = b$, how can there be any difference between "$a = a$" and "$a = b$"? Yet whereas the first is merely analytic, the second can be informative. Frege's solution is to distinguish between the meaning (sense) and the reference (nominatum) of an expression. For example, the two expressions "the morning star" and "the evening star" *refer* to the same object but are different in *meaning*. Applying this distinction to sentences, Frege was led to distinguish the proposition expressed by a sentence from the truth-value of the sentence. Emphasis on the latter is connected with the extensionality or truth-functionality of most of modern symbolic logic. Additional discussion of the problems involved here are found in Part 7's essays on modal logic. It is worth noting here that for Frege a sentence can have perfectly good sense without having any truth-value.

Russell shares Frege's interest in statements of identity, but begins his own inquiry at a different point. A "denoting phrase," for Russell, is any phrase other than a proper name that can stand as grammatical subject of a sentence. The problem here is that a phrase may be a denoting phrase without denoting anything, as "the present King of France" in "the present King of France is bald." In such a case, what can the sentence whose subject it is be about? How can a sentence be meaningful if its apparent subject is a denoting phrase that does not denote? Russell's solution depends heavily upon quantification theory, and involves analyzing such sentences into apparently more complicated—but allegedly more straightforward—sentences in which the denotationless denoting phrase no longer occurs. Although Russell does not spell it out explicitly, his reference to the law of excluded middle makes it clear that for him any sentence that makes sense must have a truth-value.

Strawson develops an extended critique of Russell's doctrine of denoting, with the theory of descriptions coming in for special attack. A number of distinctions are drawn, as between an expression, a use of an expression, and an utterance of an expression, where an expression may be either a complete sentence or what Russell called a "denoting phrase." Although different from both, Strawson's view is closer to Frege's than to Russell's. Not only does he hold that sentences can be meaningful without being either true or false, but he distinguishes meaning from reference in terms of his own distinctions, with *meaning* a function of the sentence or expression, and *referring* a function of its use. Strawson explains Russell's alleged misinterpretations as resulting from his "preoccupation with mathematics and formal logic," and ends his essay with the remark that "ordinary language has no exact logic."

Russell's reply is vigorously polemical and brings the issues separating them into sharper focus. Russell argues that Strawson is guilty of confusing two problems, that of description with that of egocentricity. It does seem clear that some of what Strawson says cannot easily be applied to problems of description where egocentricity does not enter, as in mathematical statements.

There seem to be alternative viable ways of construing and analyzing statements of identity, denoting phrases, the contrast between meaning and reference, and the relation of exact logic to ordinary language. Whatever the final decision may be, it will have to take account of the considerations presented in the following essays.

# ON SENSE AND NOMINATUM* †

GOTTLOB FREGE (1848–1925) was a German mathematician and
philosopher who is regarded as the second founder (after
Boole) of modern symbolic logic. Although his symbolic
notation was clumsy and forbidding, it was enormously
powerful. In it he was able to establish a good part of the
logistic thesis as well as to develop many strictly logical results.
Frege's *Begriffsschrift* (1879) was the first strictly formal system
of logic, and his *Grundlagen der Arithmetik* (1884) and
*Grundgesetze der Arithmetik* Volume I (1893) and Volume II
(1903) contain his derivation of arithmetic from logic.

The idea of Sameness [1] challenges reflection. It raises questions
which are not quite easily answered. Is Sameness a relation? A relation
between objects? Or between names or signs of objects? I assumed the
latter alternative in my *Begriffsschrift*. The reasons that speak in its favor
are the following: "a = a" and "a = b" are sentences of obviously different
cognitive significance: "a = a" is valid *a priori* and according to Kant is
to be called analytic, whereas sentences of the form "a = b" often contain
very valuable extensions of our knowledge and cannot always be justified
in an *a priori* manner. The discovery that it is not a different and novel
sun which rises every morning, but that it is the very same, certainly was
one of the most consequential ones in astronomy. Even nowadays the
re-cognition (identification) of a planetoid or a comet is not always a
matter of self-evidence. If we wished to view identity as a relation between
the objects designated by the names 'a' and 'b' then "a = b" and "a = a"
would not seem different if "a = b" is true. This would express a relation of a thing to itself, namely, a relation such that it holds between
every thing and itself but never between one thing and another. What one
wishes to express with "a = b" seems to be that the signs or names 'a' and
'b' name the same thing; and in that case we would be dealing with those
signs: a relation between them would be asserted. But this relation could
hold only inasmuch as they name or designate something. The relation,
as it were, is mediated through the connection of each sign with the same
nominatum. This connection, however, is arbitrary. You cannot forbid

* From: *Readings in Philosophical Analysis* by Herbert Feigl and Wilfrid Sellars.
Copyright, 1949, Appleton-Century-Crofts, Inc. Reprinted by permission of Appleton-
Century-Crofts.
† Translated by Herbert Feigl from the article, "Ueber Sinn und Bedeutung,"
*Zeitschr. f. Philos. und Philos. Kritik;* 100, 1892. The terminology adopted is largely
that used by R. Carnap in *Meaning and Necessity*, Univ. of Chicago Press, 1947.
[1] I use this word in the sense of identity and understand "a = b" in the sense of "a
is the same as b" or "a and b coincide."

the use of an arbitrarily produced process or object as a sign for something else. Hence, a sentence like "a = b" would no longer refer to a matter of fact but rather to our manner of designation; no genuine knowledge would be expressed by it. But this is just what we do want to express in many cases. If the sign 'a' differs from the sign 'b' only as an object (here by its shape) but not by its rôle as a sign, that is to say, not in the manner in which it designates anything, then the cognitive significance of "a = a" would be essentially the same as that of "a = b," if "a = b" is true. A difference could arise only if the difference of the signs corresponds to a difference in the way in which the designated objects are given. Let a, b, c be straight lines which connect the corners of a triangle with the midpoints of the opposite sides. The point of intersection of a and b is then the same as that of b and c. Thus we have different designations of the same point and these names ('intersection of a and b', 'intersection of b and c') indicate also the manner in which these points are presented. Therefore the sentence expresses a genuine cognition.

Now it is plausible to connect with a sign (name, word combination, expression) not only the designated object, which may be called the nominatum of the sign, but also the sense (connotation, meaning) of the sign in which is contained the manner and context of presentation. Accordingly, in our examples the nominata of the expressions 'the point of intersection of a and b' and 'the point of intersection of b and c' would be the same;—not their senses. The nominata of 'evening star' and 'morning star' are the same but not their senses.

From what has been said it is clear that I here understand by 'sign' or 'name' any expression which functions as a proper name, whose nominatum accordingly is a definite object (in the widest sense of this word). But no concept or relation is under consideration here. These matters are to be dealt with in another essay. The designation of a single object may consist of several words or various signs. For brevity's sake, any such designation will be considered as a proper name.

The sense of a proper name is grasped by everyone who knows the language or the totality of designations of which the proper name is a part;[2] this, however, illuminates the nominatum, if there is any, in a very one-sided fashion. A complete knowledge of the nominatum would require that we could tell immediately in the case of any given sense whether it belongs to the nominatum. This we shall never be able to do.

The regular connection between a sign, its sense and its nominatum is such that there corresponds a definite sense to the sign and to this sense

---

[2] In the case of genuinely proper names like 'Aristotle' opinions as regards their sense may diverge. As such may, e.g., be suggested: Plato's disciple and the teacher of Alexander the Great. Whoever accepts this sense will interpret the meaning of the statement "Aristotle was born in Stagira" differently from one who interpreted the sense of 'Aristotle' as the Stagirite teacher of Alexander the Great. As long as the nominatum remains the same, these fluctuations in sense are tolerable. But they should be avoided in the system of a demonstrative science and should not appear in a perfect language.

there corresponds again a definite nominatum; whereas not one sign only belongs to one nominatum (object). In different languages, and even in one language, the same sense is represented by different expressions. It is true, there are exceptions to this rule. Certainly there should be a definite sense to each expression in a complete configuration of signs, but the natural languages in many ways fall short of this requirement. We must be satisfied if the same word, at least in the same context, has the same sense. It can perhaps be granted than an expression has a sense if it is formed in a grammatically correct manner and stands for a proper name. But as to whether there is a denotation corresponding to the connotation is hereby not decided. The words 'the heavenly body which has the greatest distance from the earth' have a sense; but it is very doubtful as to whether they have a nominatum. The expression 'the series with the least convergence' has a sense; but it can be proved that it has no nominatum, since for any given convergent series, one can find another one that is less convergent. Therefore the grasping of a sense does not with certainty warrant a corresponding nominatum.

When words are used in the customary manner then what is talked about are their nominata. But it may happen that one wishes to speak about the words themselves or about their senses. The first case occurs when one quotes someone else's words in direct (ordinary) discourse. In this case one's own words immediately name (denote) the words of the other person and only the latter words have the usual nominata. We thus have signs of signs. In writing we make use of quotes enclosing the word-icons. A word-icon in quotes must therefore not be taken in the customary manner.

If we wish to speak of the sense of an expression 'A' we can do this simply through the locution 'the sense of the expression 'A'.' In indirect (oblique) discourse we speak of the sense, e.g., of the words of someone else. From this it becomes clear that also in indirect discourse words do not have their customary nominata; they here name what customarily would be their sense. In order to formulate this succinctly we shall say: words in indirect discourse are used *indirectly,* or have *indirect* nominata. Thus we distinguish the *customary* from the *indirect* nominatum of a word; and similarly, its *customary* sense from its *indirect* sense. The indirect nominatum of a word is therefore its customary sense. Such exceptions must be kept in mind if one wishes correctly to comprehend the manner of connection between signs, senses and nominata in any given case.

Both the nominatum and the sense of a sign must be distinguished from the associated image. If the nominatum of a sign is an object of sense perception, my image of the latter is an inner picture [3] arisen from mem-

---

[3] With the images we can align also the percepts in which the sense impressions and activities themselves take the place of those traces left in the mind. For our purposes the difference is unimportant, especially since besides sensations and activities recollections of such help in completing the intuitive presentation. 'Percept' may also be understood as the object, inasmuch as it is spatial or capable of sensory apprehension.

ories of sense impressions and activities of mine, internal or external. Frequently this image is suffused with feelings; the definiteness of its various parts may vary and fluctuate. Even with the same person the same sense is not always accompanied by the same image. The image is subjective; the image of one person is not that of another. Hence, the various differences between the images connected with one and the same sense. A painter, a rider, a zoölogist probably connect very different images with the name 'Bucephalus.' The image thereby differs essentially from the connotation of a sign, which latter may well be common property of many and is therefore not a part or mode of the single person's mind; for it cannot well be denied that mankind possesses a common treasure of thoughts which is transmitted from generation to generation.[4]

While, accordingly, there is no objection to speak without qualification of the sense in regard to images, we must, to be precise, add *whose* images they are and at what time they occur. One might say: just as words are connected with different images in two different persons, the same holds of the senses also. Yet this difference would consist merely in the manner of association. It does not prevent both from apprehending the same sense, but they cannot have the same image. *Si duo idem faciunt, non est idem.* When two persons imagine the same thing, each still has his own image. It is true, occasionally we can detect differences in the images or even in the sensations of different persons. But an accurate comparison is impossible because these images cannot be had together in one consciousness.

The nominatum of a proper name is the object itself which is designated thereby; the image which we may have along with it is quite subjective; the sense lies in between, not subjective as is the image, but not the object either. The following simile may help in elucidating these relationships. Someone observes the moon through a telescope. The moon is comparable with the nominatum; it is the object of the observation which is mediated through the real image projected by the object lens into the interior of the telescope, and through the retinal image of the observer. The first may be compared with the sense, the second with the presentation (or image in the psychological sense). The real image inside the telescope, however, is relative; it depends upon the standpoint; yet, it is objective in that it can serve several observers. Arrangements could be made such that several observers could utilize it. But every one of them would have only his own retinal image. Because of the different structures of the eyes not even geometrical congruence could be attained; a real coincidence would in any case be impossible. One could elaborate the simile by assuming that the retinal image of A could be made visible to B; or A could see his own retinal image in a mirror. In this manner one could possibly show

---

[4] It is therefore inexpedient to designate fundamentally different things by the one word 'image' (or 'idea').

how a presentation itself can be made into an object; but even so, it would never be to the (outside) observer what it is to the one who possesses the image. However, these lines of thought lead too far afield.

We can now recognize three levels of differences of words, expressions and complete sentences. The difference may concern at most the imagery, or else the sense but not the nominatum, or finally also the nominatum. In regard to the first level, we must note that, owing to the uncertain correlation of images with words, a difference may exist for one person that another does not discover. The difference of a translation from the original should properly not go beyond the first level. Among the differences possible in this connection we mention the shadings and colorings which poetry seeks to impart to the senses. These shadings and colorings are not objective. Every listener or reader has to add them in accordance with the hints of the poet or speaker. Surely, art would be impossible without some kinship among human imageries; but just how far the intentions of the poet are realized can never be exactly ascertained.

We shall henceforth no longer refer to the images and picturizations; they were discussed only lest the image evoked by a word be confused with its sense or its nominatum.

In order to facilitate brief and precise expression we may lay down the following formulations:

A proper name (word, sign, sign-compound, expression) expresses its sense, and designates or signifies its nominatum. We let a *sign express* its sense and *designate* its nominatum.

Perhaps the following objection, coming from idealistic or skeptical quarters, has been kept in abeyance for some time: "You have been speaking without hesitation of the moon as an object; but how do you know that the name 'the moon' has in fact a nominatum? How do you know that anything at all has a nominatum?" I reply that it is not our intention to speak of the image of the moon, nor would we be satisfied with the sense when we say 'the moon'; instead, we presuppose a nominatum here. We should miss the meaning altogether if we assumed we had reference to images in the sentence "the moon is smaller than the earth." Were this intended we would use some such locution as 'my image of the moon.' Of course, we may be in error as regards that assumption, and such errors have occurred on occasion. However, the question whether we could possibly always be mistaken in this respect may here remain unanswered; it will suffice for the moment to refer to our intention in speaking and thinking in order to justify our reference to the nominatum of a sign; even if we have to make the proviso: if there is such a nominatum.

Thus far we have considered sense and nominatum only of such expressions, words and signs which we called proper names. We are now going to inquire into the sense and the nominatum of a whole declarative sentence. Such a sentence contains a proposition.[5] Is this thought to be regarded as the sense or the nominatum of the sentence? Let us for the moment assume that the sentence has a nominatum! If we then substitute a word in it by another word with the same nominatum but with a different sense, then this substitution cannot affect the nominatum of the sentence. But we realize that in such cases the proposition is changed; e.g., the proposition of the sentence "the morning star is a body illuminated by the sun" is different from that of "the evening star is a body illuminated by the sun." Someone who did not know that the evening star is the same as the morning star could consider the one proposition true and the other false. The proposition can therefore not be the nominatum of the sentence; it will instead have to be regarded as its sense. But what about the nominatum? Can we even ask this question? A sentence as a whole has perhaps only sense and no nominatum? It may in any case be expected that there are such sentences, just as there are constituents of sentences which do have sense but no nominatum. Certainly, sentences containing proper names without nominata must be of this type. The sentence "Odysseus deeply asleep was disembarked at Ithaca" obviously has a sense. But since it is doubtful as to whether the name 'Odysseus' occurring in this sentence has a nominatum, so it is also doubtful that the whole sentence has one. However, it is certain that whoever seriously regards the sentence either as true or as false also attributes to the name 'Odysseus' a nominatum, not only a sense; for it is obviously the nominatum of this name to which the predicate is either ascribed or denied. He who does not acknowledge the nominatum cannot ascribe or deny a predicate to it. It might be urged that the consideration of the nominatum of the name is going farther than is necessary; one could be satisfied with the sense, if one stayed with the proposition. If all that mattered were only the sense of the sentence (i.e., the proposition) then it would be unnecessary to be concerned with the nominata of the sentence-components, for only the sense of the components can be relevant for the sense of the sentence. The proposition remains the same, no matter whether or not the name 'Odysseus' has a nominatum. The fact that we are at all concerned about the nominatum of a sentence-component indicates that we generally acknowledge or postulate a nominatum for the sentence itself. The proposition loses in interest as soon as we recognize that one of its parts is lacking a nominatum. We may therefore be justified to ask for a nominatum of a sentence, in addition to its sense. But why do we wish that every proper name have not only a sense but also a nominatum? Why is the proposition alone not sufficient? We answer: because what matters to us is the truth-value. This, however, is not always the case. In listening to an epic, for example, we are fascinated by the euphony of the language and also by the sense of the sentences and by the images and emotions evoked.

---

[5] By 'proposition' I do not refer to the subjective activity of thinking but rather to its objective content which is capable of being the common property of many.

In turning to the question of truth we disregard the artistic appreciation and pursue scientific considerations. Whether the name 'Odysseus' has a nominatum is therefore immaterial to us as long as we accept the poem as a work of art.[6] Thus, it is the striving for truth which urges us to penetrate beyond the sense to the nominatum.

We have realized that we are to look for the nominatum of a sentence whenever the nominata of the sentence-components are the thing that matters; and that is the case whenever and only when we ask for the truth-value.

Thus we find ourselves persuaded to accept the *truth-value* of a sentence as its nominatum. By the truth-value of a sentence I mean the circumstance of its being true or false. There are no other truth-values. For brevity's sake I shall call the one the True and the other the False. Every declarative sentence, in which what matters are the nominata of the words, is therefore to be considered as a proper name; and its nominatum, if there is any, is either the True or the False. These two objects are recognized, even if only tacitly, by everyone who at all makes judgments, holds anything as true, thus even by the skeptic. To designate truth-values as objects may thus far appear as a capricious idea or as a mere play on words, from which no important conclusion should be drawn. What I call an object can be discussed only in connection with the nature of concepts and relations. That I will reserve for another essay. But this might be clear even here: in every judgment [7]—no matter how obvious—a step is made from the level of propositions to the level of the nominata (the objective facts).

It may be tempting to regard the relation of a proposition to the True not as that of sense to nominatum but as that of the subject to the predicate. One could virtually say: "the proposition that 5 is a prime number is true." But on closer examination one notices that this does not say any more than is said in the simple sentence "5 is a prime number." This makes clear that the relation of a proposition to the True must not be compared with the relation of subject and predicate. Subject and predicate (interpreted logically) are, after all, components of a proposition; they are on the same level as regards cognition. By joining subject and predicate we always arrive only at a proposition; in this way we never move from a sense to a nominatum or from a proposition to its truth-value. We remain on the same level and never proceed from it to the next one. Just as the sun cannot be part of a proposition, so the truth-value, because it is not the sense, but an object, cannot be either.

If our conjecture (that the nominatum of a sentence is its truth-value) is correct, then the truth-value must remain unchanged if a sentence-

---

[6] It would be desirable to have an expression for signs which have sense only. If we call them 'icons' then the words of an actor on the stage would be icons; even the actor himself would be an icon.

[7] A judgment is not merely the apprehension of a thought or proposition but the acknowledgment of its truth.

component is replaced by an expression with the same nominatum but with a different sense. Indeed, Leibnitz declares: "*Eadem sunt, quae sibi mutuo substitui possunt, salva veritate.*" What else, except the truth-value, could be found, which quite generally belongs to every sentence and regarding which the nominata of the components are relevant and which would remain invariant for substitutions of the type indicated?

Now if the truth-value of a sentence is its nominatum, then all true sentences have the same nominatum, and likewise all false ones. This implies that all detail has been blurred in the nominatum of a sentence. What interests us can therefore never be merely the nominatum; but the proposition alone does not give knowledge; only the proposition together with its nominatum, i.e., its truth-value, does. Judging may be viewed as a movement from a proposition to its nominatum, i.e., its truth-value. Of course this is not intended as a definition. Judging is indeed something peculiar and unique. One might say that judging consists in the discerning of parts within the truth-value. This discernment occurs through recourse to the proposition. Every sense that belongs to a truth-value would correspond in its own manner to the analysis. I have, however, used the word 'part' in a particular manner here: I have transferred the relation of whole and part from the sentence to its nominatum. This I did by viewing the nominatum of a word as part of the nominatum of a sentence, when the word itself is part of the sentence. True enough, this way of putting things is objectionable since as regards the nominatum the whole and one part of it does not determine the other part; and also because the word 'part' in reference to bodies has a different customary usage. A special expression should be coined for what has been suggested above.

We shall now further examine the conjecture that the truth-value of a sentence is its nominatum. We have found that the truth-value of a sentence remains unaltered if an expression within the sentence is replaced by a synonymous one. But we have as yet not considered the case in which the expression-to-be-replaced is itself a sentence. If our view is correct, then the truth-value of a sentence, which contains another sentence as a part, must remain unaltered when we substitute for the part another of the same truth-value. Exceptions are to be expected if the whole or the part are either in direct or indirect discourse; for as we have seen, in that case the nominata of the words are not the usual ones. A sentence in direct discourse nominates again a sentence but in indirect discourse it nominates a proposition.

Our attention is thus directed to subordinate sentences (i.e., dependent clauses). These present themselves of course as parts of a sentence-structure which from a logical point of view appears also as a sentence, and indeed as if it were a main clause. But here we face the question whether in the case of dependent clauses it also holds that their nominata are truth-values. We know already that this is not the case with sentences in indirect discourse. The grammarians view clauses as representatives of sentence-parts and divide them accordingly into subjective, relative, and adverbial clauses. This might suggest that the nominatum of a clause is not a truth-value but rather that it is of similar nature as that of a noun or of an adjective or of an adverb; in short, of a sentence-part whose sense is not a proposition but only part thereof. Only a thorough investigation can provide clarity in this matter. We shall herein not follow strictly along grammatical lines, but rather group together what is logically of comparable type. Let us first seek out such instances in which, as we just surmised, the sense of a clause is not a self-sufficient proposition.

Among the abstract clauses beginning with 'that' there is also the indirect discourse, of which we have seen that in it the words have their indirect (oblique) nominata which coincide with what are ordinarily their senses. In this case then the clause has as its nominatum a proposition, not a truth-value; its sense is not a proposition but it is the sense of the words 'the proposition that . . .,' which is only a part of the proposition corresponding to the total sentence-structure. This occurs in connection with 'to say,' 'to hear,' 'to opine,' 'to be convinced,' 'to infer' and similar words.[8] The situation is different, and rather complicated in connection with such words as 'to recognize,' 'to know,' 'to believe,' a matter to be considered later.

One can see that in these cases the nominatum of the clause indeed consists in the proposition, because whether that proposition is true or false is immaterial for the truth of the whole sentence. Compare, e.g., the following two sentences: "Copernicus believed that the planetary orbits are circles" and "Copernicus believed that the appearance of the sun's motion is produced by the real motion of the earth." Here the one clause can be substituted for the other without affecting the truth. The sense of the principal sentence together with the clause is the single proposition; and the truth of the whole implies neither the truth nor the falsity of the clause. In cases of this type it is not permissible to replace in the clause one expression by another of the same nominatum. Such replacement may be made only by expressions of the same indirect nominatum, i.e., of the same customary sense. If one were to infer: the nominatum of a sentence is not its truth-value ("because then a sentence could always be replaced by another with the same truth-value"), he would prove too much; one could just as well maintain that the nominatum of the word 'morning star' is not Venus, for one cannot always substitute 'Venus' for 'morning star.' The only correct conclusion is that the nominatum of a sentence is *not always* its truth-value, and that 'morning star' does not always nominate the planet Venus; for this is indeed not the case when the word is used with its indirect nominatum. Such an exceptional case is before us in the clauses just considered, whose nominatum is a proposition.

When we say "it seems that . . ." then we mean to say "it seems to me

[8] In "A lied, that he had seen *B*" the clause denotes a proposition of which it is said, firstly, that A asserted it as true, and, secondly, that A was convinced of its falsity.

that . . ." or "I opine that . . .". This is the same case over again. Similarly with expressions such as: 'to be glad,' 'to regret,' 'to approve,' 'to disapprove,' 'to hope,' 'to fear.' When Wellington, toward the end of the battle of Belle-Alliance was glad that the Prussians were coming, the ground of his rejoicing was a conviction. Had he actually been deceived, he would not have been less glad, as long as his belief persisted; and before he arrived at the conviction that the Prussians were coming he could not have been glad about it, even if in fact they were already approaching.

Just as a conviction or a belief may be the ground of a sentiment, so it can also be the ground of another conviction such as in inference. In the sentence "Columbus inferred from the roundness of the earth that he could, traveling westward, reach India" we have, as nominata of its parts two propositions: that the earth is round, and that Columbus traveling westward could reach India. What matters here is only that Columbus was convinced of the one as well as of the other and that the one conviction furnishes the ground for the other. It is irrelevant for the truth of our sentence whether the earth is really round and whether Columbus could have reached India in the manner he fancied. But it is not irrelevant whether for 'the earth' we substitute 'the planet accompanied by one satellite whose diameter is larger than one-fourth of its own diameter.' Here also we deal with the indirect nominata of the words.

Adverbial clauses of purpose with 'so that,' likewise belong here; obviously the purpose is a proposition; therefore: indirect nominata of the words, expressed in subjunctive form.

The clause with 'that' after 'to command,' 'to request,' 'to forbid' would appear in imperative form in direct discourse. Imperatives have no nominata; they have only sense. It is true, commands or requests are not propositions, but they are of the same type as propositions. Therefore the words in the dependent clauses after 'to command,' 'to request,' etc. have indirect nominata. The nominatum of such a sentence is thus not a truth-value but a command, a request, and the like.

We meet a similar situation in the case of dependent questions in phrases like 'to doubt if,' 'not to know what.' It is easy to see that the words, here too, have to be interpreted in terms of their indirect nominata. The dependent interrogatory clauses containing 'who,' 'what,' 'where,' 'when,' 'how,' 'whereby,' etc. often apparently approximate closely adverbial clauses in which the words have their ordinary nominata. These cases are linguistically distinguished through the mode of the verb. In the subjunctive we have a dependent question and the indirect nominata of the words, so that a proper name cannot generally be replaced by another of the same object.

In the instances thus far considered the words in the clause had indirect nominata; this made it intelligible that the nominatum of the clause itself is indirect, i.e., not a truth-value, but a proposition, a command, a request, a question. The clause could be taken as a noun; one might even say, as a proper name of that proposition, command, etc., in whose rôle it functions in the context of the sentence-structure.

We are now going to consider clauses of another type, in which the words do have their customary nominata although there does not appear a proposition as the sense or a truth-value as the nominatum. How this is possible will best be elucidated by examples.

"He who discovered the elliptical shape of the planetary orbits, died in misery."

If, in this example, the sense of the clause were a proposition, it would have to be expressible also in a principal sentence. But this cannot be done because the grammatical subject 'he who' has no independent sense. It merely mediates the relations to the second part of the sentence: 'died in misery.' Therefore the sense of the clause is not a complete proposition and its nominatum is not a truth-value, but Kepler. It might be objected that the sense of the whole does include a proposition as its part; namely, that there was someone who first recognized the elliptical shape of the planetary orbits; for if we accept the whole as true we cannot deny this part. Indubitably so; but only because otherwise the clause "he who discovered the elliptical shape, etc." would have no nominatum. Whenever something is asserted then the presupposition taken for granted is that the employed proper names, simple or compound, have nominata. Thus, if we assert "Kepler died in misery" it is presupposed that the name 'Kepler' designates something. However, the proposition that the name 'Kepler' designates something is, the foregoing notwithstanding, not contained in the sense of the sentence "Kepler died in misery." If that were the case the denial would not read "Kepler did not die in misery" but "Kepler did not die in misery, or the name 'Kepler' is without nominatum." That the name 'Kepler' designates something is rather the presupposition of the assertion "Kepler died in misery" as well as of its denial. Now, it is a defect of languages that expressions are possible within them, which, in their grammatical form, seemingly determined to designate an object, nevertheless do not fulfill this condition in special cases; because this depends on the truth of the sentence. Thus it depends upon the truth of the sentence "there was someone who discovered the ellipticity of the orbits" whether the clause 'he who discovered the ellipticity of the orbits' really designates an object, or else merely evokes the appearance thereof, while indeed being without nominatum. Thus it may seem as if our clause, as part of its sense, contained the proposition that there existed someone who discovered the ellipticity of the orbits. If this were so, then the denial would have to read "he who first recognized the ellipticity of the orbits did not die in misery, or there was no one who discovered the ellipticity of the orbits." This, it is obvious, hinges upon an imperfection of language of which, by the way, even the symbolic language of analysis is not entirely free; there, also, sign compounds may occur which appear as if they designated something, but which at least hitherto are without nominatum, e.g., divergent infinite series. This can be avoided, e.g., through the special convention that the nominatum of divergent infinite series be the number 0. It is to be demanded that in a logically perfect language (logical symbolism) every expression constructed as a proper name in a grammatically correct manner out of already introduced symbols, in fact designate an object; and that no symbol be introduced as a proper name without assurance that it have a nominatum. It is customary in logic texts to warn against the ambiguity of expressions as a source of fallacies. I deem it at least as appropriate to issue a warning against apparent proper names that have no nominata. The history of mathematics has many a tale to tell of errors which originated from this source. The demagogic misuse is close (perhaps closer) at hand as in the case of ambiguous expressions. 'The will of the people' may serve as an example in this regard; for it is easily established that there is no generally accepted nominatum of that expression. Thus it is obviously not without importance to obstruct once for all the source of these errors, at least as regards their occurrence in science. Then such objections as the one discussed above will become impossible, for then it will be seen that whether a proper name has a nominatum can never depend upon the truth of a proposition.

Our considerations may be extended from these subjective clauses to the logically related relative and adverbial clauses.

Relative clauses, too, are employed in the formation of compound proper names—even if, in contradistinction to subjective clauses, they are not sufficient by themselves for this purpose. These relative clauses may be regarded as equivalent to appositions. Instead of 'the square root of 4 which is smaller than 0' we can also say 'the negative square root of 4.' We have here a case in which out of a conceptual expression a compound proper name is formed, with the help of the definite article in the singular. This is at any rate permissible when one and only one object is comprised by the concept.[9] Conceptual expression can be formed in such a fashion that their characteristics are indicated through relative clauses as in our example through the clause 'which is smaller than 0.' Obviously, such relative clauses, just as the subjective clauses above, do not refer to a proposition as their sense nor to a truth-value as their nominatum. Their sense is only a part of a proposition, which in many cases, can be expressed by a simple apposition. As in the subjective clauses an independent subject is missing and it is therefore impossible to represent the sense of the clause in an independent principal sentence.

Places, dates and time-intervals are objects from a logical point of view; the linguistic symbol of a definite place, moment or span of time must therefore be viewed as a proper name. Adverbial clauses of space or time can then be used in the formation of such proper names in a fashion

---

[9] According to our previous remarks such an expression should always be assured of a nominatum, e.g., through the special convention that the nominatum be the number 0 if there is no object or more than one object denoted by the expression.

analogous to the one we have just remarked in the case of subjective and relative clauses. Similarly, expressions for concepts which comprise places, etc., can be formed. Here too, it is to be remarked, the sense of the subordinate clauses cannot be rendered in a principal clause, because an essential constituent, namely the determination of place and time, is missing and only alluded to by a relative pronoun or a conjunction.[10]

In conditional clauses also, there is, just as we have realized in the case of subjective, relative and adverbial clauses, a constituent with indeterminate indication corresponding to which there is a similar one in the concluding clause. In referring to one another the two clauses combine into a whole which expresses, as a rule, only one proposition. In the sentence "if a number is smaller than 1 and greater than 0, then its square also is smaller than 1 and greater than 0" this constituent in the conditional clause is 'a number' and in the concluding clause it is 'its.' Just through this indeterminacy the sense acquires the universal character which one expects of a law. But it is in this way also that it comes about that the conditional clause alone does not possess a complete proposition as its sense, and that together with the concluding clause it expresses a single proposition whose parts are no longer propositions. It is not generally the case that a hypothetical judgment correlates two judgments. Putting it in that (or a similar) manner would amount to using the word 'judgment' in the same sense that I have attributed to the word 'proposition.' In that case I would have to say: in a hypothetical proposition two propositions are related to each other. But this could be the case only if an indeterminately denoting constituent were absent; [11] but then universality would also be missing.

If a time point is to be indeterminately indicated in a conditional and a concluding clause, then this is not infrequently effected by *tempus praesens* of the verb, which in this case does not connote the present time.

---

[10] Regarding these sentences, however, several interpretations are easily conceivable. The sense of the sentence "after Schleswig-Holstein was torn away from Denmark, Prussia and Austria fell out with one another" could also be rendered by "after the separation of Schl.-H. from Denmark, Prussia and Austria fell out with one another." In this formulation it is sufficiently clear that we should not regard it as part of this sense that Schleswig-Holstein once was separated from Denmark; but rather that this is the necessary presupposition for the very existence of a nominatum of the expression 'after the separation of Schl.-H. from D.' Yet, our sentence could also be interpreted to the effect that Schl.-H. was once separated from D. This case will be considered later. In order to grasp the difference more clearly, let us identify ourselves with the mind of a Chinese who, with his trifling knowledge of European history, regards it as false that Schl.-H. ever was separated from D. This Chinese will regard as neither true nor false the sentence as interpreted in the first manner. He would deny to it any nominatum because the dependent clause would be lacking a nominatum. The dependent clause would only apparently indicate a temporal determination. But if the Chinese interprets our sentence in the second manner, then he will find it expressing a proposition which he would consider false, in addition to a component which, for him, would be without nominatum.

[11] Occasionally there is no explicit linguistic indication and the interpretation has to depend upon the total context.

It is this grammatical form which takes the place of the indeterminately indicating constituent in the main and the dependent clause. "When the sun is at the Tropic of Cancer, the northern hemisphere has its longest day" is an example. Here, too, it is impossible to express the sense of the dependent clause in a main clause. For this sense is not a complete proposition; if we said "the sun is at the Tropic of Cancer" we would be referring to the present time and thereby alter the sense. Similarly, the sense of the main clause is not a proposition either, only the whole consisting of main and dependent clause contains a proposition. Further, it may occur that several constituents common to conditional and concluding clause are indeterminately indicated.

It is obvious that subjective clauses containing 'who,' 'what,' and adverbial clauses with 'where,' 'when,' 'wherever,' 'whenever' are frequently to be interpreted, inasmuch as their sense is concerned, as conditional sentences; e.g., "He who touches pitch soils himself."

Conditional clauses can also be replaced by relative clauses. The sense of the previously mentioned sentence can also be rendered by "the square of a number which is smaller than 1 and larger than 0, is smaller than 1 and larger than 0."

Quite different is the case in which the common constituent of main and dependent clause is represented by a proper name. In the sentence: "Napoleon who recognized the danger to his right flank, personally led his troops against the enemy's position" there are expressed two propositions:

1. Napoleon recognized the danger to his right flank.
2. Napoleon personally led his troops against the enemy's position.

When and where this happened can indeed be known only from the context, but is to be viewed as thereby determined. If we pronounce our whole sentence as an assertion we thereby assert simultaneously its two component sentences. If one of the components is false the whole is false. Here we have a case in which the dependent clause by itself has a sense in a complete proposition (if supplemented by temporal and spatial indications). The nominatum of such a clause is therefore a truth-value. We may therefore expect that we can replace it by a sentence of the same truth-value without altering the truth of the whole. This is indeed the case; but it must be kept in mind that for a purely grammatical reason, its subject must be 'Napoleon'; because only then can the sentence be rendered in the form of a relative clause attaching to 'Napoleon.' If the demand to render it in this form and if the conjunction with 'and' is admitted, then this limitation falls away.

Likewise, in dependent clauses with 'although' complete propositions are expressed. This conjunction really has no sense and does not affect the sense of the sentence; rather, it illuminates it in a peculiar fashion.[12] Without affecting the truth of the whole the implicate may be replaced by one of the same truth-value; but the illumination might then easily appear inappropriate, just as if one were to sing a song of sad content in a cheerful manner.

In these last instances the truth of the whole implied the truth of the component sentences. The situation is different if a conditional sentence expresses a complete proposition; namely, when in doing so it contains instead of a merely indicating constituent a proper name or something deemed equivalent to a proper name. In the sentence: "if the sun has already risen by now, the sky is heavily overcast," the tense is the present —therefore determinate. The place also is to be considered determinate. Here we can say that a relation is posited such that the case does not arise in which the antecedent sentence nominates the True and the consequent sentence nominates the False. Accordingly, the given (whole) sentence is true if the sun has not as yet risen (no matter whether or no the sky be heavily overcast), and also if the sun has risen and the sky is heavily overcast. Since all that matters are only the truth-values, each of the component sentences can be replaced by another one of the same truth-value, without altering the truth-value of the whole sentence. In this case also, the illumination would usually seem inappropriate; the proposition could easily appear absurd; but this has nothing to do with the truth-value of the sentence. It must always be remembered that associated thoughts are evoked on the side; but these are not really expressed and must therefore not be taken account of; their truth-values cannot be relevant.[13]

We may hope we have considered the simple types of sentences. Let us now review what we have found out!

The sense of a subordinate clause is usually not a proposition but only part of one. Its nominatum is therefore not a truth-value. The reason for this is *either*: that the words in the subordinate clause have only indirect nominata, so that the nominatum, not the sense, of the clause is a proposition, *or*, that the clause, because of a contained indeterminately indicating constituent, is incomplete, such that only together with the principal clause does it express a proposition. However, there are also instances in which the sense of the dependent clause is a complete proposition, and in this case it can be replaced by another clause of the same truth-value without altering the truth-value of the whole; that is, inasmuch as there are no grammatical obstacles in the way.

In a survey of the various occurrent clauses one will readily encounter some which will not properly fit within any of the considered divisions. As

[12] Similarly in the case of 'but,' 'yet.'

[13] The proposition of the sentence could also be formulated thus: "either the sun has not as yet risen or the sky is heavily overcast." This shows how to interpret this type of compound sentence.

far as I can see, the reason for that is that these clauses do not have quite so simple a sense. It seems that almost always we connect associated propositions with the main proposition which we express; these associated propositions, even if unexpressed, are associated with our words according to psychological laws also by the listener. And because they appear as associated automatically with our words (as in the case of the main proposition) we seem to wish, after all, to express such associated propositions along with the main propositions. The sense of the sentence thereby becomes richer and it may well happen that we may have more simple propositions than sentences. In some cases the sentence may be interpreted in this way, in others, it may be doubtful whether the associated proposition belongs to the sense of the sentence or whether it merely accompanies it.[14] One might find that in the sentence: "Napoleon, who recognized the danger to his right flank, personally led his troops against the enemy's position" there are not only the previously specified two propositions, but also the proposition that the recognition of the danger was the reason why he led his troops against the enemy. One may indeed wonder whether this proposition is merely lightly suggested or actually expressed. Consider the question whether our sentence would be false if Napoleon's resolution had been formed before the recognition of the danger. If our sentence were true even despite this, then the associated proposition should not be regarded as part of the sense of the sentence. In the alternative case the situation is rather complicated: we should then have more simple propositions than sentences. Now if we replaced the sentence: "Napoleon recognized the danger for his right flank" by another sentence of the same truth-value, e.g., by: "Napoleon was over 45 years old" this would change not only our first but also our third proposition; and this might thereby change also the truth-value of the third proposition—namely, if his age was not the reason for his resolution to lead the troops against the enemy. Hence, it is clear that in such instances sentences of the same truth-value cannot always be substituted for one another. The sentence merely by virtue of its connection with another expresses something more than it would by itself alone.

Let us now consider cases in which this occurs regularly. In the sentence: "Bebel imagines that France's desire for vengeance could be assuaged by the restitution of Alsace-Lorraine" there are expressed two propositions, which, however, do not correspond to the main and the dependent clause—namely:

1.  Bebel believes that France's desire for vengeance could be assuaged by the restitution of Alsace-Lorraine;
2.  France's desire for vengeance cannot be assuaged by the restitution of Alsace-Lorraine.

[14] This may be of importance in the question as to whether a given assertion be a lie, an oath or a perjury.

In the expression of the first proposition the words of the dependent clause have indirect nominata; while the same words, in the expression of the second proposition, have their usual nominata. Hence, we see that the dependent clause of our original sentence really is to be interpreted in a twofold way; i.e., with different nominata, one of which is a proposition and the other a truth-value. An analogous situation prevails with expressions like 'to know,' 'to recognize,' 'it is known.'

A condition clause and its related main clause express several propositions which, however, do not correspond one-to-one to the clauses. The sentence: "Since ice is specifically lighter than water, it floats on water" asserts:

1.  Ice is specifically lighter than water.
2.  If something is specifically lighter than water, it floats on water.
3.  Ice floats on water.

The third proposition, being implied by the first two, would perhaps not have to be mentioned expressly. However, neither the first and the third, nor the second and the third together would completely render the sense of our sentence. Thus we see that the dependent clause 'since ice is specifically lighter than water' expresses both our first proposition and part of the second. Hence, our clause cannot be replaced by another of the same truth-value; for thereby we are apt to alter our second proposition and could easily affect its truth-value.

A similar situation holds in the case of the sentence: "If iron were lighter than water it would float on water." Here we have the two propositions that iron is not lighter than water and that whatever is lighter than water floats on water. The clause again expresses the one proposition and part of the other. If we interpret the previously discussed sentence "After Schleswig-Holstein was separated from Denmark, Prussia and Austria fell out with one another" as containing the proposition that Schleswig-Holstein once was separated from Denmark, then we have: firstly, this proposition, secondly, the proposition that, at a time more precisely determined by the dependent clause, Prussia and Austria fell out with one another. Here, too, the dependent clause expresses not only one proposition but also part of another. Therefore, it may not generally be replaced by another clause of the same truth-value.

It is difficult to exhaust all possibilities that present themselves in language; but I hope, in essence at least, to have disclosed the reasons why, in view of the invariance of the truth of a whole sentence, a clause cannot always be replaced by another of the same truth-value. These reasons are:

1.  that the clause does not denote a truth-value in that it expresses only a part of a proposition;
2.  that the clause, while it does denote a truth-value, is not restricted to

this function in that its sense comprises, beside one proposition, also a part of another.

The first case holds

a.  with the indirect nominata of the words;
b.  if a part of the sentence indicates only indirectly without being a proper name.

In the second case the clause is to be interpreted in a twofold manner; namely, once with its usual nominatum; the other time with its indirect nominatum; or else, the sense of a part of the clause may simultaneously be a constituent of another proposition which, together with the sense expressed in the dependent clause, amounts to the total sense of the main and the dependent clause.

This makes it sufficiently plausible that instances in which a clause is not replaceable by another of the same truth-value do not disprove our view that the nominatum of a sentence is its truth-value and its sense a proposition.

Let us return to our point of departure now.

When we discerned generally a difference in cognitive significance between "a = a" and "a = b" then this is now explained by the fact that for the cognitive significance of a sentence the sense (the proposition expressed) is no less relevant than its nominatum (the truth-value). If a = b, then the nominatum of 'a' and of 'b' is indeed the same and therefore also the truth-value of "a = b" is the same as that of "a = a." Nevertheless, the sense of 'b' may differ from the sense of 'a'; and therefore the proposition expressed by "a = b" may differ from the proposition expressed by "a = a"; in that case the two sentences do not have the same cognitive significance. Thus, if, as above, we mean by 'judgment' the transition from a proposition to its truth-value, then we can also say that the judgments differ from one another.

# ON DENOTING*

BERTRAND RUSSELL (1872– ) has played a central role in determining the trend of much of contemporary philosophy. His *Principia Mathematica* (with Alfred North Whitehead) inaugurated an era of intensified logical analysis. His varied work in logic, philosophy of science, ethics, politics, history, education, and theory of knowledge has been characterized by the continuous attempt to apply scientific findings to philosophical problems. Among his very numerous books are: *Principles of Mathematics, The Problems of Philosophy, Mysticism and Logic, Our Knowledge of the External World, The Analysis of Matter, The Analysis of Mind, A History of Western Philosophy, Human Knowledge, Human Society in Ethics and Politics, Education and the Good Life.*

By a "denoting phrase" I mean a phrase such as any one of the following: a man, some man, any man, every man, all men, the present King of England, the present King of France, the centre of mass of the Solar System at the first instant of the twentieth century, the revolution of the earth round the sun, the revolution of the sun round the earth. Thus a phrase is denoting solely in virtue of its *form*. We may distinguish three cases: (1) A phrase may be denoting, and yet not denote anything; e.g., "the present King of France." (2) A phrase may denote one definite object; e.g., "the present King of England" denotes a certain man. (3) A phrase may denote ambiguously; e.g., "a man" denotes not many men, but an ambiguous man. The interpretation of such phrases is a matter of considerable difficulty; indeed, it is very hard to frame any theory not susceptible of formal refutation. All the difficulties with which I am acquainted are met, so far as I can discover, by the theory which I am about to explain.

The subject of denoting is of very great importance not only in logic and mathematics, but also in theory of knowledge. For example, we know that the centre of mass of the Solar System at a definite instant is some definite point, and we can affirm a number of propositions about it; but we have no immediate *acquaintance* with this point, which is only known to us by description. The distinction between *acquaintance* and *knowledge about* is the distinction between the things we have presentations of, and the things we only reach by means of denoting phrases. It often happens that we know that a certain phrase denotes unambiguously, although we have no acquaintance with what it denotes; this occurs in the above case of the centre of mass. In perception we have acquaintance with the objects

* Reprinted by kind permission of the author and publisher, from *Logic and Knowledge*, ed. R. C. Marsh (London: Allen & Unwin, 1956), pp. 41–56.

of perception, and in thought we have acquaintance with objects of a more abstract logical character; but we do not necessarily have acquaintance with the objects denoted by phrases composed of words with whose meanings we are acquainted. To take a very important instance: There seems no reason to believe that we are ever acquainted with other people's minds, seeing that these are not directly perceived; hence what we know about them is obtained through denoting. All thinking has to start from acquaintance; but it succeeds in thinking *about* many things with which we have no acquaintance.

The course of my argument will be as follows. I shall begin by stating the theory I intend to advocate;[1] I shall then discuss the theories of Frege and Meinong, showing why neither of them satisfies me; then I shall give the grounds in favour of my theory; and finally I shall briefly indicate the philosophical consequences of my theory.

My theory, briefly, is as follows. I take the notion of the *variable* as fundamental; I use "C $(x)$" to mean a proposition[2] in which $x$ is a constituent, where $x$, the variable, is essentially and wholly undetermined. Then we can consider the two notions "C $(x)$ is always true" and "C $(x)$ is sometimes true."[3] Then *everything* and *nothing* and *something* (which are the most primitive of denoting phrases) are to be interpreted as follows:

C (everything) means "C $(x)$ is always true";
C (nothing) means " 'C $(x)$ is false' is always true";
C (something) means "It is false that 'C $(x)$ is false' is always true."[4]

Here the notion "C $(x)$ is always true" is taken as ultimate and indefinable, and the others are defined by means of it. *Everything, nothing,* and *something* are not assumed to have any meaning in isolation, but a meaning is assigned to *every* proposition in which they occur. This is the principle of the theory of denoting I wish to advocate: that denoting phrases never have any meaning in themselves, but that every proposition in whose verbal expression they occur has a meaning. The difficulties concerning denoting are, I believe, all the result of a wrong analysis of propositions whose verbal expressions contain denoting phrases. The proper analysis, if I am not mistaken, may be further set forth as follows.

Suppose now we wish to interpret the proposition, "I met a man." If this

---

[1] I have discussed this subject in *Principles of Mathematics*, ch. v, and § 476. The theory there advocated is very nearly the same as Frege's, and is quite different from the theory to be advocated in what follows.

[2] More exactly, a propositional function.

[3] The second of these can be defined by means of the first, if we take it to mean, "It is not true that 'C $(x)$ is false' is always true."

[4] I shall sometimes use, instead of this complicated phrase, the phrase "C $(x)$ is not always false," or "C $(x)$ is sometimes true," supposed *defined* to mean the same as the complicated phrase.

is true, I met some definite man; but that is not what I affirm. What I affirm is, according to the theory I advocate:

"'I met x, and x is human' is not always false."

Generally, defining the class of men as the class of objects having the predicate *human*, we say that:

"C (a man)" means "'C (x) and x is human' is not always false."

This leaves "a man," by itself, wholly destitute of meaning, but gives a meaning to every proposition in whose verbal expression "a man" occurs.

Consider next the proposition "all men are mortal." This proposition [5] is really hypothetical and states that *if* anything is a man, it is mortal. That is, it states that if x is a man, x is mortal, whatever x may be. Hence, substituting 'x is human' for 'x is a man,' we find:

"All men are mortal" means "'If x is human, x is mortal' is always true."

This is what is expressed in symbolic logic by saying that "all men are mortal" means "'x is human' implies 'x is mortal' for all values of x." More generally, we say:

"C (all men)" means "'If x is human, then C (x) is true' is always true."

Similarly

"C (no men)" means "'If x is human, then C (x) is false' is always true."

"C (some men)" will mean the same as "C (a man)," [6] and

"C (a man)" means "It is false that 'C (x) and x is human' is always false."

"C (every man)" will mean the same as "C (all men)."

It remains to interpret phrases containing *the*. These are by far the most interesting and difficult of denoting phrases. Take as an instance "the father of Charles II was executed." This asserts that there was an x who was the father of Charles II and was executed. Now *the*, when it is strictly used, involves uniqueness; we do, it is true, speak of "*the* son of So-and-so" even when So-and-so has several sons, but it would be more correct to say "*a* son of So-and-so." Thus for our purposes we take *the* as involving uniqueness. Thus when we say "x was *the* father of Charles II" we not only assert that x had a certain relation to Charles II, but also that nothing else had this relation. The relation in question, without the assumption of

---

[5] As has been ably argued in Mr. Bradley's *Logic*, Book I, ch. ii.
[6] Psychologically "C (a man)" has a suggestion of *only one*, and "C (some men)" has a suggestion of *more than one*; but we may neglect these suggestions in a preliminary sketch.

uniqueness, and without any denoting phrases, is expressed by "x begat Charles II." To get an equivalent of "x was the father of Charles II," we must add, "If y is other than x, y did not beget Charles II," or, what is equivalent, "If y begat Charles II, y is identical with x." Hence "x is the father of Charles II" becomes "x begat Charles II; and 'if y begat Charles II, y is identical with x' is always true of y."

Thus "the father of Charles II was executed" becomes:

> "It is not always false of x that x begat Charles II and that x was executed and that 'if y begat Charles II, y is identical with x' is always true of y."

This may seem a somewhat incredible interpretation; but I am not at present giving reasons, I am merely *stating* the theory.

To interpret "C (the father of Charles II)," where C stands for any statement about him, we have only to substitute C (x) for "x was executed" in the above. Observe that, according to the above interpretation, whatever statement C may be, "C (the father of Charles II)" implies:

> "It is not always false of x that 'if y begat Charles II, y is identical with x' is always true of y,"

which is what is expressed in common language by "Charles II had one father and no more." Consequently if this condition fails, *every* proposition of the form "C (the father of Charles II)" is false. Thus, e.g., every proposition of the form "C (the present King of France)" is false. This is a great advantage in the present theory. I shall show later that it is not contrary to the law of contradiction, as might be at first supposed.

The above gives a reduction of all propositions in which denoting phrases occur to forms in which no such phrases occur. Why it is imperative to effect such a reduction, the subsequent discussion will endeavour to show.

The evidence for the above theory is derived from the difficulties which seem unavoidable if we regard denoting phrases as standing for genuine constituents of the propositions in whose verbal expressions they occur. Of the possible theories which admit such constituents the simplest is that of Meinong.[7] This theory regards any grammatically correct denoting phrase as standing for an *object*. Thus "the present King of France," "the round square," etc., are supposed to be genuine objects. It is admitted that such objects do not *subsist*, but nevertheless they are supposed to be objects. This is in itself a difficult view; but the chief objection is that such objects, admittedly, are apt to infringe the law of contradiction. It is contended, for example, that the existent present King of France exists, and also does not exist; that the round square is round, and also not round; etc.

---

[7] See *Untersuchungen zur Gegenstandstheorie und Psychologie*, Leipzig, 1904, the first three articles (by Meinong, Ameseder and Mally respectively).

But this is intolerable; and if any theory can be found to avoid this result, it is surely to be preferred.

The above breach of the law of contradiction is avoided by Frege's theory. He distinguishes, in a denoting phrase, two elements, which we may call the *meaning* and the *denotation*.[8] Thus "the centre of mass of the Solar System at the beginning of the twentieth century" is highly complex in *meaning*, but its *denotation* is a certain point, which is simple. The Solar System, the twentieth century, etc., are constituents of the *meaning*; but the *denotation* has no constituents at all.[9] One advantage of this distinction is that it shows why it is often worth while to assert identity. If we say "Scott is the author of W*averley*," we assert an identity of denotation with a difference of meaning. I shall, however, not repeat the grounds in favour of this theory, as I have urged its claims elsewhere (*loc. cit.*), and am now concerned to dispute those claims.

One of the first difficulties that confront us, when we adopt the view that denoting phrases *express* a meaning and *denote* a denotation,[10] concerns the cases in which the denotation appears to be absent. If we say "the King of England is bald," that is, it would seem, not a statement about the complex *meaning* "the King of England," but about the actual man denoted by the meaning. But now consider "the King of France is bald." By parity of form, this also ought to be about the denotation of the phrase "the King of France." But this phrase, though it has a *meaning* provided "the King of England" has a meaning, has certainly no denotation, at least in any obvious sense. Hence one would suppose that "the King of France is bald" ought to be nonsense; but it is not nonsense, since it is plainly false. Or again consider such a proposition as the following: "If *u* is a class which has only one member, then that one member is a member of *u*," or, as we may state it, "If *u* is a unit class, *the u* is a *u*." This proposition ought to be *always* true, since the conclusion is true whenever the hypothesis is true. But "the *u*" is a denoting phrase, and it is the denotation, not the meaning, that is said to be a *u*. Now if *u* is *not* a unit class, "the *u*" seems to denote nothing; hence our proposition would seem to become nonsense as soon as *u* is not a unit class.

Now it is plain that such propositions do *not* become nonsense merely because their hypotheses are false. The King in "The Tempest" might say, "If Ferdinand is not drowned, Ferdinand is my only son." Now "my only son" is a denoting phrase, which, on the face of it, has a denotation

---

[8] See his "On Sense and Nominatum," in this volume.

[9] Frege distinguishes the two elements of meaning and denotation everywhere, and not only in complex denoting phrases. Thus it is the *meanings* of the constituents of a denoting complex that enter into its *meaning*, not their *denotation*. In the proposition "Mont Blanc is over 1,000 metres high," it is, according to him, the *meaning* of "Mont Blanc," not the actual mountain, that is a constituent of the *meaning* of the proposition.

[10] In this theory, we shall say that the denoting phrase *expresses* a meaning; and we shall say both of the phrase and of the meaning that they *denote* a denotation. In the other theory, which I advocate, there is no *meaning*, and only sometimes a *denotation*.

when, and only when, I have exactly one son. But the above statement would nevertheless have remained true if Ferdinand had been in fact drowned. Thus we must either provide a denotation in cases in which it is at first sight absent, or we must abandon the view that the denotation is what is concerned in propositions which contain denoting phrases. The latter is the course that I advocate. The former course may be taken, as by Meinong, by admitting objects which do not subsist, and denying that they obey the law of contradiction; this, however, is to be avoided if possible. Another way of taking the same course (so far as our present alternative is concerned) is adopted by Frege, who provides by definition some purely conventional denotation for the cases in which otherwise there would be none. Thus "the King of France," is to denote the null-class; "the only son of Mr. So-and-so" (who has a fine family of ten), is to denote the class of all his sons; and so on. But this procedure, though it may not lead to actual logical error, is plainly artificial, and does not give an exact analysis of the matter. Thus if we allow that denoting phrases, in general, have the two sides of meaning and denotation, the cases where there seems to be no denotation cause difficulties both on the assumption that there really is a denotation and on the assumption that there really is none.

A logical theory may be tested by its capacity for dealing with puzzles, and it is a wholesome plan, in thinking about logic, to stock the mind with as many puzzles as possible, since these serve much the same purpose as is served by experiments in physical science. I shall therefore state three puzzles which a theory as to denoting ought to be able to solve; and I shall show later that my theory solves them.

1. If *a* is identical with *b*, whatever is true of the one is true of the other, and either may be substituted for the other in any proposition without altering the truth or falsehood of that proposition. Now George IV wished to know whether Scott was the author of *Waverley*; and in fact Scott *was* the author of *Waverley*. Hence we may substitute *Scott* for *the author of* "*Waverley*," and thereby prove that George IV wished to know whether Scott was Scott. Yet an interest in the law of identity can hardly be attributed to the first gentleman of Europe.

2. By the law of excluded middle, either "A is B" or "A is not B" must be true. Hence either "the present King of France is bald" or "the present King of France is not bald" must be true. Yet if we enumerated the things that are bald, and then the things that are not bald, we should not find the present King of France in either list. Hegelians, who love a synthesis, will probably conclude that he wears a wig.

3. Consider the proposition "A differs from B." If this is true, there is a difference between A and B, which fact may be expressed in the form "the difference between A and B subsists." But if it is false that A differs from B, then there is no difference between A and B, which fact may be expressed in the form "the difference between A and B does not subsist."

But how can a non-entity be the subject of a proposition? "I think, therefore I am" is no more evident than "I am the subject of a proposition, therefore I am," provided "I am" is taken to assert subsistence or being,[11] not existence. Hence, it would appear, it must always be self-contradictory to deny the being of anything; but we have seen, in connexion with Meinong, that to admit being also sometimes leads to contradictions. Thus if A and B do not differ, to suppose either that there is, or that there is not, such an object as "the difference between A and B" seems equally impossible.

The relation of the meaning to the denotation involves certain rather curious difficulties, which seem in themselves sufficient to prove that the theory which leads to such difficulties must be wrong.

When we wish to speak about the *meaning* of a denoting phrase, as opposed to its *denotation*, the natural mode of doing so is by inverted commas. Thus we say:

> The centre of mass of the Solar System is a point, not a denoting complex;
> "The centre of mass of the Solar System" is a denoting complex, not a point.

Or again,

> The first line of Gray's *Elegy* states a proposition.
> "The first line of Gray's *Elegy*" does not state a proposition.

Thus taking any denoting phrase, say C, we wish to consider the relation between C and "C," where the difference of the two is of the kind exemplified in the above two instances.

We say, to begin with, that when C occurs it is the *denotation* that we are speaking about; but when "C" occurs, it is the *meaning*. Now the relation of meaning and denotation is not merely linguistic through the phrase: there must be a logical relation involved, which we express by saying that the meaning denotes the denotation. But the difficulty which confronts us is that we cannot succeed in *both* preserving the connexion of meaning and denotation *and* preventing them from being one and the same; also that the meaning cannot be got at except by means of denoting phrases. This happens as follows.

The one phrase C was to have both meaning and denotation. But if we speak of "the meaning of C," that gives us the meaning (if any) of the denotation. "The meaning of the first line of Gray's *Elegy*" is the same as "The meaning of 'The curfew tolls the knell of parting day,' " and is not the same as "The meaning of 'the first line of Gray's *Elegy*.' " Thus in order to get the meaning we want, we must speak not of "the meaning of C," but of "the meaning of 'C,' " which is the same as "C" by itself. Similarly "the denotation of C" does not mean the denotation we want, but

---

[11] I use these as synonyms.

means something which, if it denotes at all, denotes what is denoted by the denotation we want. For example, let "C" be "the denoting complex occurring in the second of the above instances." Then C = "the first line of Gray's *Elegy*," and the denotation of C = The curfew tolls the knell of parting day. But what we *meant* to have as the denotation was "the first line of Gray's *Elegy*." Thus we have failed to get what we wanted.

The difficulty in speaking of the meaning of a denoting complex may be stated thus: The moment we put the complex in a proposition, the proposition is about the denotation; and if we make a proposition in which the subject is "the meaning of C," then the subject is the meaning (if any) of the denotation, which was not intended. This leads us to say that, when we distinguish meaning and denotation, we must be dealing with the meaning: the meaning has denotation and is a complex, and there is not something other than the meaning, which can be called the complex, and be said to *have* both meaning and denotation. The right phrase, on the view in question, is that some meanings have denotations.

But this only makes our difficulty in speaking of meanings more evident. For suppose C is our complex; then we are to say that C *is* the meaning of the complex. Nevertheless, whenever C occurs without inverted commas, what is said is not true of the meaning, but only of the denotation, as when we say: The centre of mass of the Solar System is a point. Thus to speak of C itself, i.e., to make a proposition about the meaning, our subject must not be C, but something which denotes C. Thus "C," which is what we use when we want to speak of the meaning, must be not the meaning, but something which denotes the meaning. And C must not be a constituent of this complex (as it is of "the meaning of C"); for if C occurs in the complex, it will be its denotation, not its meaning, that will occur, and there is no backward road from denotations to meanings, because every object can be denoted by an infinite number of different denoting phrases.

Thus it would seem that "C" and C are different entities, such that "C" denotes C; but this cannot be an explanation, because the relation of "C" to C remains wholly mysterious; and where are we to find the denoting complex "C" which is to denote C? Moreover, when C occurs in a proposition, it is not *only* the denotation that occurs (as we shall see in the next paragraph); yet, on the view in question, C is only the denotation, the meaning being wholly relegated to "C." This is an inextricable tangle, and seems to prove that the whole distinction of meaning and denotation has been wrongly conceived.

That the meaning is relevant when a denoting phrase occurs in a proposition is formally proved by the puzzle about the author of *Waverley*. The proposition "Scott was the author of *Waverley*" has a property not possessed by "Scott was Scott," namely the property that George IV wished to know whether it was true. Thus the two are not identical propositions; hence the meaning of "the author of *Waverley*" must be relevant as well as the denotation, if we adhere to the point of view to which this distinction belongs. Yet, as we have just seen, so long as we adhere to this point of view, we are compelled to hold that only the denotation can be relevant. Thus the point of view in question must be abandoned.

It remains to show how all the puzzles we have been considering are solved by the theory explained at the beginning of this article.

According to the view which I advocate, a denoting phrase is essentially *part* of a sentence, and does not, like most single words, have any significance on its own account. If I say "Scott was a man," that is a statement of the form "*x* was a man," and it has "Scott" for its subject. But if I say "the author of *Waverley* was a man," that is not a statement of the form "*x* was a man," and does not have "the author of *Waverley*" for its subject. Abbreviating the statement made at the beginning of this article, we may put, in place of "the author of *Waverley* was a man," the following: "One and only one entity wrote *Waverley*, and that one was a man." (This is not so strictly what is meant as what was said earlier; but it is easier to follow.) And speaking generally, suppose we wish to say that the author of *Waverley* had the property $\phi$, what we wish to say is equivalent to "One and only one entity wrote *Waverley*, and that one had the property $\phi$."

The explanation of *denotation* is now as follows. Every proposition in which "the author of *Waverley*" occurs being explained as above, the proposition "Scott was the author of *Waverley*" (i.e., "Scott was identical with the author of *Waverley*") becomes "One and only one entity wrote *Waverley*, and Scott was identical with that one"; or, reverting to the wholly explicit form: "It is not always false of *x* that *x* wrote *Waverley*, that it is always true of *y* that if *y* wrote *Waverley* *y* is identical with *x*, and that Scott is identical with *x*." Thus if "C" is a denoting phrase, it may happen that there is one entity *x* (there cannot be more than one) for which the proposition "*x* is identical with C" is true, this proposition being interpreted as above. We may then say that the entity *x* is the denotation of the phrase "C." Thus Scott is the denotation of "the author of *Waverley*." The "C" in inverted commas will be merely the *phrase*, not anything that can be called the *meaning*. The phrase *per se* has no meaning, because in any proposition in which it occurs the proposition, fully expressed, does not contain the phrase, which has been broken up.

The puzzle about George IV's curiosity is now seen to have a very simple solution. The proposition "Scott was the author of *Waverley*," which was written out in its unabbreviated form in the preceding paragraph, does not contain any constituent "the author of *Waverley*" for which we could substitute "Scott." This does not interfere with the truth of inferences resulting from making what is *verbally* the substitution of "Scott" for "the author of *Waverley*," so long as "the author of *Waverley*" has what I call a *primary* occurrence in the proposition considered. The difference of primary and secondary occurrences of denoting phrases is as follows:

When we say: "George IV wished to know whether so-and-so," or when we say "So-and-so is surprising" or "So-and-so is true," etc., the "so-and-so" must be a proposition. Suppose now that "so-and-so" contains a denoting phrase. We may either eliminate this denoting phrase from the subordinate proposition "so-and-so," or from the whole proposition in which "so-and-so" is a mere constituent. Different propositions result according to which we do. I have heard of a touchy owner of a yacht to whom a guest, on first seeing it, remarked, "I thought your yacht was larger than it is"; and the owner replied, "No, my yacht is not larger than it is." What the guest meant was, "The size that I thought your yacht was is greater than the size your yacht is"; the meaning attributed to him is, "I thought the size of your yacht was greater than the size of your yacht." To return to George IV and Waverley, when we say, "George IV wished to know whether Scott was the author of Waverley," we normally mean "George IV wished to know whether one and only one man wrote Waverley and Scott was that man"; but we *may* also mean: "One and only one man wrote Waverley, and George IV wished to know whether Scott was that man." In the latter, "the author of Waverley" has a *primary* occurrence; in the former, a *secondary*. The latter might be expressed by "George IV wished to know, concerning the man who in fact wrote Waverley, whether he was Scott." This would be true, for example, if George IV had seen Scott at a distance, and had asked "Is that Scott?" A *secondary* occurrence of a denoting phrase may be defined as one in which the phrase occurs in a proposition *p* which is a mere constituent of the proposition we are considering, and the substitution for the denoting phrase is to be effected in *p*, not in the whole proposition concerned. The ambiguity as between primary and secondary occurrences is hard to avoid in language; but it does no harm if we are on our guard against it. In symbolic logic it is of course easily avoided.

The distinction of primary and secondary occurrences also enables us to deal with the question whether the present King of France is bald or not bald, and generally with the logical status of denoting phrases that denote nothing. If "C" is a denoting phrase, say "the term having the property F," then

"C has the property $\phi$" means "one and only one term has the property F, and that one has the property $\phi$." [12]

If now the property F belongs to no terms, or to several, it follows that "C has the property $\phi$" is false for *all* values of $\phi$. Thus "the present King of France is bald" is certainly false; and "the present King of France is not bald" is false if it means

"There is an entity which is now King of France and is not bald,"

but is true if it means

"It is false that there is an entity which is now King of France and is bald."

[12] This is the abbreviated, not the stricter, interpretation.

That is, "the King of France is not bald" is false if the occurrence of "the King of France" is *primary*, and true if it is *secondary*. Thus all propositions in which "the King of France" has a primary occurrence are false; the denials of such propositions are true, but in them "the King of France" has a secondary occurrence. Thus we escape the conclusion that the King of France has a wig.

We can now see also how to deny that there is such an object as the difference between A and B in the case when A and B do not differ. If A and B do differ, there is one and only one entity $x$ such that "$x$ is the difference between A and B" is a true proposition; if A and B do not differ, there is no such entity $x$. Thus according to the meaning of denotation lately explained, "the difference between A and B" has a denotation when A and B differ, but not otherwise. This difference applies to true and false propositions generally. If "$a R b$" stands for "$a$ has the relation R to $b$," then when $a R b$ is true, there is such an entity as the relation R between $a$ and $b$; when $a R b$ is false, there is no such entity. Thus out of any proposition we can make a denoting phrase, which denotes an entity if the proposition is true, but does not denote an entity if the proposition is false. E.g., it is true (at least we will suppose so) that the earth revolves round the sun, and false that the sun revolves round the earth; hence "the revolution of the earth round the sun" denotes an entity, while "the revolution of the sun round the earth" does not denote an entity.[13]

The whole realm of non-entities, such as "the round square," "the even prime other than 2," "Apollo," "Hamlet," etc., can now be satisfactorily dealt with. All these are denoting phrases which do not denote anything. A proposition about Apollo means what we get by substituting what the classical dictionary tells us is meant by Apollo, say "the sun-god." All propositions in which Apollo occurs are to be interpreted by the above rules for denoting phrases. If "Apollo" has a primary occurrence, the proposition containing the occurrence is false; if the occurrence is secondary, the proposition may be true. So again "the round square is round" means "there is one and only one entity $x$ which is round and square, and that entity is round," which is a false proposition, not, as Meinong maintains, a true one. "The most perfect Being has all perfections; existence is a perfection; therefore the most perfect Being exists" becomes:

> "There is one and only one entity $x$ which is most perfect; that one has all perfections; existence is a perfection; therefore that one exists." As a proof, this fails for want of a proof of the premiss "there is one and only one entity $x$ which is most perfect." [14]

---

[13] The propositions from which such entities are derived are not identical either with these entities or with the propositions that these entities have being.

[14] The argument can be made to prove validly that all members of the class of most perfect Beings exist; it can also be proved formally that this class cannot have *more* than one member; but, taking the definition of perfection as possession of all positive predicates, it can be proved almost equally formally that the class does not have even one member.

Mr. MacColl (*Mind*, N.S., No. 54, and again No. 55, p. 401) regards individuals as of two sorts, real and unreal; hence he defines the null-class as the class consisting of all unreal individuals. This assumes that such phrases as "the present King of France," which do not denote a real individual, do, nevertheless, denote an individual, but an unreal one. This is essentially Meinong's theory, which we have seen reason to reject because it conflicts with the law of contradiction. With our theory of denoting, we are able to hold that there are no unreal individuals; so that the null-class is the class containing no members, not the class containing as members all unreal individuals.

It is important to observe the effect of our theory on the interpretation of definitions which proceed by means of denoting phrases. Most mathematical definitions are of this sort: for example, "$m - n$ means the number which, added to $n$, gives $m$." Thus $m - n$ is defined as meaning the same as a certain denoting phrase; but we agreed that denoting phrases have no meaning in isolation. Thus what the definition really ought to be is: "Any proposition containing $m - n$ is to mean the proposition which results from substituting for '$m - n$' 'the number which, added to $n$, gives $m$.'" The resulting proposition is interpreted according to the rules already given for interpreting propositions whose verbal expression contains a denoting phrase. In the case where $m$ and $n$ are such that there is one and only one number $x$ which, added to $n$, gives $m$, there is a number $x$ which can be substituted for $m - n$ in any proposition containing $m - n$ without altering the truth or falsehood of the proposition. But in other cases, all propositions in which "$m - n$" has a primary occurrence are false.

The usefulness of *identity* is explained by the above theory. No one outside a logic-book ever wishes to say "$x$ is $x$," and yet assertions of identity are often made in such forms as "Scott was the author of *Waverley*" or "thou art the man." The meaning of such propositions cannot be stated without the notion of identity, although they are not simply statements that Scott is identical with another term, the author of *Waverley*, or that thou art identical with another term, the man. The shortest statement of "Scott is the author of *Waverley*" seems to be: "Scott wrote *Waverley*; and it is always true of $y$ that if $y$ wrote *Waverley*, $y$ is identical with Scott." It is in this way that identity enters into "Scott is the author of *Waverley*"; and it is owing to such uses that identity is worth affirming.

One interesting result of the above theory of denoting is this: when there is anything with which we do not have immediate acquaintance, but only definition by denoting phrases, then the propositions in which this thing is introduced by means of a denoting phrase do not really contain this thing as a constituent, but contain instead the constituents expressed by the several words of the denoting phrase. Thus in every proposition that we can apprehend (i.e., not only in those whose truth or falsehood we can judge of, but in all that we can think about), all the constituents are really entities with which we have immediate acquaintance. Now such things as matter (in the sense in which matter occurs in physics) and the minds of other people are known to us only by denoting phrases, i.e., we are not *acquainted* with them, but we know them as what has such and such properties. Hence, although we can form propositional functions C (*x*) which must hold of such and such a material particle, or of So-and-so's mind, yet we are not acquainted with the propositions which affirm these things that we know must be true, because we cannot apprehend the actual entities concerned. What we know is "So-and-so has a mind which has such and such properties" but we do not know "A has such and such properties," where A *is* the mind in question. In such a case, we know the properties of a thing without having acquaintance with the things itself, and without, consequently, knowing any single proposition of which the thing itself is a constituent.

Of the many other consequences of the view I have been advocating, I will say nothing. I will only beg the reader not to make up his mind against the view—as he might be tempted to do, on account of its apparently excessive complication—until he has attempted to construct a theory of his own on the subject of denotation. This attempt, I believe, will convince him that, whatever the true theory may be, it cannot have such a simplicity as one might have expected beforehand.

# ON REFERRING*

PETER FREDERICK STRAWSON (1919–    ) of Oxford University has written extensively on logic and metaphysics. Among his books are *Introduction to Logical Theory* and *Individuals*.

## I

We very commonly use expressions of certain kinds to mention or refer to some individual person or single object or particular event or place or process, in the course of doing what we should normally describe as making a statement about that person, object, place, event, or process. I shall call this way of using expressions the "uniquely referring use." The classes of expressions which are most commonly used in this way are: singular demonstrative pronouns ("this" and "that") proper names (*e.g.,*

* Reprinted from *Essays in Conceptual Analysis*, selected and edited by Professor Anthony Flew, by permission of the author, St. Martin's Press, and Macmillan & Co., Ltd. This article appeared originally in *Mind*, Vol. 59, 1950, pp. 320–44.

"Venice," "Napoleon," "John"); singular personal and impersonal pronouns ("he," "she," "I," "you," "it"); and phrases beginning with the definite article followed by a noun, qualified or unqualified, in the singular (*e.g.*, "the table," "the old man," "the king of France"). Any expression of any of these classes can occur as the subject of what would traditionally be regarded as a singular subject-predicate sentence; and would, so occurring, exemplify the use I wish to discuss.

I do not want to say that expressions belonging to these classes never have any other use than the one I want to discuss. On the contrary, it is obvious that they do. It is obvious that anyone who uttered the sentence, "The whale is a mammal," would be using the expression "the whale" in a way quite different from the way it would be used by anyone who had occasion seriously to utter the sentence, "The whale struck the ship." In the first sentence one is obviously *not* mentioning, and in the second sentence one obviously *is* mentioning, a particular whale. Again if I said, "Napoleon was the greatest French soldier," I should be using the word "Napoleon" to mention a certain individual, but I should not be using the phrase, "the greatest French soldier," to mention an individual, but to say something about an individual I had already mentioned. It would be natural to say that in using this sentence I was talking *about* Napoleon and that what I was *saying* about him was that he was the greatest French soldier. But of course I *could* use the expression, "the greatest French soldier," to mention an individual; for example, by saying: "The greatest French soldier died in exile." So it is obvious that at least some expressions belonging to the classes I mentioned *can* have uses other than the use I am anxious to discuss. Another thing I do not want to say is that in any given sentence there is never more than one expression used in the way I propose to discuss. On the contrary, it is obvious that there may be more than one. For example, it would be natural to say that, in seriously using the sentence, "The whale struck the ship," I was saying something about both a certain whale and a certain ship, that I was using each of the expressions "the whale" and "the ship" to mention a particular object; or, in other words, that I was using each of these expressions in the uniquely referring way. In general, however, I shall confine my attention to cases where an expression used in this way occurs as the grammatical subject of a sentence.

I think it is true to say that Russell's Theory of Descriptions, which is concerned with the last of the four classes of expressions I mentioned above (*i.e.*, with expressions of the form "the so-and-so") is still widely accepted among logicians as giving a correct account of the use of such expressions in ordinary language. I want to show, in the first place, that this theory, so regarded, embodies some fundamental mistakes.

What question or questions about phrases of the form "the so-and-so" was the Theory of Descriptions designed to answer? I think that at least one of the questions may be illustrated as follows. Suppose some one were now to utter the sentence, "The king of France is wise." No one would say that the sentence which had been uttered was meaningless. Everyone would agree that it was significant. But everyone knows that there is not at present a king of France. One of the questions the Theory of Descriptions was designed to answer was the question: how can such a sentence as "The king of France is wise" be significant even when there is nothing which answers to the description it contains, *i.e.*, in this case, nothing which answers to the description "The king of France"? And one of the reasons why Russell thought it important to give a correct answer to this question was that he thought it important to show that another answer which might be given was wrong. The answer that he thought was wrong, and to which he was anxious to supply an alternative, might be exhibited as the conclusion of either of the following two fallacious arguments. Let us call the sentence "The king of France is wise" the sentence S. Then the first argument is as follows:

(1)  The phrase, "the king of France," is the subject of the sentence S.
    Therefore (2) if S is a significant sentence, S is a sentence *about* the king of France.
    But (3) if there in no sense exists a king of France, the sentence is not about anything, and hence not about the king of France.
    Therefore (4) since S is significant, there must in some sense (in some world) exist (or subsist) the king of France.

And the second argument is as follows:

(1)  If S is significant, it is either true or false.
(2)  S is true if the king of France is wise and false if the king of France is not wise.
(3)  But the statement that the king of France is wise and the statement that the king of France is not wise are alike true only if there is (in some sense, in some world) something which is the king of France.
    Hence (4) since S is significant, there follows the same conclusion as before.

These are fairly obviously bad arguments, and, as we should expect, Russell rejects them. The postulation of a world of strange entities, to which the king of France belongs, offends, he says, against "that feeling for reality which ought to be preserved even in the most abstract studies." The fact that Russell rejects these arguments is, however, less interesting than the extent to which, in rejecting their conclusion, he concedes the more important of their principles. Let me refer to the phrase, "the king of France," as the phrase D. Then I think Russell's reasons for rejecting these two arguments can be summarised as follows. The mistake arises, he says, from thinking that D, which is certainly the *grammatical* subject of S, is also the *logical* subject of S. But D is not the logical subject of S. In fact S, although grammatically it has a singular subject and a predicate, is not logically a subject-predicate sentence at all. The proposition it expresses is a complex kind of *existential* proposition, part of which might be described as a "uniquely existential" proposition. To exhibit the logical form of the proposition, we should re-write the sentence in a logically appropriate grammatical form; in such a way that the deceptive similarity of S to a sentence expressing a subject-predicate proposition would disappear, and we should be safeguarded against arguments such as the bad ones I outlined above. Before recalling the details of Russell's analysis of S, let us notice what his answer, as I have so far given it, seems to imply. His answer seems to imply that in the case of a sentence which is similar to S in that (1) it is grammatically of the subject-predicate form and (2) its grammatical subject does not refer to anything, then the only alternative to its being meaningless is that it should not really (*i.e.*, logically) be of the subject-predicate form at all, but of some quite different form. And this in its turn seems to imply that if there are any sentences which are genuinely of the subject-predicate form, then the very fact of their being significant, having a meaning, guarantees that there *is* something referred to by the logical (and grammatical) subject. Moreover, Russell's answer seems to imply that there are such sentences. For if it is true that one may be misled by the grammatical similarity of S to other sentences into thinking that it is logically of the subject-predicate form, then surely there must be other sentences grammatically similar to S, which *are* of the subject-predicate form. To show not only that Russell's answer seems to imply these conclusions, but that he accepted at least the first two of them, it is enough to consider what he says about a class of expressions which he calls "logically proper names" and contrasts with expressions, like D, which he calls "definite descriptions." Of logically proper names Russell says or implies the following things:

(1)   That they and they alone can occur as subjects of sentences which are genuinely of the subject-predicate form;
(2)   that an expression intended to be a logically proper name is *meaningless* unless there is some single object for which it stands: for the *meaning* of such an expression just is the individual object which the expression designates. To be a name at all, therefore, it *must* designate something.

It is easy to see that if anyone believes these two propositions, then the only way for him to save the significance of the sentence S is to deny that it is a logically subject-predicate sentence. Generally, we may say that Russell recognises only two ways in which sentences which seem, from their grammatical structure, to be about some particular person or individual object or event, can be significant:

(1) The first is that their grammatical form should be misleading as to their logical form, and that they should be analysable, like S, as a special kind of existential sentence.
(2) The second is that their grammatical subject should be a logically proper name, of which the meaning is the individual thing it designates.

I think that Russell is unquestionably wrong in this, and that sentences which are significant, and which begin with an expression used in the uniquely referring way fall into neither of these two classes. Expressions used in the uniquely referring way are never either logically proper names or descriptions, if what is meant by calling them "descriptions" is that they are to be analysed in accordance with the model provided by Russell's Theory of Descriptions.

There are no logically proper names and there are no descriptions (in this sense).

Let us now consider the details of Russell's analysis. According to Russell, anyone who asserted S would be asserting that:

(1) There is a king of France.
(2) There is not more than one king of France.
(3) There is nothing which is king of France and is not wise.

It is easy to see both how Russell arrived at this analysis, and how it enables him to answer the question with which we began, *viz.* the question: How can the sentence S be significant when there is no king of France? The way in which he arrived at the analysis was clearly by asking himself what would be the circumstances in which we would say that anyone who uttered the sentence S had made a true assertion. And it does seem pretty clear, and I have no wish to dispute, that the sentences (1)-(3) above do describe circumstances which are at least *necessary* conditions of anyone making a true assertion by uttering the sentence S. But, as I hope to show, to say this is not at all the same thing as to say that Russell has given a correct account of the use of the sentence S or even that he has given an account which, though incomplete, is correct as far as it goes; and is certainly not at all the same thing as to say that the model translation provided is a correct model for all (or for any) singular sentences beginning with a phrase of the form "the so-and-so."

It is also easy to see how this analysis enables Russell to answer the question of how the sentence S can be significant, even when there is no king of France. For, if this analysis is correct, anyone who utters the sentence S to-day would be jointly asserting three propositions, one of which (*viz.* that there is a king of France) would be false; and since the conjunction of three propositions, of which one is false, is itself false, the assertion as a whole would be significant, but false. So neither of the bad arguments for subsistent entities would apply to such an assertion.

## II

As a step towards showing that Russell's solution of his problem is mistaken, and towards providing the correct solution, I want now to draw certain distinctions. For this purpose I shall, for the remainder of this section, refer to an expression which has a uniquely referring use as "an expression" for short; and to a sentence beginning with such an expression as "a sentence" for short. The distinctions I shall draw are rather rough and ready, and, no doubt, difficult cases could be produced which would call for their refinement. But I think they will serve my purpose. The distinctions are between:

(A1)    a sentence,
(A2)    a use of a sentence,
(A3)    an utterance of a sentence,

and, correspondingly, between:

(B1)    an expression,
(B2)    a use of an expression,
(B3)    an utterance of an expression.

Consider again the sentence, "The king of France is wise." It is easy to imagine that this sentence was uttered at various times from, say, the beginning of the seventeenth century onwards, during the reigns of each successive French monarch; and easy to imagine that it was also uttered during the subsequent periods in which France was not a monarchy. Notice that it was natural for me to speak of "the sentence" or "this sentence" being uttered at various times during this period; or, in other words, that it would be natural and correct to speak of *one and the same* sentence being uttered on all these various occasions. It is in the sense in which it would be correct to speak of one and the same sentence being uttered on all these various occasions that I want to use the expression (A1) "a sentence." There are, however, obvious differences between different *occasions of the use* of this sentence. For instance, if one man uttered it in the reign of Louis XIV and another man uttered it in the reign of Louis XV, it would be natural to say (to assume) that they were respectively talking about different people; and it might be held that the first man, in using the sentence, made a true assertion, while the second man, in using the same sentence, made a false assertion. If on the other hand two different men simultaneously uttered the sentence (*e.g.* if one wrote it and the other spoke it) during the reign of Louis XIV, it would be natural to say (assume) that they were both talking about the same person, and, in that case, in using the sentence, they *must* either both have made a true assertion or both have made a false assertion. And this illustrates what I mean by *a use* of a sentence. The two men who uttered the sentence, one in the reign of Louis XV and one in the reign of Louis XIV, each made a different use of the same sentence; whereas the two men who uttered the sentence simultaneously in the reign of Louis XIV, made the same use [1] of the same sentence. Obviously in the case of this sentence, and equally obviously in the case of many others, we cannot talk of *the sentence* being true or false, but only of its being used to make a true or false assertion, or (if this is preferred) to express a true or a false proposition. And equally obviously we cannot talk of *the sentence* being *about* a particular person, for the same sentence may be used at different times to talk about quite different particular persons, but only of *a use* of the sentence to talk about a particular person. Finally it will make sufficiently clear what I mean by an utterance of a sentence if I say that the two men who simultaneously uttered the sentence in the reign of Louis XIV made two different utterances of the same sentence, though they made the same *use* of the sentence.

If we now consider not the whole sentence, "The king of France is wise," but that part of it which is the expression, "the king of France," it is obvious that we can make analogous, though not identical distinctions between (1) the expression, (2) a use of the expression and (3) an utterance of the expression. The distinctions will not be identical; we obviously cannot correctly talk of the expression "the king of France" being used to express a true or false proposition, since in general only sentences can be used truly or falsely; and similarly it is only by using a sentence and not by using an expression alone, that you can talk about a particular person. Instead, we shall say in this case that you *use* the expression to *mention* or *refer to* a particular person in the course of using the sentence to talk about him. But obviously in this case, and a great many others, the *expression* (B1) cannot be said to mention, or refer to, anything, any more than the *sentence* can be said to be true or false. The same expression can have different mentioning-uses, as the same sentence can be used to make statements with different truth-values. "Mentioning," or "referring," is not something an expression does; it is something that some one can use an expression to do. Mentioning, or referring to, something is a characteristic of *a use* of an expression, just as "being about" something, and truth-or-falsity, are characteristics of *a use* of a sentence.

---

[1] This usage of 'use' is, of course, different from (*a*) the current usage in which 'use' (of a particular word, phrase, sentence) = (roughly) 'rules for using' = (roughly) 'meaning'; and from (*b*) my own usage in the phrase "uniquely referring use of expressions" in which 'use' = (roughly) 'way of using.'

A very different example may help to make these distinctions clearer. Consider another case of an expression which has a uniquely referring use, *viz.* the expression "I"; and consider the sentence, "I am hot." Countless people may use this same sentence; but it is logically impossible for two different people to make *the same use* of this sentence: or, if this is preferred, to use it to express the same proposition. The expression "I" may correctly be used by (and only by) any one of innumerable people to refer to himself. To say this is to say something about the expression "I": it is, in a sense, to give its meaning. This is the sort of thing that can be said about *expressions*. But it makes no sense to say of the *expression* "I" that it refers to a particular person. This is the sort of thing that can be said only of a particular use of the expression.

Let me use "type" as an abbreviation for "sentence or expression." Then I am not saying that there are sentences and expression (types), *and* uses of them, *and* utterances of them, as there are ships *and* shoes *and* sealing-wax. I am saying that we cannot say *the same things* about types, uses of types, and utterances of types. And the fact is that we do talk about types; and that confusion is apt to result from the failure to notice the differences between what we can say about these and what we can say only about the *uses* of types. We are apt to fancy we are talking about sentences and expressions when we are talking about the uses of sentences and expressions.

This is what Russell does. Generally, as against Russell, I shall say this. Meaning ( in at least one important sense) is a function of the sentence or expression; mentioning and referring and truth or falsity, are functions of the use of the sentence or expression. To give the meaning of an expression (in the sense in which I am using the word) is to give *general directions* for its use to refer to or mention particular objects or persons; to give the meaning of a sentence is to give *general directions* for its use in making true or false assertions. It is not to talk about any particular occasion of the use of the sentence or expression. The meaning of an expression cannot be identified with the object it is used, on a particular occasion, to refer to. The meaning of a sentence cannot be identified with the assertion it is used, on a particular occasion, to make. For to talk about the meaning of an expression or sentence is not to talk about its use on a particular occasion, but about the rules, habits, conventions governing its correct use, on all occasions, to refer or to assert. So the question of whether a sentence or expression *is significant or not* has nothing whatever to do with the question of whether the sentence, *uttered on a particular occasion*, is, on that occasion, being used to make a true-or-false assertion or not, or of whether the expression is, on that occasion, being used to refer to, or mention, anything at all.

The source of Russell's mistake was that he thought that referring or mentioning, if it occurred at all, must be meaning. He did not distinguish B1 from B2; he confused expressions with their use in a particular context; and so confused meaning with mentioning, with referring. If I talk about my handkerchief, I can, perhaps, produce the object I am referring to out of my pocket. I cannot produce the meaning of the expression, "my handkerchief," out of my pocket. Because Russell confused meaning with mentioning, he thought that if there were any expressions having a uniquely referring use, which were what they seemed (*i.e.* logical subjects) and not something else in disguise, their meaning must *be* the particular object which they were used to refer to. Hence the troublesome mythology of the logically proper name. But if some one asks me the meaning of the expression "this"—once Russell's favourite candidate for this status—I do not hand him the object I have just used the expression to refer to, adding at the same time that the meaning of the word changes every time it is used. Nor do I hand him all the objects it ever has been, or might be, used to refer to. I explain and illustrate the conventions governing the use of the expression. This *is* giving the meaning of the expression. It is quite different from giving (in any sense of giving) the object to which it refers; for the expression itself does not refer to anything; though it can be used, on different occasions, to refer to innumerable things. Now as a matter of fact there is, in English, a sense of the word "mean" in which this word does approximate to "indicate, mention or refer to"; *e.g.* when somebody (unpleasantly) says, "I mean you"; or when I point and say, "That's the one I mean." But *the one I meant* is quite different from *the meaning of the expression* I used to talk of it. In this special sense of "mean," it is people who mean, not expressions. People use expressions to refer to particular things. But the meaning of an expression is not the set of things or the single thing it may correctly be used to refer to: the meaning is the set of rules, habits, conventions for its use in referring.

It is the same with sentences: even more obviously so. Every one knows that the sentence, "The table is covered with books," is significant, and every one knows what it means. But if I ask, "What object is that sentence about?" I am asking an absurd question—a question which cannot be asked about the sentence, but only some use of the sentence: and in this case the sentence has not been used to talk about something, it has only been taken as an example. In knowing what it means, you are knowing how it could correctly be used to talk about things: so knowing the meaning has nothing to do with knowing about any particular use of the sentence to talk about anything. Similarly, if I ask: "Is the sentence true or false?" I am asking an absurd question, which becomes no less absurd if I add, "It must be one or the other since it is significant." The question is absurd, because the *sentence* is neither true nor false any more than it is *about* some object. Of course the fact that it is significant is the same as the fact that it *can* correctly be used to talk about something and that, in so using it, some one will be making a true or false assertion. And I will add that it will be used to make a true or false assertion *only* if the person using it *is* talking about something. If, when he utters it, he is not talking about anything, then his use is not a genuine one, but a spurious or pseudo-use: he is not making either a true or a false assertion, though he may think he is. And this points the way to the correct answer to the puzzle to which the Theory of Descriptions gives a fatally incorrect answer. The important point is that the question of whether the sentence is significant or not is quite independent of the question that can be raised about a particular use of it, *viz.* the question whether it is a genuine or a spurious use, whether it is being used to talk about something, or in make-believe, or as an example in philosophy. The question whether the sentence is significant or not is the question whether there exist such language habits, conventions or rules that the sentence logically could be used to talk about something; and is hence quite independent of the question whether it is being so used on a particular occasion.

## III

Consider again the sentence, "The king of France is wise," and the true and false things Russell says about it.

There are at least two true things which Russell would say about the sentence:

(1)    The first is that it is significant; that if anyone were now to utter it, he would be uttering a significant sentence.
(2)    The second is that anyone now uttering the sentence would be making a true assertion only if there in fact at present existed one and only one king of France, and if he were wise.

What are the false things which Russell would say about the sentence? They are:

(1)    That anyone now uttering it would be making a true assertion or a false assertion;
(2)    That part of what he would be asserting would be that there at present existed one and only one king of France.

I have already given some reasons for thinking that these two statements are incorrect. Now suppose some one were in fact to say to you with a perfectly serious air: "The king of France is wise." Would you say, "That's untrue"? I think it is quite certain that you would not. But suppose he went on to *ask* you whether you thought that what he had just said was true, or was false; whether you agreed or disagreed with what he had just said. I think you would be inclined, with some hesitation, to say that you did not do either; that the question of whether his statement was true or false simply *did not arise*, because there was no such person as the king of France.[2] You might, if he were obviously serious (had a dazed astray-in-the-centuries look), say something like: "I'm afraid you must be under a misapprehension. France is not a monarchy. There is no king of France." And this

---

[2] Since this article was written, there has appeared a clear statement of this point by Mr Geach in *Analysis* Vol. 10, No. 4, March, 1950.

brings out the point that if a man seriously uttered the sentence, his uttering it would in some sense be *evidence* that he *believed* that there was a king of France. It would not be evidence for his believing this simply in the way in which a man's reaching for his raincoat is evidence for his believing that it is raining. But nor would it be evidence for his believing this in the way in which a man's saying, "It's raining" is evidence for his believing that it is raining. We might put it as follows. To say, "The king of France is wise" is, in some sense of "imply," to *imply* that there is a king of France. But this is a very special and odd sense of "imply." "Implies" in this sense is certainly not equivalent to "entails" (or "logically implies")'. And this comes out from the fact that when, in response to his statement, we say (as we should) "There is no king of France," we should certainly *not* say we were *contradicting* the statement that the king of France is wise. We are certainly not saying that it is false. We are, rather, giving a reason for saying that the question of whether it is true or false simply does not arise.

And this is where the distinction I drew earlier can help us. The sentence, "The king of France is wise," is certainly significant; but this does not mean that any particular use of it is true or false. We use it truly or falsely when we use it to talk about some one; when, in using the expression, "The king of France," we are in fact mentioning some one. The fact that the sentence and the expression, respectively, are significant just is the fact that the sentence *could* be used, in certain circumstances, to say something true or false, that the expression *could* be used, in certain circumstances to mention a particular person; and to know their meaning is to know what sort of circumstances these are. So when we utter the sentence without in fact mentioning anybody by the use of the phrase, "The king of France," the sentence does not cease to be significant: we simply *fail* to say anything true or false because we simply fail to mention anybody by this particular use of that perfectly significant phrase. It is, if you like, a spurious use of the sentence, and a spurious use of the expression; though we may (or may not) mistakenly think it a genuine use.

And such spurious uses [3] are very familiar. Sophisticated romancing, sophisticated fiction,[4] depend upon them. If I began, "The king of France is wise," and went on, "and he lives in a golden castle and has a hundred wives," and so on, a hearer would understand me perfectly well, without supposing *either* that I was talking about a particular person, *or* that I was making a false statement to the effect that there existed such a person as my words described. (It is worth adding that where the use of sentences and expressions is overtly fictional, the sense of the word "about" may change. As Moore said, it is perfectly natural and correct to say that some of the statements in *Pickwick Papers* are *about* Mr. Pickwick. But where

---

[3] [The choice of the word 'spurious' now seems to me unfortunate, at least for some nonstandard uses. I should now prefer to call some of these 'secondary' uses.]

[4] The unsophisticated kind begins: "Once upon a time there was . . ."

the use of sentences and expressions is not overtly fictional, this use of "about" seems less correct; *i.e.* it would not *in general* be correct to say that a statement was about Mr. X or the so-and-so, unless there were such a person or thing. So it is where the romancing is in danger of being taken seriously that we might answer the question, "Who is he talking about?" with "He's not talking about anybody"; but, in saying this, we are not saying that what he is saying is either false or nonsense.)

Overtly fictional uses apart, however, I said just now that to use such an expression as "The king of France" at the beginning of a sentence was, in some sense of "imply," to imply that there was a king of France. When a man uses such an expression, he does not *assert*, nor does what he says *entail*, a uniquely existential proposition. But one of the conventional functions of the definite article is to act as a *signal* that a unique reference is being made—a signal, not a disguised assertion. When we begin a sentence with "the such-and-such" the use of "the" shows, but does not state, that we are, or intend to be, referring to one particular individual of the species "such-and-such." *Which* particular individual is a matter to be determined from context, time, place and any other features of the situation of utterance. Now, whenever a man uses any expression, the presumption is that he thinks he is using it correctly so when he uses the expression, "the such-and-such," in a uniquely referring way, the presumption is that he thinks both that there is *some* individual of that species, and that the context of use will sufficiently determine which one he has in mind. To use the word "the" in this way is then to imply (in the relevant sense of "imply") that the existential conditions described by Russell are fulfilled. But to use "the" in this way is not to *state* that those conditions are fulfilled. If I begin a sentence with an expression of the form, "the so-and-so," and then am prevented from saying more, I have made no statement of any kind; but I may have succeeded in mentioning some one or something.

The uniquely existential assertion supposed by Russell to be part of any assertion in which a uniquely referring use is made of an expression of the form "the so-and-so" is, he observes, a compound of two assertions. To say that there is a $\phi$ is to say something compatible with there being several $\phi$s; to say there is not more than one $\phi$ is to say something compatible with there being none. To say there is one $\phi$ and one only is to compound these two assertions. I have so far been concerned mostly with the alleged assertion of existence and less with the alleged assertion of uniqueness. An example which throws the emphasis on to the latter will serve to bring out more clearly the sense of "implied" in which a uniquely existential assertion is implied, but not entailed, by the use of expressions in the uniquely referring way. Consider the sentence, "The table is covered with books." It is quite certain that in any normal use of this sentence, the expression "the table" would be used to make a unique reference, *i.e.* to refer to some one table. It is a quite strict use of the definite article, in the sense in which

Russell talks on p. 30 of *Principia Mathematica*, of using the article "*strictly*, so as to imply uniqueness." On the same page Russell says that a phrase of the form "the so-and-so," used strictly, "will only have an application in the event of there being one so-and-so and no more." Now it is obviously quite false that the phrase "the table" in the sentence "the table is covered with books," used normally, will "only have an application in the event of there being one table and no more." It is indeed tautologically true that, in such a use, the phrase will have an application only in the event of there being one table and no more *which is being referred to*, and that it will be understood to have an application only in the event of there being one table and no more which it is understood as being used to refer to. To use the sentence is not to assert, but it is (in the special sense discussed) to imply, that there is only one thing which is *both* of the kind specified (*i.e.*, a table) *and is being referred to* by the speaker. It is obviously not to assert this. To refer is not to say you are referring. To say there is *some table or other* to which you are referring is not the same as referring to a particular table. We should have no use for such phrases as "the individual I referred to" unless there were something which counted as referring. (It would make no sense to say you had pointed if there were nothing which counted as pointing.) So once more I draw the conclusion that referring to or mentioning a particular thing cannot be dissolved into any kind of assertion. To refer is not to assert, though you refer in order to go on to assert.

Let me now take an example of the uniquely referring use of an expression not of the form, "the so-and-so." Suppose I advance my hands, cautiously cupped, towards someone, saying, as I do so, "This is a fine red one." He, looking into my hands and seeing nothing there, may say: "What is? What are you talking about?" Or perhaps, "But there's nothing in your hands." Of course it would be absurd to say that in saying "But you've got nothing in your hands," he was *denying* or *contradicting* what I said. So "this" is not a disguised description in Russell's sense. Nor is it a logically proper name. For one must know what the sentence means in order to react in that way to the utterance of it. It is precisely because the significance of the word "this" is independent of any particular reference it may be used to make, though not independent of the way it may be used to refer, that I can, as in this example, use it to *pretend* to be referring to something.

The general moral of all this is that communication is much less a matter of explicit or disguised assertion than logicians used to suppose. The particular application of this general moral in which I am interested is its application to the case of making a unique reference. It is a part of the significance of expressions of the kind I am discussing that they can be used, in an immense variety of contexts, to make unique references. It is no part of their significance to assert that they are being so used or that the conditions of their being so used are fulfilled. So the wholly important distinction we are required to draw is between:

(1)    using an expression to make a unique reference; and
(2)    asserting that there is one and only one individual which has certain characteristics (*e.g.*, is of a certain kind, or stands in a certain relation to the speaker, or both).

This is, in other words, the distinction between

(1)    sentences containing an expression used to indicate or mention or refer to a particular person or thing; and
(2)    uniquely existential sentences.

What Russell does is progressively to assimilate more and more sentences of class (1) to sentences of class (2), and consequently to involve himself in insuperable difficulties about logical subjects, and about values for individual variables generally: difficulties which have led him finally to the logically disastrous theory of names developed in the *Enquiry into Meaning and Truth* and in *Human Knowledge*. That view of the meaning of logical-subject-expressions which provides the whole incentive to the Theory of Descriptions at the same time precludes the possibility of Russell's ever finding any satisfactory substitutes for those expressions which, beginning with substantival phrases, he progressively degrades from the status of logical subjects.[5] It is not simply, as is sometimes said, the fascination of the relation between a name and its bearer, that is the root of the trouble. Not even names come up to the impossible standard set. It is rather the combination of two more radical misconceptions: first, the failure to grasp the importance of the distinction (section II above) between what may be said of an expression and what may be said of a particular use of it; second, a failure to recognise the uniquely referring use of expressions for the harmless, necessary thing it is, distinct from, but complementary to, the predicative or ascriptive use of expressions. The expressions which can in fact occur as singular logical subjects are expressions of the class I listed at the outset (demonstratives, substantival phrases, proper names, pronouns): to say this is to say that these expressions, together with context (in the widest sense) are what one uses to make unique references. The point of the conventions governing the uses of such expressions is, along with the situation of utterance, to secure uniqueness of reference. But to do this, enough is enough. We do not, and we cannot, while referring, attain the point of complete explicitness at which the referring function is no longer performed. The actual unique reference made, if any, is a matter of the particular use in the particular context; the significance of the expression used is the set of rules or conventions which permit such references to be made. Hence we can, using significant expressions, pretend

[5] And this in spite of the danger-signal of that phrase, "*misleading* grammatical form."

to refer, in make-believe or in fiction, or mistakenly think we are referring when we are not referring to anything.[6]

This shows the need for distinguishing two kinds (among many others) of linguistic conventions or rules: rules for referring, and rules for attributing and ascribing; and for an investigation of the former. If we recognise this distinction of use for what it is, we are on the way to solving a number of ancient logical and metaphysical puzzles.

My last two sections are concerned, but only in the barest outline, with these questions.

## IV

One of the main purposes for which we use language is the purpose of stating facts about things and persons and events. If we want to fulfil this purpose, we must have some way of forestalling the question, "What (who, which one) are you talking about?" as well as the question, "What are you saying about it (him, her)?" The task of forestalling the first question is the referring (or identifying) task. The task of forestalling the second is the attributive (or descriptive or classificatory or ascriptive) task. In the conventional English sentence which is used to state, or to claim to state, a fact about an individual thing or person or event, the performance of these two tasks can be roughly and approximately assigned to separable expressions.[7] And in such a sentence, this assigning of expressions to their separate roles corresponds to the conventional grammatical classification of subject and predicate. There is nothing sacrosanct about the employment of separable expressions for these two tasks. Other methods could be, and are, employed. There is, for instance, the method of uttering a single word or attributive phrase in the conspicuous presence of the object referred to; or that analogous method exemplified by, *e.g.*, the painting of the words "unsafe for lorries" on a bridge, or the tying of a label reading "first prize" on a vegetable marrow. Or one can imagine an elaborate game in which one never used an expression in the uniquely referring way at all, but uttered only uniquely existential sentences, trying to enable the hearer to identify what was being talked of by means of an accumulation of relative clauses. (This description of the purposes of the game shows in what sense it would be a game: this is not the normal use we make of existential sentences.) Two points require emphasis. The first is that the necessity of performing these two tasks in order to state particular facts requires no transcendental explanation: to call attention to it is partly to elucidate the meaning of the phrase, "stating a fact." The second is that even this eluci-

---

[6] [This sentence now seems to me objectionable in a number of ways, notably because of an unexplicitly restrictive use of the word 'refer.' It could be more exactly phrased as follows: 'Hence we can, using significant expressions, refer in secondary ways, as in make-believe or in fiction, or mistakenly think we are referring to something in the primary way when we are not, in that way, referring to anything ]

[7] I neglect relational sentences; for these require, not a modification in the principle of what I say, but a complication of the detail.

dation is made in terms derivative from the grammar of the conventional singular sentence; that even the overtly functional, linguistic distinction between the identifying and attributive roles that words may play in language is prompted by the fact that ordinary speech offers us separable expressions to which the different functions may be plausibly and approximately assigned. And this functional distinction has cast long philosophical shadows. The distinctions between particular and universal, between substance and quality, are such pseudo-material shadows, cast by the grammar of the conventional sentence, in which separable expressions play distinguishable roles.[8]

To use a separate expression to perform the first of these tasks is to use an expression in the uniquely referring way. I want now to say something in general about the conventions of use for expressions used in this way, and to contrast them with conventions of ascriptive use. I then proceed to the brief illustration of these general remarks and to some further applications of them.

What in general is required for making a unique reference is, obviously, some device, or devices, for showing both *that* a unique reference is intended and *what* unique reference it is; some device requiring and enabling the hearer or reader to identify what is being talked about. In securing this result, the context of utterance is of an importance which it is almost impossible to exaggerate; and by "context" I mean, at least, the time, the place, the situation, the identity of the speaker, the subjects which form the immediate focus of interest, and the personal histories of both the speaker and those he is addressing. Besides context, there is, of course, convention;—linguistic convention. But, except in the case of genuine proper names, of which I shall have more to say later, the fulfilment of more or less precisely stateable contextual conditions is *conventionally* (or, in a wide sense of the word, *logically*) required for the correct referring use of expressions in a sense in which this is not true of correct ascriptive uses. The requirement for the correct application of an expression in its ascriptive use to a certain thing is simply that the thing should be of a certain kind, have certain characteristics. The requirement for the correct application of an expression in its referring use to a certain thing is something over and above any requirement derived from such ascriptive meaning as the expression may have; it is, namely, the requirement that the thing should be in a certain relation to the speaker and to the context of utterance. Let me call this the contextual requirement. Thus, for example, in the limiting case of the word "I" the contextual requirement is that the thing should be identical with the speaker; but in the case of most expressions which have a referring use this requirement cannot be so precisely specified. A further, and perfectly general, difference between conventions for referring and conventions for describing is one we have already encountered, *viz.*

---

[8] [What is said or implied in the last two sentences of this paragraph no longer seems to me true, unless considerably qualified.]

that the fulfilment of the conditions for a correct ascriptive use of an expression is a part of what is stated by such a use; but the fulfilment of the conditions for a correct referring use of an expression is never part of what is stated, though it is (in the relevant sense of "implied") implied by such a use.

Conventions for referring have been neglected or misinterpreted by logicians. The reasons for this neglect are not hard to see, though they are hard to state briefly. Two of them are, roughly: (1) the preoccupation of most logicians with definitions; (2) the preoccupation of some logicians with formal systems. (1) A definition, in the most familiar sense, is a specification of the conditions of the correct ascriptive or classificatory use of an expression. Definitions take no account of contextual requirements. So that in so far as the search for the meaning or the search for the analysis of an expression is conceived as the search for a definition, the neglect or misinterpretation of conventions other than ascriptive is inevitable. Perhaps it would be better to say (for I do not wish to legislate about "meaning" or "analysis") that logicians have failed to notice that problems of use are wider than problems of analysis and meaning. (2) The influence of the preoccupation with mathematics and formal logic is most clearly seen (to take no more recent examples) in the cases of Leibniz and Russell. The constructor of calculuses, not concerned or required to make factual statements, approaches applied logic with a prejudice. It is natural that he should assume that the types of convention with whose adequacy in one field he is familiar should be really adequate, if only one could see how, in a quite different field—that of statements of fact. Thus we have Leibniz striving desperately to make the uniqueness of unique references a matter of logic in the narrow sense, and Russell striving desperately to do the same thing, in a different way, both for the implication of uniqueness and for that of existence.

It should be clear that the distinction I am trying to draw is primarily one between different rôles or parts that expressions may play in language, and not primarily one between different groups of expressions; for some expressions may appear in either rôle. Some of the kinds of words I shall speak of have predominantly, if not exclusively, a referring rôle. This is most obviously true of pronouns and ordinary proper names. Some can occur as wholes or parts of expressions which have a predominantly referring use, and as wholes or parts of expressions which have a predominantly ascriptive or classificatory use. The obvious cases are common nouns; or common nouns preceded by adjectives, including participial adjectives; or, less obviously, adjectives or participial adjectives alone. Expressions capable of having a referring use also differ from one another in at least the three following, not mutually independent, ways:

(1)   They differ in the extent to which the reference they are used to make is dependent on the context of their utterance. Words like "I"

and "it" stand at one end of this scale—the end of maximum dependence—and phrases like "the author of W*averley*" and "the eighteenth king of France" at the other.

(2)   They differ in the degree of "descriptive meaning" they possess: by "descriptive meaning" I intend "conventional limitation, in application, to things of a certain general kind, or possessing certain general characteristics." At one end of this scale stand the proper names we most commonly use in ordinary discourse; men, dogs and motor-bicycles may be called "Horace." The pure name has no descriptive meaning (except such as it may acquire *as a result of* some one of its uses as a name). A word like "he" has minimal descriptive meaning, but has some. Substantival phrases like "the round table" have the maximum descriptive meaning. An interesting intermediate position is occupied by 'impure' proper names like "The Round Table"— substantival phrases which have grown capital letters.

(3)   Finally, they may be divided into the following two classes: (i) those of which the correct referring use is regulated by some *general* referring-cum-ascriptive conventions; (ii) those of which the correct referring use is regulated by no general conventions, either of the contextual or the ascriptive kind, but by conventions which are *ad hoc* for each particular use (though not for each particular utterance). To the first class belong both pronouns (which have the least descriptive meaning) and substantival phrases (which have the most). To the second class belong, roughly speaking, the most familiar kind of proper names. Ignorance of a man's name is not ignorance of the language. This is why we do not speak of the meaning of proper names. (But it won't do to say they are meaningless.) Again an intermediate position is occupied by such phrases as "The Old Pretender." Only an old pretender may be so referred to; but to know which old pretender is not to know a general, but an *ad hoc*, convention.

In the case of phrases of the form "the so-and-so" used referringly, the use of "the" together with the position of the phrase in the sentence (*i.e.*, at the beginning, or following a transitive verb or preposition) acts as a signal *that* a unique reference is being made; and the following noun, or noun and adjective, together with the context of utterance, shows *what* unique reference is being made. In general the functional difference between common nouns and adjectives is that the former are naturally and commonly used referringly, while the latter are not commonly, or so naturally, used in this way, except as qualifying nouns; though they can be and are, so used alone. And of course this functional difference is not independent of the descriptive force peculiar to each word. In general we should expect the descriptive force of nouns to be such that they are more efficient tools for the job of showing what unique reference is intended when such a reference is signalised; and we should also expect the descriptive force of the words we naturally and commonly use to make unique references to mirror our interest in the salient, relatively permanent and behavioural characteristics of things. These two expectations are not independent of one another; and, if we look at the differences between the commoner sort of common nouns and the commoner sort of adjectives, we find them both fulfilled. These are differences of the kind that Locke quaintly reports, when he speaks of our ideas of substances being *collections* of simple ideas; when he says that "powers make up a great part of our ideas of substances"; and when he goes on to contrast the identity of real and nominal essence in the case of simple ideas with their lack of identity and the shiftingness of the nominal essence in the case of substances. "Substance" itself is the troublesome tribute Locke pays to his dim awareness of the difference in predominant linguistic function that lingered even when the noun had been expanded into a more or less indefinite string of adjectives. Russell repeats Locke's mistake with a difference when, admitting the inference from syntax to reality to the extent of feeling that he can get rid of this metaphysical unknown only if he can purify language of the referring function altogether, he draws up his programme for "abolishing particulars"; a programme, in fact, for abolishing the distinction of logical use which I am here at pains to emphasise.

The contextual requirement for the referring use of pronouns may be stated with the greatest precision in some cases (*e.g.* "I" and "you") and only with the greatest vagueness in others ("it" and "this"). I propose to say nothing further about pronouns, except to point to an additional symptom of the failure to recognise the uniquely referring use for what it is; the fact, namely, that certain logicians have actually sought to elucidate the nature of a variable by offering such *sentences* as "he is sick," "it is green," as examples of something in ordinary speech like a *sentential function*. Now of course it is true that the word "he" may be used on different occasions to refer to different people or different animals: so may the word "John" and the phrase "the cat." What deters such logicians from treating these two expressions as quasi-variables is, in the first case, the lingering superstition that a name is logically tied to a single individual, and, in the second case, the descriptive meaning of the word "cat." But "he," which has a wide range of applications and minimal descriptive force, only acquires a use as a referring word. It is this fact, together with the failure to accord to expressions used referringly, the place in logic which belongs to them (the place held open for the mythical logically proper name), that accounts for the misleading attempt to elucidate the nature of the variable by reference to such words as "he," "she," "it."

Of ordinary proper names it is sometimes said that they are essentially words each of which is used to refer to just one individual. This is obviously false. Many ordinary personal names—names par excellence—are correctly used to refer to numbers of people. An ordinary personal name, is, roughly, a word, used referringly, of which the use is *not* dictated by any descriptive meaning the word may have, and is *not* prescribed by any such general rule for use as a referring expression (or a part of a referring expression) as we find in the case of such words as "I," "this" and "the," but is governed by *ad hoc* conventions for each particular set of applications of the word to a given person. The important point is that the correctness of such applications does not follow from any *general* rule or convention for the use of the word as such. (The limit of absurdity and obvious circularity is reached in the attempt to treat names as disguised description in Russell's sense; for what is in the special sense implied, but not entailed, by my now referring to some one by name is simply the existence of some one, *now being referred to*, who is *conventionally referred to* by that name.) Even this feature of names, however, is only a symptom of the purpose for which they are employed. At present our choice of names is partly arbitrary, partly dependent on legal and social observances. It would be perfectly possible to have a thorough-going *system* of names, based *e.g.*, on dates of birth, or on a minute classification of physiological and anatomical differences. But the success of any such system would depend entirely on the convenience of the resulting name-allotments for the purpose of making unique references; and this would depend on the multiplicity of the classifications used and the degree to which they cut haphazard across normal social groupings. Given a sufficient degree of both, the selectivity supplied by context would do the rest; just as is the case with our present naming habits. Had we such a system, we could use name-words descriptively (as we do at present, to a limited extent and in a different way, with some famous names) as well as referringly. But it is by criteria derived from consideration of the requirements of the referring task that we should assess the adequacy of any system of naming. From the naming point of view, no kind of classification would be better or worse than any other simply because of the kind of classification—natal or anatomical—that it was.

I have already mentioned the class of quasi-names, of substantival phrases which grow capital letters, and of which such phrases as "the Glorious Revolution," "the Great War," "the Annunciation," "the Round Table" are examples. While the descriptive meaning of the words which follow the definite article is still relevant to their referring role, the capital letters are a sign of that extra-logical selectivity in their referring use, which is characteristic of pure names. Such phrases are found in print or in writing when one member of some class of events or things is of quite outstanding interest in a certain society. These phrases are embryonic names. A phrase may, for obvious reasons, pass into, and out of, this class (*e.g.*, "the Great War").

# V

I want to conclude by considering, all too briefly, three further problems about referring uses.

(*a*) *Indefinite references*. Not all referring uses of singular expressions forestall the question "What (who, which one) are you talking about?" There are some which either invite this question, or disclaim the intention or ability to answer it. Examples are such sentence-beginnings as "A man told me that . . . ," "Some one told me that. . . ." The orthodox (Russellian) doctrine is that such sentences are existential, but not uniquely existential. This seems wrong in several ways. It is ludicrous to suggest that part of what is asserted is that the class of men or persons is not empty. Certainly this is *implied* in the by now familiar sense of implication; but the implication is also as much an implication of the *uniqueness* of the particular object of reference as when I begin a sentence with such a phrase as "the table." The difference between the use of the definite and indefinite articles is, very roughly, as follows. We use "the" either when a previous reference has been made, and when "the" signalises that the same reference is being made; or when, in the absence of a previous indefinite reference, the context (including the hearer's assumed knowledge) is expected to enable the hearer to tell *what* reference is being made. We use "a" either when these conditions are not fulfilled, or when, although a definite reference *could* be made, we wish to keep dark the identity of the individual to whom, or to which, we are referring. This is the *arch* use of such a phrase as "a certain person" or "some one"; where it could be expanded, not into "some one, but you wouldn't (or I don't) know who" but into "some one, but I'm not telling you who."

(*b*) *Identification statements*. By this label I intend statements like the following:

(*ia*) That is the man who swam the channel twice on one day.
(*iia*) Napoleon was the man who ordered the execution of the Duc D'Enghien.

The puzzle about these statements is that their grammatical predicates do not seem to be used in a straightforwardly ascriptive way as are the grammatical predicates of the statements:

(*ib*) That man swam the channel twice in one day.
(*iib*) Napoleon ordered the execution of the Duc D'Enghien.

But if, in order to avoid blurring the difference between (*ia*) and (*ib*) and (*iia*) and (*iib*), one says that the phrases which form the grammatical complements of (*ia*) and (*iia*) are being used referringly, one becomes puzzled about what is being said in these sentences. We seem then to be referring to the same person twice over and either saying nothing about him and thus making no statement, or identifying him with himself and thus producing a trivial identity.

The bogey of triviality can be dismissed. This only arises for those who think of the object referred to by the use of an expression as its meaning, and thus think of the subject and complement of these sentences as meaning the same because they could be used to refer to the same person.

I think the differences between sentences in the (*a*) group and sentences in the (*b*) group can best be understood by considering the differences between the circumstances in which you would say (*ia*) and the circumstances in which you would say (*ib*). You would say (*ia*) instead of (*ib*) if you knew or believed that your hearer knew or believed that *some one* had swum the channel twice in one day. You say (*ia*) when you take your hearer to be in the position of one who can ask: "Who swam the channel twice in one day?" (And in asking this, he is not saying that anyone did, though his asking it implies—in the relevant sense—that some one did.) Such sentences are like answers to such questions. They are better called "identification-statements" than "identities." Sentence (*ia*) does not assert more or less than sentence (*ib*). It is just that you say (*ia*) to a man whom you take to know certain things that you take to be unknown to the man to whom you say (*ib*).

This is, in the barest essentials, the solution to Russell's puzzle about "denoting phrases" joined by "is"; one of the puzzles which he claims for the Theory of Descriptions the merit of solving.

(*c*) *The logic of subjects and predicates.* Much of what I have said of the uniquely referring use of expressions can be extended, with suitable modifications, to the non-uniquely referring use of expressions; *i.e.* to some uses of expressions consisting of "the" "all the," "all," "some," "some of the," etc. followed by a noun, qualified or unqualified, in the *plural*; to some uses of "they," "them," "those," "these"; and to conjunctions of names. Expressions of the first kind have a special interest. Roughly speaking, orthodox modern criticism, inspired by mathematical logic, of such traditional doctrines as that of the Square of Opposition and of some of the forms of the syllogism traditionally recognised as valid, rests on the familiar failure to recognise the special sense in which existential assertions may be implied by the referring use of expressions. The universal propositions of the fourfold schedule, it is said, must *either* be given a negatively existential interpretation (*e.g.*, for A, "there are no Xs which are not Ys") *or* they must be interpreted as conjunctions of negatively and positively existential statements of, *e.g.*, the form (for A) "there are no Xs which are not Ys, and there are Xs." The I and O forms are normally given a positively existential interpretation. It is then seen that, whichever of the above alternatives is selected, some of the traditional laws have to be abandoned. The dilemma, however, is a bogus one. If we interpret the propositions of the schedule as neither positively, nor negatively, nor positively *and* negatively, existential, but as sentences such that *the question of whether they are being used to make true or false assertions does not arise except when the existential condition is fulfilled for the subject term*, then all the traditional laws hold good together. And this interpretation is far closer to the most common uses of expressions beginning with "all" and "some" than is any Russellian alternative. For these expressions are most commonly used in the referring way. A literal-minded and childless man asked whether all his children are asleep will certainly not answer "Yes" on the ground that he has none; but nor will he answer "No" on this ground. Since he has no children, the question does not arise. To say this is not to say that I may not use the sentence, "All my children are asleep," with the intention of letting some one know that I have children, or of deceiving him into thinking that I have. Nor is it any weakening of my thesis to concede that singular phrases of the form "the so-and-so" may sometimes be used with a similar purpose. Neither Aristotelian nor Russellian rules give the exact logic of any expression of ordinary language; for ordinary language has no exact logic.

# MR. STRAWSON ON REFERRING*

Bertrand Russell (1872–    ). See page 93.

Mr. P. F. Strawson published in *Mind* of 1950 an article called "On Referring." This article is reprinted in *Essays in Conceptual Analysis*, selected and edited by Professor Antony Flew. The references that follow are to this reprint. The main purpose of the article is to refute my theory of descriptions. As I find that some philosophers whom I respect consider that it has achieved its purpose successfully, I have come to the conclusion that a polemical reply is called for. I may say, to begin with, that I am totally unable to see any validity whatever in any of Mr. Strawson's arguments. Whether this inability is due to senility on my part or to some other cause, I must leave readers to judge.

The gist of Mr. Strawson's argument consists in identifying two problems which I have regarded as quite distinct—namely, the problem of descriptions and the problem of egocentricity. I have dealt with both these problems at considerable length, but as I have considered them to be different problems, I have not dealt with the one when I was considering the other. This enables Mr. Strawson to pretend that I have overlooked the problem of egocentricity.

He is helped in this pretence by a careful selection of material. In the article in which I first set forth the theory of descriptions, I dealt specially

* Copyright © 1959, by George Allen & Unwin, Ltd. Reprinted by permission of Simon & Schuster, Inc., the author, and Allen & Unwin. From Bertrand Russell, *My Philosophical Development* (London: Allen & Unwin), 1959, pp. 238–245.

with two examples: "The present King of France is bald" and "Scott is the author of *Waverley*." The latter example does not suit Mr. Strawson, and he therefore entirely ignores it except for one quite perfunctory reference. As regards "the present King of France," he fastens upon the egocentric word "present" and does not seem able to grasp that, if for the word "present" I had substituted the words "in 1905," the whole of his argument would have collapsed.

Or perhaps not quite the whole for reasons which I had set forth before Mr. Strawson wrote. It is, however, not difficult to give other examples of the use of descriptive phrases from which egocentricity is wholly absent. I should like to see him apply his doctrine to such sentences as the following: "the square-root of minus one is half the square-root of minus four," or "the cube of three is the integer immediately preceding the second perfect number." There are no egocentric words in either of these two sentences, but the problem of interpreting the descriptive phrases is exactly the same as if there were.

There is not a word in Mr. Strawson's article to suggest that I ever considered egocentric words, still less, that the theory which he advocates in regard to them is the very one which I had set forth at great length and in considerable detail.[1] The gist of what he has to say about such words is the entirely correct statement that what they refer to depends upon when and where they are used. As to this, I need only quote one paragraph from *Human Knowledge* (p. 107):

> 'This' denotes whatever, at the moment when the word is used, occupies the centre of attention. With words which are not egocentric what is constant is something about the object indicated, but 'this' denotes a different object on each occasion of its use: what is constant is not the object denoted, but its relation to the particular use of the word. Whenever the word is used, the person using it is attending to something, and the word indicates this something. When a word is not egocentric, there is no need to distinguish between different occasions when it is used, but we must make this distinction with egocentric words, since what they indicate is something having a given relation to the particular use of the word.

I must refer also to the case that I discuss (pp. 101 ff.) in which I am walking with a friend on a dark night. We lose touch with each other and he calls, "Where are you?" and I reply "Here I am!" It is of the essence of a scientific account of the world to reduce to a minimum the egocentric element in an assertion, but success in this attempt is a matter of degree, and is never complete where empirical material is concerned. This is due to the fact that the meanings of all empirical words depend ultimately upon ostensive definitions, that ostensive definitions depend upon experi-

---

[1] *Cf. An Inquiry into Meaning and Truth*, chap. vii, and *Human Knowledge*. Part II, chap. iv.

ence, and that experience is egocentric. We can, however, by means of egocentric words, *describe* something which is not egocentric; it is this that enables us to use a common language.

All this may be right or wrong, but, whichever it is, Mr. Strawson should not expound it as if it were a theory that he had invented, whereas, in fact, I had set it forth before he wrote, though perhaps he did not grasp the purport of what I said. I shall say no more about egocentricity since, for the reasons I have already given, I think Mr. Strawson completely mistaken in connecting it with the problem of descriptions.

I am at a loss to understand Mr. Strawson's position on the subject of names. When he is writing about me, he says: "There are no logically proper names and there are no descriptions (in this sense)" (p. 109). But when he is writing about Quine, in *Mind*, October, 1956, he takes a quite different line. Quine has a theory that names are unnecessary and can always be replaced by descriptions. This theory shocks Mr. Strawson for reasons which, to me, remain obscure. However, I will leave the defence of Quine to Quine, who is quite capable of looking after himself. What is important for my purpose is to elucidate the meaning of the words "in this sense," which Mr. Strawson puts in brackets. So far as I can discover from the context, what he objects to is the belief that there are words which are only significant because there is something that they mean, and if there were not this something, they would be empty noises, not words. For my part, I think that there must be such words if language is to have any relation to fact. The necessity for such words is made obvious by the process of ostensive definition. How do we know what is meant by such words as "red" and "blue"? We cannot know what these words mean unless we have seen red and seen blue. If there were no red and no blue in our experience, we might, perhaps, invent some elaborate description which we could substitute for the word "red" or for the word "blue." For example, if you were dealing with a blind man, you could hold a red-hot poker near enough for him to feel the heat, and you could tell him that red is what he would see if he could see—but of course for the word "see" you would have to substitute another elaborate description. Any description which the blind man could understand would have to be in terms of words expressing experiences which he had had. Unless fundamental words in the individual's vocabulary had this kind of direct relation to fact, language in general would have no such relation. I defy Mr. Strawson to give the usual meaning to the word "red" unless there is something which the word designates.

This brings me to a further point. "Red" is usually regarded as a predicate and as designating a universal. I prefer for purposes of philosophical analysis a language in which "red" is a subject, and, while I should not say that it is a positive error to call it a universal, I should say that calling it so invites confusion. This is connected with what Mr. Strawson calls my "logically disastrous theory of names" (p. 118). He does not deign to mention why he considers this theory "logically disastrous." I hope that on some future occasion he will enlighten me on this point.

This brings me to a fundamental divergence between myself and many philosophers with whom Mr. Strawson appears to be in general agreement. They are persuaded that common speech is good enough not only for daily life, but also for philosophy. I, on the contrary, am persuaded that common speech is full of vagueness and inaccuracy, and that any attempt to be precise and accurate requires modification of common speech both as regards vocabulary and as regards syntax. Everybody admits that physics and chemisty and medicine each require a language which is not that of everyday life. I fail to see why philosophy, alone, should be forbidden to make a similar approach towards precision and accuracy. Let us take, in illustration, one of the commonest words of everyday speech: namely, the word "day." The most august use of this word is in the first chapter of *Genesis* and in the Ten Commandments. The desire to keep holy the Sabbath "day" has led orthodox Jews to give a precision to the word "day" which it does not have in common speech: they have defined it as the period from one sunset to the next. Astronomers, with other reasons for seeking precision, have three sorts of day: the true solar day: the mean solar day; and the sidereal day. These have different uses: the true solar day is relevant if you are considering lighting-up time; the mean solar day is relevant if you are sentenced to fourteen days without the option; and the sidereal day is relevant if you are trying to estimate the influence of the tides in retarding the earth's rotation. All these four kinds of day—decalogical, true, mean, and sidereal—are more precise than the common use of the word "day." If astronomers were subject to the prohibition of precision which some recent philosophers apparently favour, the whole science of astronomy would be impossible.

For technical purposes, technical languages differing from those of daily life are indispensable. I feel that those who object to linguistic novelties, if they had lived a hundred and fifty years ago, would have stuck to feet and ounces, and would have maintained that centimetres and grams savour of the guillotine.

In philosophy, it is syntax, even more than vocabulary, that needs to be corrected. The subject-predicate logic to which we are accustomed depends for its convenience upon the fact that at the usual temperatures of the earth there are approximately permanent "things." This would not be true at the temperature of the sun, and is only roughly true at the temperatures to which we are accustomed.

My theory of descriptions was never intended as an analysis of the state of mind of those who utter sentences containing descriptions. Mr. Strawson gives the name "S" to the sentence "The King of France is wise," and he says of me "The way in which he arrived at the analysis was clearly by asking himself what would be the circumstances in which we would say that anyone who uttered the sentence S had made a true assertion." This does not seem to me a correct account of what I was doing. Suppose (which God forbid) Mr. Strawson were so rash as to accuse his char-lady of thieving: she would reply indignantly, "I ain't never done no harm to no one." Assuming her a pattern of virtue, I should say that she was making a true assertion, although, according to the rules of syntax which Mr. Strawson would adopt in his own speech, what she said should have meant: "there was at least one moment when I was injuring the whole human race." Mr. Strawson would not have supposed that this was what she meant to assert, although he would not have used her words to express the same sentiment. Similarly, I was concerned to find a more accurate and analysed thought to replace the somewhat confused thoughts which most people at most times have in their heads.

Mr. Strawson objects to my saying that "the King of France is wise" is false if there is no King of France. He admits that the sentence is significant and not true, but not that it is false. This is a mere question of verbal convenience. He considers that the word "false" has an unalterable meaning which it would be sinful to regard as adjustable, though he prudently avoids telling us what this meaning is. For my part, I find it more convenient to define the word "false" so that every significant sentence is either true or false. This is a purely verbal question; and although I have no wish to claim the support of common usage, I do not think that he can claim it either. Suppose, for example, that in some country there was a law that no person could hold public office if he considered it false that the Ruler of the Universe is wise. I think an avowed atheist who took advantage of Mr. Strawson's doctrine to say that he did not hold this proposition false, would be regarded as a somewhat shifty character.

It is not only as to names and as to falsehood that Mr. Strawson shows his conviction that there is an unalterably right way of using words and that no change is to be tolerated however convenient it may be. He shows the same feeling as regards universal affirmatives—*i.e.*, sentences of the form "All A is B." Traditionally, such sentences are supposed to imply that there are A's, but it is much more convenient in mathematical logic to drop this implication and to consider that "All A is B" is true if there are no A's. This is wholly and solely a question of convenience. For some purposes the one convention is more convenient, and for others, the other. We shall prefer the one convention or the other according to the purpose we have in view. I agree, however, with Mr. Strawson's statement (p. 127) that ordinary language has no exact logic.

Mr. Strawson, in spite of his very real logical competence, has a curious prejudice against logic. On page 121, he has a sudden dithyrambic outburst, to the effect that life is greater than logic, which he uses to give a quite false interpretation of my doctrines.

Leaving detail aside, I think we may sum up Mr. Strawson's argument and my reply to it as follows:

There are two problems, that of descriptions and that of egocentricity.

Mr. Strawson thinks they are one and the same problem, but it is obvious from his discussion that he has not considered as many kinds of descriptive phrases as are relevant to the argument. Having confused the two problems, he asserts dogmatically that it is only the egocentric problem that needs to be solved, and he offers a solution of this problem which he seems to believe to be new, but which in fact was familiar before he wrote. He then thinks that he has offered an adequate theory of descriptions, and announces his supposed achievement with astonishing dogmatic certainty. Perhaps I am doing him an injustice, but I am unable to see in what respect this is the case.

## SUGGESTIONS FOR FURTHER READING
## ON MEANING AND REFERENCE

Carnap, R.  *Introduction to Semantics.* Cambridge, Mass.: Harvard University Press, 1946.

Caton, C. E.  "Strawson on Referring," *Mind*, Vol. 68 (1959), pp. 539–544.

Donnellan, K. S.  "Reference and Definite Descriptions," *The Philosophical Review*, Vol. 75 (1966), pp. 281–304.

Frege, G.  *Translations from the Philosophical Writings of Gottlob Frege.* P. Geach and M. Black eds. Oxford. Oxford University Press, 1952.

Geach, P. T.  *Reference and Generality.* Ithaca, N.Y.: Cornell University Press, 1962.

Linsky, L.  "Reference and Referents," *Philosophy and Ordinary Language*, C. E. Caton, ed. Urbana, Ill.: University of Illinois Press, 1963.

Quine, W. V. O.  *Word and Object.* Cambridge, Mass.: The M.I.T. Press, 1960.

Russell, B.  "Descriptions," Chapter XVI of *Introduction to Mathematical Philosophy.* New York: Macmillan, 1919.

Searle, John R.  "Proper Names," *Mind*, Vol. 67 (1958), pp. 166–173; reprinted in *Philosophy and Ordinary Language*, C. E. Caton, ed. Urbana. Ill.: University of Illinois Press, 1963, pp. 154–161.

Tarski, A.  *Logic, Semantics, Metamathematics.* J. H. Woodger, trans. Oxford. Oxford University Press, 1956.

# Part

## 4 THE THEORY OF TYPES

*Introduction*

Some of the contradictions reported in the following essay began to appear in logic and mathematics around the turn of the century. The earliest of them occurred in the new mathematics of the infinite; later the famous Russell Paradox was discovered to infect the very notion of class or set as used in the main body of mathematics of the time. Russell devised his Theory of Types to explain and eliminate those contradictions. He had included a preliminary, highly tentative, version of the "Doctrine of Types" as Appendix B to his *Principles of Mathematics* in 1903. Five years later he published a revised and enlarged version, the first five sections of which are reproduced here. That same year also saw the publication by Ernst Zermelo of an altogether different method for avoiding the contradictions, consisting of a carefully restricted axiomatic development of set theory. By and large the mathematical community has tended to prefer avoiding the contradictions by using a Zermelo type of set theory, while philosophical logicians have taken more interest in Russell's Theory of Types. It should be mentioned that as recently as 1943 Russell wrote:

*I have never been satisfied that the theory of types, as I have presented it, is final. I am convinced that some sort of hierarchy is necessary, and I am not sure that a purely extensional hierarchy suffices. But I hope that, in time, some theory will be developed which will be simple and adequate, and at the same time be satis-*

*factory from the point of view of what might be called logical common sense.**

Fitch presents an exceptionally clear formulation of some criticisms of the Theory of Types. Agreeing that the "vicious" sorts of self-reference that lead to contradictions must be eliminated, Fitch argues that there are other desirable sorts of self-reference which are necessary both in philosophy and in mathematics. And because they are not permitted by the Theory of Types, the latter must be rejected. Fitch's remarks about the *semantics* of type theory, although brief, are deserving of more serious consideration than they have yet been given.

* From *The Philosophy of Betrand Russell*, ed. P. A. Schilpp. The Library of Living Philosophers, New York, Harper & Row, 1944, p. 692.

# MATHEMATICAL LOGIC AS BASED ON THE THEORY OF TYPES*

BERTRAND RUSSELL (1872–    ). See page 93.

The following theory of symbolic logic recommended itself to me in the first instance by its ability to solve certain contradictions, of which the one best known to mathematicians is Burali-Forti's concerning the greatest ordinal.[1] But the theory in question seems not wholly dependent on this indirect recommendation; it has also, if I am not mistaken, a certain consonance with common sense which makes it inherently credible. This, however, is not a merit upon which much stress should be laid; for common sense is far more fallible than it likes to believe. I shall therefore begin by stating some of the contradictions to be solved, and shall then show how the theory of logical types effects their solution.

## 1. THE CONTRADICTIONS

(1) The oldest contradiction of the kind in question is the *Epimenides*. Epimenides the Cretan said that all Cretans were liars, and all other statements made by Cretans were certainly lies. Was this a lie? The simplest form of this contradiction is afforded by the man who says 'I am lying'; if he is lying, he is speaking the truth, and vice versa.

(2) Let $w$ be the class of all those classes which are not members of themselves. Then, whatever class $x$ may be, '$x$ is a $w$' is equivalent[2] to '$x$ is not an $x$.' Hence, giving to $x$ the value $w$, '$w$ is a $w$' is equivalent to '$w$ is not a $w$.'

(3) Let $T$ be the relation which subsists between two relations $R$ and $S$ whenever $R$ does not have the relation $R$ to $S$. Then, whatever relations $R$ and $S$ may be, '$R$ has the relation $T$ to $S$' is equivalent to '$R$ does not have the relation $R$ to $S$.' Hence, giving the value $T$ to both $R$ and $S$, '$T$ has the relation $T$ to $T$' is equivalent to '$T$ does not have the relation $T$ to $T$.'

(4) The number of syllables in the English names of finite integers tends to increase as the integers grow larger, and must gradually increase

---

* Reprinted by kind permission of the author and publisher, from Bertrand Russell, *Logic and Knowledge*, Robert Charles Marsh, editor (London: Allen & Unwin, 1956), pp. 59–83. This article appeared originally in the *American Journal of Mathematics*, Vol. 30 (1908), pp. 222–262.

[1] See below.

[2] Two propositions are called *equivalent* when both are true or both are false.

indefinitely, since only a finite number of names can be made with a given finite number of syllables. Hence the names of some integers must consist of at least nineteen syllables, and among these there must be a least. Hence 'the least integer not nameable in fewer than nineteen syllables' must denote a definite integer; in fact, it denotes 111,777. But 'the least integer not nameable in fewer than nineteen syllables' is itself a name consisting of eighteen syllables; hence the least integer not nameable in fewer than nineteen syllables can be named in eighteen syllables, which is a contradiction.[3]

(5) Among transfinite ordinals some can be defined, while others can not; for the total number of possible definitions is $\aleph_0$, while the number of transfinite ordinals exceeds $\aleph_0$. Hence there must be indefinable ordinals, and among these there must be a least. But this is defined as 'the least indefinable ordinal', which is a contradiction.[4]

(6) Richard's paradox[5] is akin to that of the least indefinable ordinal. It is as follows: Consider all decimals that can be defined by means of a finite number of words; let $E$ be the class of such decimals. Then $E$ has $\aleph_0$ terms; hence its members can be ordered as the 1st, 2nd, 3rd, . . . Let $N$ be a number defined as follows: If the $n$th figure in the $n$th decimal is $p$, let the $n$th figure in $N$ be $p + 1$ (or 0, if $p = 9$). Then $N$ is different from all the members of $E$, since, whatever finite value $n$ may have, the $n$th figure in $N$ is different from the $n$th figure in the $n$th of the decimals composing $E$, and therefore $N$ is different from the $n$th decimal. Nevertheless we have defined $N$ in a finite number of words, and therefore $N$ ought to be a member of $E$. Thus $N$ both is and is not a member of $E$.

(7) Burali-Forti's contradiction[6] may be stated as follows: It can be shown that every well-ordered series has an ordinal number, that the series of ordinals up to and including any given ordinal exceeds the given ordinal by one, and (on certain very natural assumptions) that the series of all ordinals (in order of magnitude) is well ordered. It follows that the series of all ordinals has an ordinal number, $\Omega$ say. But in that case the series of all ordinals including $\Omega$ has the ordinal number $\Omega + 1$, which must be greater than $\Omega$. Hence $\Omega$ is not the ordinal number of all ordinals.

In all the above contradictions (which are merely selections from an indefinite number) there is a common characteristic, which we may describe as self-reference or reflexiveness. The remark of Epimenides must include itself in its own scope. If *all* classes, provided they are not mem-

---

[3] This contradiction was suggested to me by Mr. G. G. Berry of the Bodleian Library.

[4] Cf. König, 'Über die Grundlagen der Mengenlehre und das Kontinuum-problem,' *Math. Annalen*, Vol. LXI (1905); A. C. Dixon, 'On "well-ordered" aggregates,' *Proc. London Math. Soc.*, Series 2, Vol. IV, Part I (1906); and E. W. Hobson, 'On the Arithmetic Continuum,' ibid. The solution offered in the last of these papers does not seem to me adequate.

[5] Cf. Poincaré, 'Les mathématiques et la logique,' *Revue de Métaphysique et de Morale* (May, 1906), especially sections VII and IX; also Peano, *Revista de Mathematica*, Vol. VIII, No. 5 (1906), pp. 149 ff.

[6] 'Una questione sui numeri transfiniti,' *Rendiconti del circolo matematico di Palermo*, Vol. XI (1897).

bers of themselves, are members of $w$, this must also apply to $w$; and similarly for the analogous relational contradiction. In the cases of names and definitions, the paradoxes result from considering non-nameability and indefinability as elements in names and definitions. In the case of Burali-Forti's paradox, the series whose ordinal number causes the difficulty is the series of all ordinal numbers. In each contradiction something is said about *all* cases of some kind, and from what is said a new case seems to be generated, which both is and is not of the same kind as the cases of which *all* were concerned in what was said. Let us go through the contradictions one by one and see how this occurs.

(1) When a man says 'I am lying,' we may interpret his statement as: 'There is a proposition which I am affirming and which is false.' All statements that 'there is' so-and-so may be regarded as denying that the opposite is always true; thus 'I am lying' becomes: 'It is not true of all propositions that either I am not affirming them or they are true'; in other words, 'It is not true for all propositions $p$ that if I affirm $p$, $p$ is true.' The paradox results from regarding this statement as affirming a proposition, which must therefore come within the scope of the statement. This, however, makes it evident that the notion of 'all propositions' is illegitimate; for otherwise, there must be propositions (such as the above) which are about all propositions, and yet can not, without contradiction, be included among the propositions they are about. Whatever we suppose to be the totality of propositions, statements about this totality generate new propositions which, on pain of contradiction, must lie outside the totality. It is useless to enlarge the totality, for that equally enlarges the scope of statements about the totality. Hence there must be no totality of propositions, and 'all propositions' must be a meaningless phrase.

(2) In this case, the class $w$ is defined by reference to 'all classes,' and then turns out to be one among classes. If we seek help by deciding that no class is a member of itself, then $w$ becomes the class of all classes, and we have to decide that this is not a member of itself, i.e., is not a class. This is only possible if there is no such thing as the class of all classes in the sense required by the paradox. That there is no such class results from the fact that, if we suppose there is, the supposition immediately gives rise (as in the above contradiction) to new classes lying outside the supposed total of all classes.

(3) This case is exactly analogous to (2), and shows that we can not legitimately speak of 'all relations.'

(4) 'The least integer not nameable in fewer than nineteen syllables' involves the totality of names, for it is 'the least integer such that all names either do not apply to it or have more than nineteen syllables.' Here we assume, in obtaining the contradiction, that a phrase containing 'all names' is itself a name, though it appears from the contradiction that it can not be one of the names which were supposed to be all the names there are. Hence 'all names' is an illegitimate notion.

(5) This case, similarly, shows that 'all definitions' is an illegitimate notion.

(6) This is solved, like (5), by remarking that 'all definitions' is an illegitimate notion. Thus the number $E$ is *not* defined in a finite number of words, being in fact not defined at all.[7]

(7) Burali-Forti's contradiction shows that 'all ordinals' is an illegitimate notion; for if not, all ordinals in order of magnitude form a well-ordered series, which must have an ordinal number greater than all ordinals.

Thus all our contradictions have in common the assumption of a totality such that, if it were legitimate, it would at once be enlarged by new members defined in terms of itself.

This leads us to the rule: 'Whatever involves *all* of a collection must not be one of the collection'; or, conversely: 'If, provided a certain collection had a total, it would have members only definable in terms of that total, then the said collection has no total.'[8]

The above principle is, however, purely negative in its scope. It suffices to show that many theories are wrong, but it does not show how the errors are to be rectified. We can not say: 'When I speak of *all* propositions, I mean all except those in which "all propositions" are mentioned'; for in this explanation we have mentioned the propositions in which all propositions are mentioned, which we can not do significantly. It is impossible to avoid mentioning a thing by mentioning that we won't mention it. One might as well, in talking to a man with a long nose, say: 'When I speak of noses, I except such as are inordinately long,' which would not be a very successful effort to avoid a painful topic. Thus it is necessary, if we are not to sin against the above negative principle, to construct our logic without mentioning such things as 'all propositions' or 'all properties,' and without even having to say that we are excluding such things. The exclusion must result naturally and inevitably from our positive doctrines, which must make it plain that 'all propositions' and 'all properties' are meaningless phrases.

The first difficulty that confronts us is as to the fundamental principles of logic known under the quaint name of 'laws of thought.' 'All propositions are either true or false,' for example, has become meaningless. If it were significant, it would be a proposition, and would come under its own scope. Nevertheless, some substitute must be found, or all general accounts of deduction become impossible.

Another more special difficulty is illustrated by the particular case of mathematical induction. We want to be able to say: 'If $n$ is a finite integer, $n$ has all properties possessed by 0 and by the successors of all numbers

---

[7] Cf. 'Les paradoxes de la logique,' by the present author, *Revue de Métaphysique et de Morale* (September, 1906), p. 645.

[8] When I say that a collection has no total, I mean that statements about *all* its members are nonsense. Furthermore, it will be found that the use of this principle requires the distinction of *all* and *any* considered in Section II.

possessing them.' But here 'all properties' must be replaced by some other phrase not open to the same objections. It might be thought that 'all properties possessed by 0 and by the successors of all numbers possessing them' might be legitimate even if 'all properties' were not. But in fact this is not so. We shall find that phrases of the form 'all properties which *etc.*' involve *all* properties of which the '*etc.*' can be significantly either affirmed or denied, and not only those which in fact have whatever characteristic is in question; for, in the absence of a catalogue of properties having this characteristic, a statement about all those that have the characteristic must be hypothetical, and of the form: 'It is always true that, if a property has the said characteristic, then etc.' Thus mathematical induction is *prima facie* incapable of being significantly enunciated, if 'all properties' is a phrase destitute of meaning. This difficulty, as we shall see later, can be avoided; for the present we must consider the laws of logic, since these are far more fundamental.

## 2.   ALL AND ANY

Given a statement containing a variable $x$, say '$x = x$,' we may affirm that this holds in all instances, or we may affirm any one of the instances without deciding as to which instance we are affirming. The distinction is roughly the same as that between the general and particular enunciation in Euclid. The general enunciation tells us something about (say) all triangles, while the particular enunciation takes one triangle, and asserts the same thing of this one triangle. But the triangle taken is *any* triangle, not some one special triangle; and thus although, throughout the proof, only one triangle is dealt with, yet the proof retains its generality. If we say: 'Let $ABC$ be a triangle, then the sides $AB$, $AC$ are together greater than the side $BC$,' we are saying something about *one* triangle, not about *all* triangles; but the one triangle concerned is absolutely ambiguous, and our statement consequently is also absolutely ambiguous. We do not affirm any one definite proposition, but an undetermined one of all the propositions resulting from supposing $ABC$ to be this or that triangle. This notion of ambiguous assertion is very important, and it is vital not to confound an ambiguous assertion with the definite assertion that the same thing holds in *all* cases.

The distinction between (1) asserting any value of a propositional function, and (2) asserting that the function is always true, is present throughout mathematics, as it is in Euclid's distinction of general and particular enunciations. In any chain of mathematical reasoning, the objects whose properties are being investigated are the arguments to *any* value of some propositional function. Take as an illustration the following definition:

'We call $f(x)$ continuous for $x = a$ if, for every positive number $\sigma$, different from 0, there exists a positive number $\epsilon$, different from 0, such that, for all values of $\delta$ which are numerically less than $\epsilon$, the difference $f(a + \delta) - f(a)$ is numerically less than $\sigma$.'

Here the function $f$ is *any* function for which the above statement has a meaning; the statement is *about* $f$, and varies as $f$ varies. But the statement is not *about* $\sigma$ or $\epsilon$ or $\delta$, because *all* possible values of these are concerned, not one undetermined value. (In regard to $\epsilon$, the statement 'there exists a positive number $\epsilon$ such that *etc.*' is the denial that the denial of '*etc.*' is true of *all* positive numbers.) For this reason, when *any* value of a propositional function is asserted, the argument (e.g., $f$ in the above) is called a *real* variable; whereas, when a function is said to be *always* true, or to be not always true, the argument is called an *apparent* variable.[9] Thus in the above definition, $f$ is a real variable, and $\sigma$, $\epsilon$, $\delta$ are apparent variables.

When we assert *any* value of a propositional function, we shall say simply that we assert the *propositional function*. Thus if we enunciate the law of identity in the form '$x = x$,' we are asserting the function '$x = x$'; i.e., we are asserting any value of this function. Similarly we may be said to deny a propositional function when we deny any instance of it. We can only truly assert a propositional function if, whatever value we choose, that value is true; similarly we can only truly deny it if, whatever value we choose, that value is false. Hence in the general case, in which some values are true and some false, we can neither assert nor deny a propositional function.[10]

If $\phi x$ is a propositional function, we will denote by '$(x) . \phi x$' the proposition '$\phi x$ is always true.' Similarly '$(x, y) . \phi(x, y)$' will mean '$\phi(x, y)$ is always true,' and so on. Then the distinction between the assertion of all values and the assertion of any is the distinction between (1) asserting $(x) . \phi x$ and (2) asserting $\phi x$ where $x$ is undetermined. The latter differs from the former in that it can not be treated as one determinate proposition.

The distinction between asserting $\phi x$ and asserting $(x) . \phi x$ was, I believe, first emphasized by Frege.[11] His reason for introducing the distinction explicitly was the same which had caused it to be present in the practice of mathematicians; namely, that deduction can only be effected with *real* variables, not with apparent variables. In the case of Euclid's proofs, this is evident: we need (say) some one triangle $ABC$ to reason about, though it does not matter what triangle it is. The triangle $ABC$ is a *real* variable; and although it is *any* triangle, it remains the *same* triangle throughout the argument. But in the general enunciation, the

---

[9] These two terms are due to Peano, who uses them approximately in the above sense. Cf., e.g., *Formulaire Mathématique* (Turin, 1903), Vol. IV, p. 5.

[10] Mr. MacColl speaks of 'propositions' as divided into the three classes of certain, variable, and impossible. We may accept this division as applying to propositional functions. A function which can be asserted is certain, one which can be denied is impossible, and all others are (in Mr. MacColl's sense) variable.

[11] See his *Grundgesetze der Arithmetik* (Jena, 1893), Vol. I, § 17, p. 31.

triangle is an apparent variable. If we adhere to the apparent variable, we can not perform any deductions, and this is why in all proofs, real variables have to be used. Suppose, to take the simplest case, that we know '$\phi x$ is always true,' i.e. '$(x)$. $\phi x$,' and we know '$\phi x$ always implies $\psi x$,' i.e. '$(x)$. $\{\phi x$ implies $\psi x\}$.' How shall we infer '$\psi x$ is always true,' i.e. '$(x)$. $\psi x$'? We know it is always true that if $\phi x$ is true, and if $\phi x$ implies $\psi x$, then $\psi x$ is true. But we have no premises to the effect that $\phi x$ is true and $\phi x$ implies $\psi x$; what we have is: $\phi x$ is *always* true, and $\phi x$ *always* implies $\psi x$. In order to make our inference, we must go from '$\phi x$ is always true' to $\phi x$, and from '$\phi x$ always implies $\psi x$' to '$\phi x$ implies $\psi x$,' where the $x$, while remaining any possible argument, is to be the same in both. Then, from '$\phi x$' and '$\phi x$ implies $\psi x$,' we infer '$\psi x$'; thus $\psi x$ is true for any possible argument, and therefore is always true. Thus in order to infer '$(x)$. $\psi x$' from '$(x)$. $\phi x$' and '$(x)$. $\{\phi x$ implies $\psi x\}$,' we have to pass from the apparent to the real variable, and then back again to the apparent variable. This process is required in all mathematical reasoning which proceeds from the assertion of all values of one or more propositional functions to the assertion of all values of some other propositional function, as, e.g., from 'all isosceles triangles have equal angles at the base' to 'all triangles having equal angles at the base are isosceles.' In particular, this process is required in proving *Barbara* and the other moods of the syllogism. In a word, *all deduction operates with real variables* (or with constants).

It might be supposed that we could dispense with apparent variables altogether, contenting ourselves with *any* as a substitute for *all*. This, however, is not the case. Take, for example, the definition of a continuous function quoted above: in this definition $\sigma$, $\epsilon$, and $\delta$ must be apparent variables. Apparent variables are constantly required for definitions. Take, e.g., the following: 'An integer is called a *prime* when it has no integral factors except 1 and itself.' This definition unavoidably involves an apparent variable in the form: 'If $n$ is an integer other than 1 or the given integer, $n$ is not a factor of the given integer, for all possible values of $n$.'

The distinction between *all* and *any* is, therefore, necessary to deductive reasoning, and occurs throughout mathematics; though, so far as I know, its importance remained unnoticed until Frege pointed it out.

For our purposes it has a different utility, which is very great. In the case of such variables as propositions or properties, 'any value' is legitimate, though 'all values' is not. Thus we may say: '$p$ is true or false, where $p$ is any proposition,' though we can not say 'all propositions are true or false.' The reason is that, in the former, we merely affirm an undetermined one of the propositions of the form '$p$ is true or false,' whereas in the latter we affirm (if anything) a new proposition, different from all the propositions of the form '$p$ is true or false.' Thus we may admit 'any value' of a variable in cases where 'all values' would lead to reflexive fallacies; for the admission of 'any value' does not in the same way create new values. Hence the fundamental laws of logic can be stated concerning *any* proposition, though we can not significantly say that they hold of *all* propositions. These laws have, so to speak, a particular enunciation but no general enunciation. There is no one proposition which *is* the law of contradiction (say); there are only the various instances of the law. Of any proposition $p$, we can say: '$p$ and not-$p$ can not both be true'; but there is no such proposition as: 'Every proposition $p$ is such that $p$ and not-$p$ can not both be true.'

A similar explanation applies to properties. We can speak of *any* property of $x$, but not of *all* properties, because new properties would be thereby generated. Thus we can say 'If $n$ is a finite integer, and if 0 has the property $\phi$, and $m + 1$ has the property $\phi$ provided $m$ has it, it follows that $n$ has the property $\phi$.' Here we need not specify $\phi$; $\phi$ stands for 'any property.' But we can not say: 'A finite integer is defined as one which has *every* property $\phi$ possessed by 0 and by the successors of possessors.' For here it is essential to consider *every* property,[12] not *any* property; and in using such a definition we assume that it embodies a *property* distinctive of finite integers, which is just the kind of assumption from which, as we saw, the reflexive contradictions spring.

In the above instance, it is necessary to avoid the suggestions of ordinary language, which is not suitable for expressing the distinction required. The point may be illustrated further as follows: If induction is to be used for defining finite integers, induction must state a definite property of finite integers, not an ambiguous property. But if $\phi$ is a real variable, the statement '$n$ has the property $\phi$ provided this property is possessed by 0 and by the successors of possessors' assigns to $n$ a property which varies as $\phi$ varies, and such a property can not be used to define the class of finite integers. We wish to say: ' "$n$ is a finite integer" means: "Whatever property $\phi$ may be, $n$ has the property $\phi$ provided $\phi$ is possessed by 0 and by the successors of possessors." ' But here $\phi$ has become an *apparent* variable. To keep it a real variable, we should have to say: 'Whatever property $\phi$ may be, "$n$ is a finite integer" means: "$n$ has the property $\phi$ provided $\phi$ is possessed by 0 and by the successors of possessors." ' But here the meaning of "$n$ is a finite integer" varies as $\phi$ varies, and thus such a definition is impossible. This case illustrates an important point, namely the following: 'The scope [13] of a real variable can never be less than the whole propositional function in the assertion of which the said variable occurs.' That is, if our propositional function is (say) '$\phi x$ implies $p$,' the assertion of this function will mean 'any value of "$\phi x$ implies $p$" is true,' *not* ' "any value of $\phi x$ is true" implies $p$.' In the latter, we have really '*all* values of $\phi x$ are true,' and the $x$ is an *apparent* variable.

---

[12] This is indistinguishable from 'all properties.'

[13] The *scope* of a real variable is the whole function of which 'any value' is in ques-tion. Thus in '$\phi x$ implies $p$' the scope of $x$ is not $\phi x$, but '$\phi x$ implies $p$.'

## 3. THE MEANING AND RANGE OF GENERALIZED PROPOSITIONS

In this section we have to consider first the meaning of propositions in which the word *all* occurs, and then the kind of collections which admit of propositions about all their members.

It is convenient to give the name *generalized propositions* not only to such as contain *all*, but also to such as contain *some* (undefined). The proposition '$\phi x$ is sometimes true' is equivalent to the denial of 'not-$\phi x$ is always true'; 'some A is B' is equivalent to the denial of 'all A is not B'; i.e., of 'no A is B.' Whether is it possible to find interpretations which distinguish '$\phi x$ is sometimes true' from the denial of 'not-$\phi x$ is always true,' it is unnecessary to inquire; for our purposes we may *define* '$\phi x$ is sometimes true' as the denial of 'not-$\phi x$ is always true.' In any case, the two kinds of propositions require the same kind of interpretation, and are subject to the same limitations. In each there is an apparent variable; and it is the presence of an apparent variable which constitutes what I mean by a generalized proposition. (Note that there can not be a *real* variable in any proposition; for what contains a real variable is a propositional function, not a proposition.)

The first question we have to ask in this section is: How are we to interpret the word *all* in such propositions as 'all men are mortal'? At first sight, it might be thought that there could be no difficulty, that 'all men' is a perfectly clear idea, and that we say of all men that they are mortal. But to this view there are many objections.

(1) If this view were right, it would seem that 'all men are mortal' could not be true if there were no men. Yet, as Mr. Bradley has urged,[14] 'Trespassers will be prosecuted' may be perfectly true even if no one trespasses; and hence, as he further argues, we are driven to interpret such propositions as hypotheticals, meaning 'if anyone trespasses, he will be prosecuted'; i.e., 'if $x$ trespasses, $x$ will be prosecuted,' where the range of values which $x$ may have, whatever it is, is certainly not confined to those who really trespass. Similarly 'all men are mortal' will mean 'if $x$ is a man, $x$ is mortal, where $x$ may have any value within a certain range.' What this range is, remains to be determined; but in any case it is wider than 'men,' for the above hypothetical is certainly often true when $x$ is not a man.

(2) 'All men' is a denoting phrase; and it would appear, for reasons which I have set forth elsewhere,[15] that denoting phrases never have any meaning in isolation, but only enter as constituents into the verbal expression of propositions which contain no constituent corresponding to the denoting phrases in question. That is to say, a denoting phrase is

[14] *Logic*, Part I, Chapter II.
[15] 'On Denoting,' *Mind* (October, 1905).

defined by means of the propositions in whose verbal expression it occurs. Hence it is impossible that these propositions should acquire their meaning through the denoting phrases; we must find an independent interpretation of the propositions containing such phrases, and must not use these phrases in explaining what such propositions mean. Hence we can not regard 'all men are mortal' as a statement about 'all men.'

(3) Even if there were such an object as 'all men,' it is plain that it is not this object to which we attribute mortality when we say 'all men are mortal.' If we were attributing mortality to this object, we should have to say '*all men* is mortal.' Thus the supposition that there is such an object as 'all men' will not help us to interpret 'all men are mortal.'

(4) It seems obvious that, if we meet something which may be a man or may be an angel in disguise, it comes within the scope of 'all men are mortal' to assert 'if this is a man, it is mortal.' Thus again, as in the case of the trespassers, it seems plain that we are really saying 'if anything is a man, it is mortal,' and that the question whether this or that is a man does not fall within the scope of our assertion, as it would do if the *all* really referred to 'all men.'

(5) We thus arrive at the view that what is meant by 'all men are mortal' may be more explicitly stated in some such form as 'it is always true that if $x$ is a man, $x$ is mortal.' Here we have to inquire as to the scope of the word *always*.

(6) It is obvious that *always* includes some cases in which $x$ is not a man, as we saw in the case of the disguised angel. If $x$ were limited to the case when $x$ is a man, we could infer that $x$ is a mortal, since if $x$ is a man, $x$ is a mortal. Hence, with the same meaning of *always*, we should find 'it is always true that $x$ is mortal.' But it is plain that, without altering the meaning of *always*, this new proposition is false, though the other was true.

(7) One might hope that 'always' would mean 'for all values of $x$.' But 'all values of $x$,' if legitimate, would include as parts 'all propositions' and 'all functions,' and such illegitimate totalities. Hence the values of $x$ must be somehow restricted within some legitimate totality. This seems to lead us to the traditional doctrine of a 'universe of discourse' within which $x$ must be supposed to lie.

(8) Yet it is quite essential that we should have some meaning of *always* which does not have to be expressed in a restrictive hypothesis as to $x$. For suppose 'always' means 'whenever $x$ belongs to the class $i$.' Then 'all men are mortal' becomes 'whenever $x$ belongs to the class $i$, if $x$ is a man, $x$ is mortal'; i.e., 'it is always true that if $x$ belongs to the class $i$, then, if $x$ is a man, $x$ is mortal.' But what is our new *always* to mean? There seems no more reason for restricting $x$, in this new proposition, to the class $i$, than there was before for restricting it to the class *man*. Thus we shall be led on to a new wider universe, and so on *ad infinitum*, unless we can discover some natural restriction upon the possible values of (i.e., some re-

striction given with) the function 'if $x$ is a man, $x$ is mortal,' and not needing to be imposed from without.

(9) It seems obvious that, since all men are mortal, there can not be any *false* proposition which is a value of the function 'if $x$ is a man, $x$ is mortal.' For if this is a proposition at all, the hypothesis '$x$ is a man' must be a proposition, and so must be the conclusion '$x$ is mortal.' But if the hypothesis is false, the hypothetical is true; and if the hypothesis is true, the hypothetical is true. Hence there can be no false propositions of the form 'if $x$ is a man, $x$ is mortal.'

(10) It follows that, if any values of $x$ are to be excluded, they can only be values for which there is no proposition of the form 'if $x$ is a man, $x$ is mortal'; i.e., for which this phrase is meaningless. Since, as we saw in (7), there must be excluded values of $x$, it follows that the function 'if $x$ is a man, $x$ is mortal' must have a certain *range of significance,*[16] which falls short of all imaginable values of $x$, though it exceeds the values which are men. The restriction on $x$ is therefore a restriction to the range of significance of the function 'if $x$ is a man, $x$ is mortal.'

(11) We thus reach the conclusion that 'all men are mortal' means 'if $x$ is a man, $x$ is mortal, always,' where *always* means 'for all values of the function "if $x$ is a man, $x$ is mortal." ' This is an *internal* limitation upon $x$, given by the nature of the function; and it is a limitation which does not require explicit statement, since it is impossible for a function to be true more generally than for all its values. Moreover, if the range of significance of the function is $i$, the function 'if $x$ is an $i$, then if $x$ is a man, $x$ is mortal' has the same range of significance, since it can not be significant unless its constituent 'if $x$ is a man, $x$ is mortal' is significant. But here the range of significance is again implicit, as it was in "if $x$ is a man, $x$ is mortal"; thus we can not make ranges of significance explicit, since the attempt to do so only gives rise to a new proposition in which the same range of significance is implicit.

Thus generally: '$(x) . \phi x$' is to mean '$\phi x$ always.' This may be interpreted, though with less exactitude, as '$\phi x$ is always true,' or, more explicitly: 'All propositions of the form $\phi x$ are true,' or 'All values of the function $\phi x$ are true.' [17] Thus the fundamental *all* is 'all values of a propositional function,' and every other *all* is derivative from this. And every propositional function has a certain *range of significance*, within which lie the arguments for which the function has values. Within this range of arguments, the function is true or false; outside this range, it is nonsense.

---

[16] A function is said to be significant for the argument $x$ if it has a value for this argument. Thus we may say shortly '$\phi x$ is significant,' meaning 'the function $\phi$ has a value for the argument $x$.' The range of significance of a function consists of all the arguments for which the function is true, together with all the arguments for which it is false.

[17] A linguistically convenient expression for this idea is: '$\phi x$ is true for all *possible* values of $x$,' a possible value being understood to be one for which $\phi x$ is significant.

The above argumentation may be summed up as follows:

The difficulty which besets attempts to restrict the variable is, that restrictions naturally express themselves as hypotheses that the variable is of such or such a kind, and that, when so expressed, the resulting hypothetical is free from the intended restriction. For example, let us attempt to restrict the variable to *men*, and assert that, subject to this restriction, '*x* is mortal' is always true. Then what is always true is that if *x* is a man, *x* is mortal; and this hypothetical is true even when *x* is not a man. Thus a variable can never be restricted within a certain range if the propositional function in which the variable occurs remains significant when the variable is outside that range. But if the function ceases to be significant when the variable goes outside a certain range, then the variable is *ipso facto* confined to that range, without the need of any explicit statement to that effect. This principle is to be borne in mind in the development of logical types, to which we shall shortly proceed.

We can now begin to see how it comes that 'all so-and-so's' is sometimes a legitimate phrase and sometimes not. Suppose we say 'all terms which have the property $\phi$ have the property $\psi$.' That means, according to the above interpretation, '$\phi x$ always implies $\psi x$.' Provided the range of significance of $\phi x$ is the same as that of $\psi x$, this statement is significant; thus, given any definite function $\phi x$, there are propositions about 'all the terms satisfying $\phi x$.' But it sometimes happens (as we shall see more fully later on) that what appears verbally as one function is really many analogous functions with different ranges of significance. This applies, for example, to '*p* is true,' which, we shall find, is not really one function of *p*, but is different functions according to the kind of proposition that *p* is. In such a case, the *phrase* expressing the ambiguous function may, owing to the ambiguity, be significant throughout a set of values of the argument exceeding the range of significance of any one function. In such a case, *all* is not legitimate. Thus if we try to say 'all true propositions have the property $\phi$,' i.e., ' "*p* is true" always implies $\phi p$,' the possible arguments to "*p* is true" necessarily exceed the possible arguments to $\phi$, and therefore the attempted general statement is impossible. For this reason, genuine general statements about all true propositions can not be made. It may happen, however, that the supposed function $\phi$ is really ambiguous like "*p* is true," and if it happens to have an ambiguity precisely of the same kind as that of "*p* is true," we may be able always to give an interpretation to the proposition ' "*p* is true" implies $\phi p$.' This will occur, e.g., if $\phi p$ is 'not-*p* is false.' Thus we get an appearance, in such cases, of a general proposition concerning *all* propositions; but this appearance is due to a systematic ambiguity about such words as *true* and *false*. (This systematic ambiguity results from the hierarchy of propositions which will be explained later on.) We may, in all such cases, make our statement about *any* proposition, since the meaning of the ambiguous words will adapt itself to any proposition. But if we turn our proposition into an apparent variable, and say something about *all*, we must suppose the ambiguous words fixed to this or that possible meaning, though it may be quite irrelevant which of their possible meanings they are to have. This is how it happens both that *all* has limitations which exclude 'all propositions,' and that there nevertheless *seem* to be true statements about 'all propositions.' Both these points will become plainer when the theory of types has been explained.

It has often been suggested [18] that what is required in order that it may be legitimate to speak of *all* of a collection is that the collection should be finite. Thus 'all men are mortal' will be legitimate because men form a finite class. But that is not really the reason why we can speak of 'all men.' What is essential, as appears from the above discussion, is not finitude, but what may be called *logical homogeneity*. This property is to belong to any collection whose terms are all contained within the range of significance of some one function. It would always be obvious at a glance whether a collection possessed this property or not, if it were not for the concealed ambiguity in common logical terms such as *true* and *false*, which gives an appearance of being a single function to what is really a conglomeration of many functions with different ranges of significance.

The conclusions of this section are as follows: Every proposition containing *all* asserts that some propositional function is always true; and this means that all values of the said function are true, not that the function is true for all arguments, since there are arguments for which any given function is meaningless, i.e., has no value. Hence we can speak of *all* of a collection when and only when the collection forms part of the whole of the *range of significance* of some propositional function, the range of significance being defined as the collection of those arguments for which the function in question is significant, i.e., has a value.

## 4.  THE HIERARCHY OF TYPES

A *type* is defined as the range of significance of a propositional function, i.e., as the collection of arguments for which the said function has values. Whenever an apparent variable occurs in a proposition, the range of values of the apparent variable is a type, the type being fixed by the function of which 'all values' are concerned. The division of objects into types is necessitated by the reflexive fallacies which otherwise arise. These fallacies, as we saw, are to be avoided by what may be called the 'vicious-circle principle'; i.e., 'no totality can contain members defined in terms of itself.' This principle, in our technical language, becomes: 'Whatever contains an apparent variable must not be a possible value of that variable.' Thus whatever contains an apparent variable must be of a different type from the possible values of that variable; we will say that it is of a *higher* type. Thus the apparent variables contained in an expression are what determines its type. This is the guiding principle in what follows.

[18] E.g., by M. Poincaré, *Revue de Métaphysique et de Morale* (May, 1906).

Propositions which contain apparent variables are generated from such as do not contain these apparent variables by processes of which one is always the process of *generalization*, i.e., the substitution of a variable for one of the terms of a proposition, and the assertion of the resulting function for all possible values of the variable. Hence a proposition is called a *generalized* proposition when it contains an apparent variable. A proposition containing no apparent variable we will call an *elementary* proposition. It is plain that a proposition containing an apparent variable presupposes others from which it can be obtained by generalization; hence all generalized propositions presuppose elementary propositions. In an elementary proposition we can distinguish one or more *terms* from one or more *concepts*; the *terms* are whatever can be regarded as the *subject* of the proposition, while the concepts are the predicates or relations asserted of these terms.[19] The terms of elementary propositions we will call *individuals*; these form the first or lowest type.

It is unnecessary, in practice, to know what objects belong to the lowest type, or even whether the lowest type of variable occurring in a given context is that of individuals or some other. For in practice only the *relative* types of variables are relevant; thus the lowest type occurring in a given context may be called that of individuals, so far as that context is concerned. It follows that the above account of individuals is not essential to the truth of what follows; all that is essential is the way in which other types are generated from individuals, however the type of individuals may be constituted.

By applying the process of generalization to individuals occurring in elementary propositions, we obtain new propositions. The legitimacy of this process requires only that no individuals should be propositions. That this is so, is to be secured by the meaning we give to the word *individual*. We may define an individual as something destitute of complexity; it is then obviously not a proposition, since propositions are essentially complex. Hence in applying the process of generalization to individuals we run no risk of incurring reflexive fallacies.

Elementary propositions together with such as contain only individuals as apparent variables we will call *first-order propositions*. These form the second logical type.

We have thus a new totality, that of *first-order propositions*. We can thus form new propositions in which first-order propositions occur as apparent variables. These we will call *second-order propositions*; these form the third logical type. Thus, e.g., if Epimenides asserts 'all first-order propositions affirmed by me are false', he asserts a second-order proposition; he may assert this truly, without asserting truly any first-order proposition, and thus no contradiction arises.

The above process can be continued indefinitely. The $n + 1$th logical type will consist of propositions of order $n$, which will be such as contain

[19] See *Principles of Mathematics*, § 48.

propositions of order $n - 1$, but of no higher order, as apparent variables. The types so obtained are mutually exclusive, and thus no reflexive fallacies are possible so long as we remember that an apparent variable must always be confined within some one type.

In practice, a hierarchy of *functions* is more convenient than one of propositions. Functions of various orders may be obtained from propositions of various orders by the method of *substitution*. If $p$ is a proposition, and $a$ a constituent of $p$, let '$p/a$;$x$' denote the proposition which results from substituting $x$ for $a$ wherever $a$ occurs in $p$. Then $p/a$, which we will call a *matrix*, may take the place of a function; its value for the argument $x$ is $p/a$;$x$, and its value for the argument $a$ is $p$. Similarly, if '$p/(a, b)$;$(x, y)$' denotes the result of first substituting $x$ for $a$ and then substituting $y$ for $b$, we may use the double matrix $p/(a, b)$ to represent a double function. In this way we can avoid apparent variables other than individuals and propositions of various orders. The *order* of a matrix will be defined as being the order of the proposition in which the substitution is effected, which proposition we will call the *prototype*. The order of a matrix does not determine its type: in the first place because it does not determine the number of arguments for which others are to be substituted (i.e., whether the matrix is of the form $p/a$ or $p/(a, b)$ or $p/(a, b, c)$ etc.); in the second place because, if the prototype is of more than the first order, the arguments may be either propositions or individuals. But it is plain that the type of a matrix is definable always by means of the hierarchy of propositions.

Although it is *possible* to replace functions by matrices, and although this procedure introduces a certain simplicity into the explanation of types, it is technically inconvenient. Technically, it is convenient to replace the prototype $p$ by $\phi a$, and to replace $p/a$;$x$ by $\phi x$; thus where, if matrices were being employed, $p$ and $a$ would appear as apparent variables, we now have $\phi$ as our apparent variable. In order that $\phi$ may be legitimate as an apparent variable, it is necessary that its values should be confined to propositions of some one type. Hence we proceed as follows.

A function whose argument is an individual and whose value is always a first-order proposition will be called a first-order function. A function involving a first-order function or proposition as apparent variable will be called a second-order function, and so on. A function of one variable which is of the order next above that of its argument will be called a *predicative* function; the same name will be given to a function of several variables if there is one among these variables in respect of which the function becomes predicative when values are assigned to all the other variables. Then the type of a function is determined by the type of its values and the number and type of its arguments.

The hierarchy of functions may be further explained as follows. A first-order function of an individual $x$ will be denoted by $\phi ! x$ (the letters $\psi$, $\chi$, $\theta$, $f$, $g$, $F$, $G$ will also be used for functions). No first-order function contains a function as apparent variable; hence such functions form a well-defined totality, and the $\phi$ in $\phi \,!\, x$ can be turned into an apparent variable. Any proposition in which $\phi$ appears as apparent variable, and there is no apparent variable of higher type than $\phi$, is a second-order proposition. If such a proposition contains an individual $x$, it is not a predicative function of $x$; but if it contains a first-order function $\phi$, it is a predicative function of $\phi$, and will be written $f\,!\,(\psi\,!\,\hat{z})$. Then $f$ is a *second-order predicative function*; the possible values of $f$ again form a well-defined totality, and we can turn $f$ into an apparent variable. We can thus define *third-order predicative functions*, which will be such as have third-order propositions for their values and second-order predicative functions for their arguments. And in this way we can proceed indefinitely. A precisely similar development applies to functions of several variables.

We will adopt the following conventions. Variables of the lowest type occurring in any context will be denoted by small Latin letters (excluding $f$ and $g$, which are reserved for functions); a predicative function of an argument $x$ (where $x$ may be of any type) will be denoted by $\phi \,!\, x$ (where $\psi$, $\chi$, $\theta$, $f$, $g$, $F$ or $G$ may replace $\phi$); similarly a predicative function of two arguments $x$ and $y$ will be denoted by $\phi \,!\,(x, y)$; a general function of $x$ will be denoted by $\phi x$, and a general function of $x$ and $y$ by $\phi(x, y)$. In $\phi x$, $\phi$ can not be made into an apparent variable, since its type is indeterminate; but in $\phi \,!\, x$, where $\phi$ is a *predicative* function whose argument is of some given type, $\phi$ *can* be made into an apparent variable.

It is important to observe that since there are various types of propositions and functions, and since generalization can only be applied within some one type, all phrases containing the words 'all propositions' or 'all functions' are prima facie meaningless, though in certain cases they are capable of an unobjectionable interpretation. The contradictions arise from the use of such phrases in cases where no innocent meaning can be found.

If we now revert to the contradictions, we see at once that some of them are solved by the theory of types. Wherever 'all propositions' are mentioned, we must ⌐ubstitute 'all propositions of order $n$,' where it is indifferent what value we give to $n$, but it is essential that $n$ should have *some* value. Thus when a man says 'I am lying', we must interpret him as meaning: 'There is a proposition of order $n$, which I affirm, and which is false.' This is a proposition of order $n + 1$; hence the man is not affirming any proposition of order $n$; hence his statement is false, and yet its falsehood does not imply, as that of 'I am lying' appeared to do, that he is making a true statement. This solves the liar.

Consider next 'the least integer not nameable in fewer than nineteen syllables.' It is to be observed, in the first place, that *nameable* must mean 'nameable by means of such-and-such assigned names,' and that the number of assigned names must be finite. For if it is not finite, there is no reason why there should be any integer not nameable in fewer than nineteen syllables, and the paradox collapses. We may next suppose that 'nameable in terms of names of the class N' means 'being the only term satisfying some function composed wholly of names of the class N.' The solution of this paradox lies, I think, in the simple observation that 'nameable in terms of names of the class N' is never itself nameable in terms of names of that class. If we enlarge N by adding the name 'nameable in terms of names of the class N,' our fundamental apparatus of names is enlarged; calling the new apparatus N', 'nameable in terms of names of the class N″ remains not nameable in terms of names of the class N'. If we try to enlarge N till it embraces *all* names, 'nameable' becomes (by what was said above) 'being the only term satisfying some function composed wholly of names.' But here there is a function as apparent variable; hence we are confined to predicative functions of some one type (for non-predicative functions can not be apparent variables). Hence we have only to observe that nameability in terms of such functions is non-predicative in order to escape the paradox.

The case of 'the least indefinable ordinal' is closely analogous to the case we have just discussed. Here, as before, 'definable' must be relative to some given apparatus of fundamental ideas; and there is reason to suppose that 'definable in terms of ideas of the class N' is not definable in terms of ideas of the class N. It will be true that there is some definite segment of the series of ordinals consisting wholly of definable ordinals, and having the least indefinable ordinal as its limit. This least indefinable ordinal will be definable by a slight enlargement of our fundamental apparatus; but there will then be a new ordinal which will be the least that is indefinable with the new apparatus. If we enlarge our apparatus so as to include all possible ideas, there is no longer any reason to believe that there is any indefinable ordinal. The apparent force of the paradox lies largely, I think, in the supposition that if all the ordinals of a certain class are definable, the class must be definable, in which case its successor is of course also definable; but there is no reason for accepting this supposition.

The other contradictions, that of Burali-Forti in particular, require some further developments for their solution.

## 5. THE AXIOM OF REDUCIBILITY

A propositional function of *x* may, as we have seen, be of any order; hence any statement about 'all properties of *x*' is meaningless. (A 'property of *x*' is the same thing as a 'propositional function which holds of *x*.') But it is absolutely necessary, if mathematics is to be possible, that we should have some method of making statements which will usually be equivalent to what we have in mind when we (inaccurately) speak of 'all properties of *x*.' This necessity appears in many cases, but especially in connexion with mathematical induction. We can say, by the use of *any* instead of *all*, 'Any property possessed by 0, and by the successors of all numbers possessing it, is possessed by all finite numbers.' But we can not go on to: 'A finite number is one which possesses *all* properties possessed by o and by the successors of all numbers possessing them.' If we confine this statement to all first-order properties of numbers, we can not infer that it holds of second-order properties. For example, we shall be unable to prove that if $m, n$ are finite numbers, then $m + n$ is a finite number. For, with the above definition, '$m$ is a finite number' is a second-order property of $m$; hence the fact that $m + o$ is a finite number, and that, if $m + n$ is a finite number, so is $m + n + 1$, does not allow us to conclude by induction that $m + n$ is a finite number. It is obvious that such a state of things renders much of elementary mathematics impossible.

The other definition of finitude, by the non-similarity of whole and part, fares no better. For this definition is: 'A class is said to be finite when every one-one relation whose domain is the class and whose converse domain is contained in the class has the whole class for its converse domain.' Here a variable relation appears, i.e., a variable function of two variables; we have to take *all* values of this function, which requires that it should be of some assigned order; but any assigned order will not enable us to deduce many of the propositions of elementary mathematics.

Hence we must find, if possible, some method of reducing the order of a propositional function without affecting the truth or falsehood of its values. This seems to be what common sense effects by the admission of *classes*. Given any propositional function $\phi x$, of whatever order, this is assumed to be equivalent, for all values of $x$, to a statement of the form '$x$ belongs to the class $\alpha$.' Now this statement is of the first order, since it makes no allusion to 'all functions of such-and-such a type.' Indeed its only practical advantage over the original statement $\phi x$ is that it is of the first order. There is no advantage in assuming that there really are such things as classes, and the contradiction about the classes which are not members of themselves shows that, if there are classes, they must be something radically different from individuals. I believe the chief purpose which classes serve, and the chief reason which makes them linguistically convenient, is that they provide a method of reducing the order of a propositional function. I shall, therefore, not assume anything of what may seem to be involved in the common sense admission of classes, except this: that every propositional function is equivalent, for all its values, to some predicative function.

This assumption with regard to functions is to be made whatever may be the type of their arguments. Let $\phi x$ be a function, of any order, of an argument $x$, which may itself be either an individual or a function of any order. If $\phi$ is of the order next above $x$, we write the function in the form $\phi \,!\, x$; in such a case we will call $\phi$ a *predicative* function. Thus a predicative function of an individual is a first-order function; and for higher types of arguments, predicative functions take the place that first-order functions take in respect of individuals. We assume, then, that every function is equivalent, for all its values, to some predicative function of the same argument. This assumption seems to be the essence of the usual assumption of classes; at any rate, it retains as much of classes as we have any use for, and little enough to avoid the contradictions which a less grudging admission of classes is apt to entail. We will call this assumption the *axiom of classes*, or the *axiom of reducibility*.

We shall assume similarly that every function of two variables is equivalent, for all its values, to a predicative function of those variables, where a predicative function of two variables is one such that there is one of the variables in respect of which the function becomes predicative (in our previous sense) when a value is assigned to the other variable. This assumption is what seems to be meant by saying that any statement about two variables defines a relation between them. We will call this assumption the *axiom of relations* or the *axiom of reducibility*.

In dealing with relations between more than two terms, similar assumptions would be needed for three, four, . . . variables. But these assumptions are not indispensable for our purpose, and are therefore not made in this paper.

By the help of the axiom of reducibility, statements about 'all first-order functions of $x$' or 'all predicative functions of $\alpha$' yield most of the results which otherwise would require 'all functions.' The essential point is that such results are obtained in all cases where only the truth or falsehood of values of the functions concerned are relevant, as is invariably the case in mathematics. Thus mathematical induction, for example, need now only be stated for all predicative functions of numbers; it then follows from the axiom of classes that it holds of *any* function of whatever order. It might be thought that the paradoxes for the sake of which we invented the hierarchy of types would now reappear. But this is not the case, because, in such paradoxes, either something beyond the truth or falsehood of values of functions is relevant, or expressions occur which are unmeaning even after the introduction of the axiom of reducibility. For example, such a statement as 'Epimenides asserts $\psi x$' is not equivalent to 'Epimenides asserts $\phi \,!\, x$,' even though $\psi x$ and $\phi \,!\, x$ are equivalent. Thus 'I am lying' remains unmeaning if we attempt to include *all* propositions among those which I may be falsely affirming, and is unaffected by the axiom of classes if we confine it to propositions of order $n$. The hierarchy of propositions and functions, therefore, remains relevant in just those cases in which there is a paradox to be avoided. . . .

# SELF-REFERENCE IN PHILOSOPHY[*][1]

FREDERIC B. FITCH (1908–     ) of Yale University has written extensively on logic and religion. He is the author of *Symbolic Logic*.

A theory always has a particular subject matter associated with it. We say that the theory is "about" its subject matter. For example, Darwin's theory of natural selection is about living organisms, and species of living organisms, and genetic relationships among such species. Newton's theory of universal gravitation is about particles of matter and about certain relationships of attraction between such particles. In so far as a theory is vague, the exact extent of its subject matter tends to be hard to specify. A precisely stated theory, on the other hand, tends to have a clearly delineated subject matter. We may ordinarily regard the subject matter of a theory as consisting of some class of entities, together with certain subclasses of that class and certain relations among its members. The notion of "subject matter" could be more carefully analyzed, but this concept should be clear enough in the light of the informal examples just given.

Some theories are about theories. Others are not. Theories which do not include theories in their subject matter will be said to be of *ordinal level zero*. A theory which includes in its subject matter some theories of *ordinal level zero*, but none of higher ordinal level, will be said to be of ordinal *level one*. And so on. In general: A theory of ordinal level $n + 1$ includes in its subject matter no theories of ordinal level greater than $n$, but it does include some of ordinal level $n$. Here $n$ may be thought of as any finite or infinite ordinal number. Many theories proposed in the empirical sciences can be seen to be of some fairly low finite ordinal level. This is because empirical science is not generally concerned with framing theories about all theories.

---

* Reprinted by kind permission of the author, the editor of *Mind*, and The Ronald Press, Inc., from Frederic B. Fitch, *Symbolic Logic* (New York: The Ronald Press, 1952), pp. 217–225.
[1] This is a slightly revised form of an article which I published under the same title in *Mind*, vol. 55, n.s. (1946), pp. 64–73. It is reprinted here in order to indicate more fully my motives for rejecting the Russell-Whitehead theory of types and in order to emphasize the philosophical importance of self-referential propositions and the need for a logic, such as the present one, which can handle such propositions. I have not discussed Russell's theory of "typical ambiguity" as constituting a possible reply to my objections, but I do not believe that such a theory can be developed in detail without encountering type difficulties of an insuperable sort at the semantical level. I wish to thank the Editor of *Mind* for permission to reprint this material. See also, in connection with some of these problems, the article by Weiss referred to in the first footnote of the Foreword [to Fitch, *Symbolic Logic*], and the remarks by W. M. Urban on p. 209 of his book *Humanity and Deity* (London, 1951).

A different situation prevails in philosophical research. Here extreme comprehensiveness is sought for. Theories are constructed which purport to deal with all entities whatsoever and which therefore have an unrestrictedly extensive subject matter. In dealing with all entities, such theories in particular deal with all theories, since theories are themselves entities of a special sort. In philosophy we thus encounter theories about the general nature of theories. If a theory has an ordinal level, its ordinal level must be greater than the ordinal levels of all theories occurring within its subject matter. Hence a theory about the general nature of theories can have no ordinal level, for its ordinal level would have to be greater than itself. Theories having no ordinal level will be said to be "vertical" or "non-ordinal" theories. Theories having ordinal levels will be said to be "horizontal" or "ordinal" theories.

If a theory is included in its own subject matter, we say that it is a *self-referential* theory. Since no ordinal level can be assigned to a self-referential theory, every self-referential theory is vertical and non-ordinal. The converse, however, is not true, because a theory might contain vertical theories in its subject matter without containing itself in its subject matter. Such a theory would be vertical but not self-referential.

An example of a vertical and self-referential theory is Whitehead's philosophical system as presented in *Process and Reality*. Among the entities considered in his system are not only actual occasions, eternal objects, prehensions, nexūs, contrasts, and multiplicities, but also propositions or theories. His whole doctrine of these entities is itself a theory. Since it is a theory about all theories, it includes itself in its subject matter.

Whitehead's identification of propositions with theories raises the question as to whether theories should be treated as classes of propositions or as individual propositions. Either view seems equally tenable. For present purposes Whitehead's view will be accepted. This means that every proposition is a theory, and conversely, so that every proposition is regarded as having a subject matter. One might say that all entities mentioned by a proposition belong to the subject matter of the proposition, and that if a class or a relation is among the entities that belong to the subject matter so are all members of the class and so are all entities related by the relation.

Some writers attempt to abandon the notion of "proposition" altogether, and to replace it by the notion of "statement" or "sentence," regarding the latter as a mere string of symbols. Such a procedure is useful as a matter of method in the field of syntax, where the meanings of symbols are not of interest so much as the symbols themselves. When questions of meaning are raised, however, this sort of nominalism seems very inadequate. Even Carnap, who formerly advocated some such nominalism, has now largely relinquished it.

Any system of philosophy which takes a position on the nature of theories or propositions is itself a vertical self-referential theory. Particular views as to what constitutes a valid or acceptable theory are also themselves vertical self-referential theories. For example, consider the view that every valid theory must be obtained from observed empirical data. This is a theory about theories and their validity. Incidentally it is a theory which does not seem to conform to its own criterion as to what constitutes a valid theory, at least not unless it can itself be shown to have been obtained as a generalization from observed empirical data. A vertical theory is always open to just this sort of danger. It may not itself conform to some principle that it lays down concerning theories in general. A horizontal theory, on the other hand, is open to no such danger. It may be internally inconsistent, or it may be inconsistent with known facts, and hence "externally" inconsistent, but it cannot be inconsistent with its own nature in the way that a self-referential theory can. If a self-referential theory $T$ implies that $T$ has the property $P$, and if $T$ in fact does not have the property $P$, then we shall call $T$ self-referentially inconsistent.

Self-referential inconsistency is important in at least two respects. In the first place, a standard method for attempting to refute a philosophical view is to show that it is self-referentially inconsistent. This is a method which can be applied only to vertical, or at least self-referential, theories. Hence it is a method which is for the most part peculiar to philosophy and philosophical logic. In the second place, self-referential inconsistency, or something almost the same, is at the heart of many important problems in logic and mathematics. Some of the most interesting problems of modern logic center around the paradoxes of set theory and the closely analogous semantical paradoxes. All these paradoxes involve propositions which refer directly or indirectly to themselves. Any system of mathematics or logic in which such paradoxes can arise is both vertical and inconsistent, though it might not be actually self-referential itself. The vertical or non-ordinal aspect would arise from the fact that self-referential propositions would be part of its subject matter. There exist restricted vertical systems of logic and mathematics which seem to be free from the paradoxes of set theory, though consistency has not yet been definitely established in the case of the most important and useful of such systems. Even within such restricted systems it is possible to prove certain fundamental theorems due to Cantor and Gödel which are closely similar to the paradoxes of set theory both with respect to the presence of something analogous to self-reference (or even self-reference itself, in the case of Cantor's theorem) and with respect to the role played by the concept of negation. More will be said about these mathematical matters later. First let us consider the importance of the notion of self-reference in philosophical methodology.

It may be that nobody has ever seriously proposed or tried to defend a system of philosophy which was actually self-referentially inconsistent, though many systems of philosophy superficially *seem* (to those attacking such systems) to be self-referentially inconsistent. For example, consider the skeptical point of view according to which nothing is "absolutely" true. This view casts some element of doubt on every proposition. According to it no proposition can be asserted as true for certain. All theories are open to some doubt, it holds. But this view is itself a theory about all theories, and the doubt it casts on all theories it casts equally well upon itself. If it is really a valid theory, then it is wrongly questioning its own validity in questioning the validity of all theories. Therefore, if it is valid it is self-referentially inconsistent and hence not valid after all. Therefore it cannot be valid. A similar situation is to be found in Descartes' method of doubt. He could not doubt that he was doubting, and hence he found something indubitable. Complete doubt of everything led to a self-referentially inconsistent view and so had to be abandoned. We thus get the positive result that some propositions may be affirmed with certainty. In fact we can conclude that doubt "presupposes" certainty.

The notion of "presupposition" suggests various sorts of philosophical idealism and related types of philosophy. In such philosophies a "presupposition" often seems to mean some hypothesis that cannot be systematically denied without in some sense being already assumed. The very denial itself, or some important aspect of it, or some assumption or method involved in presenting and defending it, constitutes an exception to the denial. A presupposition might be defined as an assumption whose denial is self-referentially inconsistent. For example, any systematic consideration of and rejection of the accepted principles of logic already involves the use of at least some of those principles of logic. Hence it is a presupposition that at least some of the principles of logic are valid. Similarly, any attempt to reduce the principles of logic to mere conventions regarding the use of symbols must already employ those principles themselves in carrying out the reduction. Hence the reduction is really a reduction of logic to *conventions-plus-logic*, and logic is not completely "analyzed away" into something else.

The concept of presupposition may also be considered in connection with the theory of value. This is because value judgments enter into the theory of value, or rather into specific theories of value, not only as part of the subject matter but also as part of the intellectual apparatus used for defending or attacking particular theses concerning value. For example, one value theorist might attack the scientific or philosophical methodology of another value theorist as "bad" or "unsound" methodology. But the attacking theorist might be assuming a theory of value according to which the phrase, "X is bad," should always be replaced by a phrase of the form, "Y dislikes X," and nevertheless might be unwilling to restate his attack in the form of a mere statement of personal dislike. If so, the attack becomes self-referentially inconsistent, inasmuch as it is based on a theory to which it does not itself conform. The rejection of the demand that phrases of the form, "X is bad," be restated in the form, "Y dislikes X," is a presupposition of every theory which makes value assumptions ("good" and "bad") about methodology and fails to treat such value assumptions as mere matters of personal like or dislike.

The type of argument in which one accuses one's opponent of self-referential inconsistency is really a very ancient type of argument. It has often been called the *ad hominem* type of argument, since it may involve the pointing out of some fact about the opponent himself which contradicts or is an exception to the view he propounds. It is perhaps best understood as a request that the opponent clarify his position sufficiently to destroy some superficial appearance of self-referential inconsistency. A solipsist, for example, might be expected to hold the view that his solipsism needs no defence against the attack of an opponent, since the solipsist maintains that nobody else, and hence no opponent, exists. Thus solipsism seems to presuppose the existence of other minds insofar as the solipsist takes the trouble to reply to objections to his view. But this is perhaps a superficial interpretation of solipsism, and a careful solipsist might state his position in such a way that it would be evident that he was stating his position for the benefit of no other mind but his own.

The *ad hominem* type of argument is probably more liable to stir up the resentment of an opponent than any other type of argument. This is because it has the appearance of being directed at the opponent himself, as well as against his thesis. It may therefore be treated as if it were a personal insult of some sort, involving even ridicule and irony. The opponent is made to look like very much of a fool when the *ad hominem* argument is well presented, because the exception to the opponent's view is found to exist not in some distant situation but, of all places, in some situation or fact immediately involving the opponent himself. Not only does self-referential inconsistency involve a definite sort of irony, but consideration seems to reveal that all cases of irony, conversely, have in them some element of self-referential inconsistency, or something approximating to it.

The personal aspect of the *ad hominem* type of argument tends to cause it to be regarded as an "unfair" type of argument, and indeed unsound. The present writer, however, regards it as a very important sort of argument, and one that is perfectly valid against certain kinds of vertical theories. The mere fact that it cannot be used in connection with horizontal theories arising in the special sciences does not mean that it can have no application in philosophy. On the contrary, the possibility of using it in philosophical speculation and in the criticism of systems of philosophy is a mark which distinguishes philosophy from the empirical sciences. W. M. Urban in his book, *The Intelligible World*, makes repeated use of the *ad hominem* argument. On page 45 he quotes Lowes Dickinson as holding that in ultimate matters the *argumentum ad hominem* is "the only argument possible and, indeed, the only one in which anyone much believes."

Although no *ordinal* level can be assigned to a theory which is about all theories, still we may speak of its "level" in some broader sense. A theory about all theories may be said to have attained the level of maximum theoretical generality. At such a level all other levels may be dealt with. There is no level which is higher in the sense that it can deal with theories not dealt with on the level of maximum theoretical generality. To deny that there is such a level is already to be proposing a theory about all theories and hence to be presenting a theory which is itself of the level of maximum theoretical generality. Thus an *ad hominem* argument can be used against the contention that no such level is to be found. It is characteristic of philosophy to reach this maximum level and to be able to use the self-referential sorts of reasoning which are possible on this level.

An analogous situation is to be found in the classical theory of real numbers. The real numbers can be defined as classes of rational numbers. We thus obtain numbers (namely, the irrational real numbers) having various properties not possessed by the rational numbers. If we attempt to go a step further and define some other sort of number in terms of classes of real numbers in exactly the same way that the real numbers are defined as classes of rational numbers, then nothing essentially new or different is obtained. This is because the class of real numbers has a sort of "level of maximum numerical generality," just as a theory about all theories has a level of maximum theoretical generality. The analogy can be seen from the fact that on the classical theory of real numbers it is permissible for an individual real number to be defined in terms of the class of all real numbers. This is similar to the situation where we have a theory dealing with all theories. On the classical theory of real numbers, generally speaking, it is permissible for an entity to be defined in terms of a class (e.g., the class of real numbers) having that entity as a member. Such a definition is not "circular" in the objectionable sense of defining an entity in terms of itself, but it is nevertheless circular in a secondary sense, since a class having the definiendum as a member is a factor in the definiens. Real numbers defined in terms of the class of all real numbers are thus circularly defined (in a secondary sense of "circularity") and involve self-reference. Cantor's proof that the class of real numbers cannot be put into a one-to-one correspondence with the class of rational numbers consists in supposing that the correspondence has been set up and then in defining *in terms of the correspondence* (and hence in terms of the whole class of real numbers) a particular real number that must have been omitted from the correspondence. The particular real number, of course, involves a sort of self-reference. Russell's "branched" or "ramified" theory of types of the first edition of *Principia Mathematica* was designed to do away with all self-reference in logic and mathematics in order to provide protection against the paradoxes of set theory and the paradoxes of semantics, since Russell believed these paradoxes to be due to a "vicious" circularity. Russell proposed the Axiom of Reducibility, however, as a device to moderate (in effect, if not in theory) the elimination of all circularity and to permit the sort of secondary circularity required for Cantor's theorem. (A similar effect is obtained more simply by replacing the branched theory of types by the "simplified theory of types." This method, however, can be safely used only where semantical concepts are not being assigned type.) Unless some appropriate sort of circularity and self-reference is allowed, Cantor's theorem no longer holds and the real numbers no longer represent a genuine maximum level. In order to get enough real numbers for mathematical purposes without some such circularity, it becomes necessary to keep proceeding to higher and higher levels (or "orders") without ever reaching a final level on which all the real numbers may be handled. For this reason the branched theory of types, unless moderated by the required reducibility principle (or, equivalently, transformed into the simplified theory of types), is not held in esteem by most mathematicians. Something very much like the branched ("ramified") theory of types, not too much moderated by a reducibility principle, has often been urged for avoiding the paradoxes of semantics in those theories which are concerned with *semantical* as well as mathematical concepts. The ramified theory of types, however, cannot be taken as laying down ultimate restrictions which eliminate all sorts of self-reference whatsoever. Not only would the theory of real numbers be crippled, but all theories about the totality of theories would be eliminated. Furthermore, such a ramified theory of types could not even be stated. Its sweeping restrictions against self-reference would apply to every theory, including itself, and so it would be self-referential in violation of its own edicts. A similar criticism can be made even against the more moderate simplified theory of types, if regarded as universally applicable. This sort of criticism is clearly just another instance of a use of the *ad hominem* argument. One way of attempting to meet this objection to the ramified or simplified theory of types is to assert that a formulation of a theory of types is simply the formulation of certain more or less arbitrary or conventional stipulations about the permitted ways of combining symbols. This answer seems to be all right so long as one is restricting oneself to the realm of uninterpreted symbols, but as soon as one enters the realm of semantical concepts it becomes necessary to apply distinctions of "type" to *meanings* of symbols as well as to symbols themselves, and the element of self-reference reappears. For example, the ramified theory of types cannot assign a type to the meaning of the word "type," and yet it must do so if the theory applies to all meanings. In a similar way, no "order" (in the sense used in the ramified theory of types) can be assigned to a proposition which is about all propositions, hence no order can be assigned to the proposition which states the ramified theory of types.

The problem is to find a logic which eliminates the "vicious" sorts of self-reference that lead to the mathematical and semantical paradoxes but not those sorts of self-reference that seem to be such an important part of philosophical logic, or are required in developing the theory of real numbers. The system of logic of this book seems to satisfy these demands. On the other hand, Russell's theory of types, in its various forms, excludes the sort of self-reference that is essential to philosophy. At the same time the theory of types requires for its own statement the sort of inclusive generality that it treats as meaningless. It is therefore self-referentially inconsistent.

## SUGGESTIONS FOR FURTHER READING
## ON THE THEORY OF TYPES

BLACK, M.　"Russell's Philosophy of Language," *The Philosophy of Bertrand Russell*, P. A. Schilpp, ed. Evanston, Ill.: Northwestern University Press, 1946.

CHURCH, A.　"A Formulation of the Simple Theory of Types," *The Journal of Symbolic Logic*, Vol. 5 (1940), pp. 56–68.

FITCH, F. B.　"The Consistency of the Ramified Principia," *The Journal of Symbolic Logic*, Vol. 3 (1938), pp. 140–149.

HENKIN, L.　"Completeness in the Theory of Types," *The Journal of Symbolic Logic*, Vol. 15 (1950), pp. 81–91.

QUINE, W. V. O.　"On the Theory of Types," *The Journal of Symbolic Logic*, Vol. 3 (1938), pp. 125–139.

———.　*Set Theory and Its Logic*. Cambridge, Mass.: Harvard University Press, 1963.

RAMSEY, F. P.　*The Foundations of Mathematics*. New York: Harcourt, Brace, & World, Inc., 1931.

SCHÜTTE, K.　"Syntactical and Semantical Properties of Simple Type Theory," *The Journal of Symbolic Logic*, Vol. 25 (1960), pp. 305–326.

SOMMERS, F.　"Types and Ontology," *The Philosophical Review*, Vol. 72 (1963), pp. 327–363.

TURING, A. M.　"Practical Forms of Type Theory," *The Journal of Symbolic Logic*, Vol. 13 (1948), pp. 80–94.

# *Part*
# 5 LOGIC AND ONTOLOGY

## *Introduction*

In his extremely influential essay "On What There Is," Quine discusses some of the problems raised by Russell in "On Denoting." Questions of meaning and reference are reëxamined to discover their bearing on ontology. Where Russell analyzed denoting phrases in terms of quantification theory, Quine uses quantification theory to formulate, if not to decide, ontological questions of denotation. He explains and defends the semantical formula "To be is to be the value of a variable," but insists that it does not provide a basis for adjudicating among rival ontologies. It is, however, useful in discovering the ontological commitments of a given theory or language.

Carnap welcomes and accepts Quine's formulation of ontological commitment in terms of admissible values of variables, but goes on to distinguish two different kinds of existential questions. *Internal questions* about existence are questions to be answered within the linguistic framework devised for speaking of entities of the type asked about. The answers to internal questions are to be found either by empirical investigation or by logical analysis. On the other hand, an *external question* asks about "the existence or reality *of the system of entities as a whole*," which amounts to questioning the acceptability of the linguistic framework itself. These external questions are the philosophical ones. But from Carnap's point of view, they are not theoretical questions but practical ones, "a matter of decision rather than assertion." Alternatively, Carnap concedes that an external question *may be meant in the following sense:* "Are our experiences such that the use of the linguistic forms in question will be expedient and fruitful?" *This is a theoretical question of a factual, empirical nature. But it concerns a matter of degree; therefore a formulation in the form "real or not?" would be inadequate.*

Church outlines a system of semantics embodying a modified form of Frege's theory of sense and denotation. Such a system is strongly Platonic, presupposing a considerable array of abstract entities. In discussing the ontological issue involved here, Church suggests that the nominalist's

*extreme demand for a simple prohibition of abstract entities under all circumstances perhaps arises from a desire to maintain the connection between theory and observation. But the preference of (say) seeing over understanding as a method of observation seems to me capricious. For just as an opaque body may be seen, so a concept may be understood or grasped.*

In the same tone of reasonableness that Quine and Carnap voiced, Church urges that alternative approaches be studied for their possible utility.

Goodman's eloquent and closely reasoned essay is devoted to expounding, clarifying, and defending a nominalist position. His exposition is clear and his defense vigorous, but what Goodman calls "nominalism" is rather different from what has traditionally gone by that name. Goodman is not opposed to abstract entities as such: for him nominalism "consists specifically in the refusal to recognize classes." Regardless of the historical question, Goodman's doctrine is interesting and important in its own right and deserves careful attention.

# ON WHAT THERE IS*

WILLARD VAN ORMAN QUINE (1908–    ) of Harvard University
has made major contributions to logic and philosophy of
language. Among his books are A *System of Logistic,
Mathematical Logic, Methods of Logic, Word and Object,*
and *Set Theory and Its Logic.*

A curious thing about the ontological problem is its simplicity.
It can be put in three Anglo-Saxon monosyllables: 'What is there?' It can
be answered, moreover, in a word—'Everything'—and everyone will accept
this answer as true. However, this is merely to say that there is what there
is. There remains room for disagreement over cases; and so the issue has
stayed alive down the centuries.

Suppose now that two philosophers, McX and I, differ over ontology.
Suppose McX maintains there is something which I maintain there is not.
McX can, quite consistently with his own point of view, describe our
difference of opinion by saying that I refuse to recognize certain entities.
I should protest, of course, that he is wrong in his formulation of our disagreement, for I maintain that there are no entities, of the kind which he
alleges, for me to recognize; but my finding him wrong in his formulation
of our disagreement is unimportant, for I am committed to considering
him wrong in his ontology anyway.

When *I* try to formulate our difference of opinion, on the other hand, I
seem to be in a predicament. I cannot admit that there are some things
which McX countenances and I do not, for in admitting that there are
such things I should be contradicting my own rejection of them.

It would appear, if this reasoning were sound, that in any ontological
dispute the proponent of the negative side suffers the disadvantage of not
being able to admit that his opponent disagrees with him.

This is the old Platonic riddle of nonbeing. Nonbeing must in some
sense be, otherwise what is it that there is not? This tangled doctrine might
be nicknamed *Plato's beard*; historically it has proved tough, frequently
dulling the edge of Occam's razor.

It is some such line of thought that leads philosophers like McX to
impute being where they might otherwise be quite content to recognize
that there is nothing. Thus, take Pegasus. If Pegasus *were* not, McX argues,
we should not be talking about anything when we use the word; therefore

---

* Reprinted by permission of the publishers from Willard Van Orman Quine, *From
a Logical Point of View: 9 Logico-Philosophical Essays,* Cambridge, Mass.: Harvard
University Press, Copyright 1953, 1961, by the President and Fellows of Harvard
College.

it would be nonsense to say even that Pegasus is not. Thinking to show thus that the denial of Pegasus cannot be coherently maintained, he concludes that Pegasus is.

McX cannot, indeed, quite persuade himself that any region of space-time, near or remote, contains a flying horse of flesh and blood. Pressed for further details on Pegasus, then, he says that Pegasus is an idea in men's minds. Here, however, a confusion begins to be apparent. We may for the sake of argument concede that there is an entity, and even a unique entity (though this is rather implausible), which is the mental Pegasus-idea; but this mental entity is not what people are talking about when they deny Pegasus.

McX never confuses the Parthenon with the Parthenon-idea. The Parthenon is physical; the Parthenon-idea is mental (according anyway to McX's version of ideas, and I have no better to offer). The Parthenon is visible; the Parthenon-idea is invisible. We cannot easily imagine two things more unlike, and less liable to confusion, than the Parthenon and the Parthenon-idea. But when we shift from the Parthenon to Pegasus, the confusion sets in—for no other reason than that McX would sooner be deceived by the crudest and most flagrant counterfeit than grant the non-being of Pegasus.

The notion that Pegasus must be, because it would otherwise be nonsense to say even that Pegasus is not, has been seen to lead McX into an elementary confusion. Subtler minds, taking the same precept as their starting point, come out with theories of Pegasus which are less patently misguided than McX's, and correspondingly more difficult to eradicate. One of these subtler minds is named, let us say, Wyman. Pegasus, Wyman maintains, has his being as an unactualized possible. When we say of Pegasus that there is no such thing, we are saying, more precisely, that Pegasus does not have the special attribute of actuality. Saying that Pegasus is not actual is on a par, logically, with saying that the Parthenon is not red; in either case we are saying something about an entity whose being is unquestioned.

Wyman, by the way, is one of those philosophers who have united in ruining the good old word 'exist.' Despite his espousal of unactualized possibles, he limits the word 'existence' to actuality—thus preserving an illusion of ontological agreement between himself and us who repudiate the rest of his bloated universe. We have all been prone to say, in our common-sense usage of 'exist,' that Pegasus does not exist, meaning simply that there is no such entity at all. If Pegasus existed he would indeed be in space and time, but only because the word 'Pegasus' has spatio-temporal connotations, and not because 'exists' has spatio-temporal connotations. If spatio-temporal reference is lacking when we affirm the existence of the cube root of 27, this is simply because a cube root is not a spatio-temporal kind of thing, and not because we are being ambiguous in our use of 'exist.' [1] However, Wyman, in an ill-conceived effort to appear agreeable, genially grants us the nonexistence of Pegasus and then, contrary to what *we* meant by nonexistence of Pegasus, insists that Pegasus *is*. Existence is one thing, he says, and subsistence is another. The only way I know of coping with this obfuscation of issues is to *give* Wyman the word 'exist.' I'll try not to use it again; I still have 'is.' So much for lexicography; let's get back to Wyman's ontology.

Wyman's overpopulated universe is in many ways unlovely. It offends the aesthetic sense of us who have a taste for desert landscapes, but this is not the worst of it. Wyman's slum of possibles is a breeding ground for disorderly elements. Take, for instance, the possible fat man in that doorway; and, again, the possible bald man in that doorway. Are they the same possible man, or two possible men? How do we decide? How many possible men are there in that doorway? Are there more possible thin ones than fat ones? How many of them are alike? Or would their being alike make them one? Are no *two* possible things alike? Is this the same as saying that it is impossible for two things to be alike? Or, finally, is the concept of identity simply inapplicable to unactualized possibles? But what sense can be found in talking of entities which cannot meaningfully be said to be identical with themselves and distinct from one another? These elements are well-nigh incorrigible. By a Fregean therapy of individual concepts, some effort might be made at rehabilitation; but I feel we'd do better simply to clear Wyman's slum and be done with it.

Possibility, along with the other modalities of necessity and impossibility and contingency, raises problems upon which I do not mean to imply that we should turn our backs. But we can at least limit modalities to whole statements. We may impose the adverb 'possibly' upon a statement as a whole, and we may well worry about the semantical analysis of such usage; but little real advance in such analysis is to be hoped for in expanding our universe to include so-called *possible entities*. I suspect that the main motive for this expansion is simply the old notion that Pegasus, for example, must be because otherwise it would be nonsense to say even that he is not. Still, all the rank luxuriance of Wyman's universe of possibles would seem to come to naught when we make a slight change in the example and speak not of Pegasus but of the round square cupola on Berkeley College. If, unless Pegasus were, it would be nonsense to say that he is not, then by the same token, unless the round square cupola on Berkeley College were, it would be nonsense to say that it is not. But, unlike Pegasus, the round

[1] The impulse to distinguish terminologically between existence as applied to objects actualized somewhere in space-time and existence (or subsistence or being) as applied to other entities arises in part, perhaps, from an idea that the observation of nature is relevant only to questions of existence of the first kind. But this idea is readily refuted by counter-instances such as 'the ratio of the number of centaurs to the number of unicorns.' If there were such a ratio, it would be an abstract entity, viz. a number. Yet it is only by studying nature that we conclude that the number of centaurs and the number of unicorns are both 0 and hence that there is no such ratio.

square cupola on Berkeley College cannot be admitted even as an unactualized *possible*. Can we drive Wyman now to admitting also a realm of unactualizable impossibles? If so, a good many embarrassing questions could be asked about them. We might hope even to trap Wyman in contradictions, by getting him to admit that certain of these entities are at once round and square. But the wily Wyman chooses the other horn of the dilemma and concedes that it is nonsense to say that the round square cupola on Berkeley College is not. He says that the phrase 'round square cupola' is meaningless.

Wyman was not the first to embrace this alternative. The doctrine of the meaninglessness of contradictions runs away back. The tradition survives, moreover, in writers who seem to share none of Wyman's motivations. Still, I wonder whether the first temptation to such a doctrine may not have been substantially the motivation which we have observed in Wyman. Certainly the doctrine has no intrinsic appeal; and it has led its devotees to such quixotic extremes as that of challenging the method of proof by *reductio ad absurdum*—a challenge in which I sense a *reductio ad absurdum* of the doctrine itself.

Moreover, the doctrine of meaninglessness of contradictions has the severe methodological drawback that it makes it impossible, in principle, ever to devise an effective test of what is meaningful and what is not. It would be forever impossible for us to devise systematic ways of deciding whether a string of signs made sense—even to us individually, let alone other people—or not. For it follows from a discovery in mathematical logic, due to Church, that there can be no generally applicable test of contradictoriness.

I have spoken disparagingly of Plato's beard, and hinted that it is tangled. I have dwelt at length on the inconveniences of putting up with it. It is time to think about taking steps.

Russell, in his theory of so-called singular descriptions, showed clearly how we might meaningfully use seeming names without supposing that there be the entities allegedly named. The names to which Russell's theory directly applies are complex descriptive names such as 'the author of *Waverley*,' 'the present King of France,' 'the round square cupola on Berkeley College.' Russell analyzes such phrases systematically as fragments of the whole sentences in which they occur. The sentence 'The author of *Waverley* was a poet,' for example, is explained as a whole as meaning 'Someone (better: something) wrote *Waverley* and was a poet, and nothing else wrote *Waverley*.' (The point of this added clause is to affirm the uniqueness which is implicit in the word 'the,' in '*the* author of *Waverley*.') The sentence 'The round square cupola on Berkeley College is pink' is explained as 'Something is round and square and is a cupola on Berkeley College and is pink, and nothing else is round and square and a cupola on Berkeley College.'

The virtue of this analysis is that the seeming name, a descriptive phrase, is paraphrased *in context* as a so-called incomplete symbol. No unified expression is offered as an analysis of the descriptive phrase, but the statement as a whole which was the context of that phrase still gets its full quota of meaning—whether true or false.

The unanalyzed statement 'The author of *Waverley* was a poet' contains a part, 'the author of *Waverley*,' which is wrongly supposed by McX and Wyman to demand objective reference in order to be meaningful at all. But in Russell's translation, 'Something wrote *Waverley* and was a poet and nothing else wrote *Waverley*,' the burden of objective reference which had been put upon the descriptive phrase is now taken over by words of the kind that logicians call bound variables, variables of quantification, namely, words like 'something,' 'nothing,' 'everything.' These words, far from purporting to be names specifically of the author of *Waverley*, do not purport to be names at all; they refer to entities generally, with a kind of studied ambiguity peculiar to themselves. These quantificational words or bound variables are of course a basic part of language, and their meaningfulness, at least in context, is not to be challenged. But their meaningfulness in no way presupposes there being either the author of *Waverley* or the round square cupola on Berkeley College or any other specifically preassigned objects.

Where descriptions are concerned, there is no longer any difficulty in affirming or denying being. 'There *is* the author of *Waverley*' is explained by Russell as meaning 'Someone (or, more strictly, something) wrote *Waverley* and nothing else wrote *Waverley*.' 'The author of *Waverley* is not' is explained, correspondingly, as the alternation 'Either each thing failed to write *Waverley* or two or more things wrote *Waverley*.' This alternation is false, but meaningful; and it contains no expression purporting to name the author of *Waverley*. The statement 'The round square cupola on Berkeley College is not' is analyzed in similar fashion. So the old notion that statements of nonbeing defeat themselves goes by the board. When a statement of being or nonbeing is analyzed by Russell's theory of descriptions, it ceases to contain any expression which even purports to name the alleged entity whose being is in question, so that the meaningfulness of the statement no longer can be thought to presuppose that there be such an entity.

Now what of 'Pegasus'? This being a word rather than a descriptive phrase, Russell's argument does not immediately apply to it. However, it can easily be made to apply. We have only to rephrase 'Pegasus' as a description, in any way that seems adequately to single out our idea; say, 'the winged horse that was captured by Bellerophon.' Substituting such a phrase for 'Pegasus,' we can then proceed to analyze the statement 'Pegasus is,' or 'Pegasus is not,' precisely on the analogy of Russell's analysis of 'The author of *Waverley* is' and 'The author of *Waverley* is not.'

In order thus to subsume a one-word name or alleged name such as 'Pegasus' under Russell's theory of description, we must, of course, be able first to translate the word into a description. But this is no real restriction. If the notion of Pegasus had been so obscure or so basic a one that no pat translation into a descriptive phrase had offered itself along familiar lines, we could still have availed ourselves of the following artificial and trivial-seeming device: we could have appealed to the *ex hypothesi* unanalyzable, irreducible attribute of *being Pegasus*, adopting, for its expression, the verb 'is-Pegasus,' or 'pegasizes.' The noun 'Pegasus' itself could then be treated as derivative, and identified after all with a description: 'the thing that is-Pegasus,' 'the thing that pegasizes.'

If the importing of such a predicate as 'pegasizes' seems to commit us to recognizing that there is a corresponding attribute, pegasizing, in Plato's heaven or in the minds of men, well and good. Neither we nor Wyman nor McX have been contending, thus far, about the being or nonbeing of universals, but rather about that of Pegasus. If in terms of pegasizing we can interpret the noun 'Pegasus' as a description subject to Russell's theory of descriptions, then we have disposed of the old notion that Pegasus cannot be said not to be without presupposing that in some sense Pegasus is.

Our argument is now quite general. McX and Wyman supposed that we could not meaningfully affirm a statement of the form 'So-and-so is not,' with a simple or descriptive singular noun in place of 'so-and-so,' unless so-and-so is. This supposition is now seen to be quite generally groundless, since the singular noun in question can always be expanded into a singular description, trivially or otherwise, and then analyzed out *à la* Russell.

We commit ourselves to an ontology containing numbers when we say there are prime numbers larger than a million; we commit ourselves to an ontology containing centaurs when we say there are centaurs; and we commit ourselves to an ontology containing Pegasus when we say Pegasus is. But we do not commit ourselves to an ontology containing Pegasus or the author of *Waverley* or the round square cupola on Berkeley College when we say that Pegasus or the author of *Waverley* or the cupola in question is *not*. We need no longer labor under the delusion that the meaningfulness of a statement containing a singular term presupposes an entity named by the term. A singular term need not name to be significant.

An inkling of this might have dawned on Wyman and McX even without benefit of Russell if they had only noticed—as so few of us do—that there is a gulf between *meaning* and *naming* even in the case of a singular term which is genuinely a name of an object. The following example from Frege will serve. The phrase 'Evening Star' names a certain large physical object of spherical form, which is hurtling through space some scores of millions of miles from here. The phrase 'Morning Star' names the same thing, as was probably first established by some observant Babylonian. But the two phrases cannot be regarded as having the same meaning; otherwise that Babylonian could have dispensed with his observations and contented himself with reflecting on the meanings of his words. The meanings then, being different from one another, must be other than the named object, which is one and the same in both cases.

Confusion of meaning with naming not only made McX think he could not meaningfully repudiate Pegasus; a continuing confusion of meaning with naming no doubt helped engender his absurd notion that Pegasus is an idea, a mental entity. The structure of his confusion is as follows. He confused the alleged *named object* Pegasus with the *meaning* of the word 'Pegasus,' therefore concluding that Pegasus must be in order that the word have meaning. But what sorts of things are meanings? This is a moot point; however, one might quite plausibly explain meanings as ideas in the mind, supposing we can make clear sense in turn of the idea of ideas in the mind. Therefore Pegasus, initially confused with a meaning, ends up as an idea in the mind. It is the more remarkable that Wyman, subject to the same initial motivation as McX, should have avoided this particular blunder and wound up with unactualized possibles instead.

Now let us turn to the ontological problem of universals: the question whether there are such entities as attributes, relations, classes, numbers, functions. McX, characteristically enough, thinks there are. Speaking of attributes, he says: "There are red houses, red roses, red sunsets; this much is prephilosophical common sense in which we must all agree. These houses, roses, and sunsets, then, have something in common; and this which they have in common is all I mean by the attribute of redness." For McX, thus, there being attributes is even more obvious and trivial than the obvious and trivial fact of there being red houses, roses, and sunsets. This, I think, is characteristic of metaphysics, or at least of that part of metaphysics called ontology: one who regards a statement on this subject as true at all must regard it as trivially true. One's ontology is basic to the conceptual scheme by which he interprets all experiences, even the most commonplace ones. Judged within some particular conceptual scheme— and how else is judgment possible?—an ontological statement goes without saying, standing in need of no separate justification at all. Ontological statements follow immediately from all manner of casual statements of commonplace fact, just as—from the point of view, anyway, of McX's conceptual scheme—'There is an attribute' follows from 'There are red houses, red roses, red sunsets.'

Judged in another conceptual scheme, an ontological statement which is axiomatic to McX's mind may, with equal immediacy and triviality, be adjudged false. One may admit that there are red houses, roses, and sunsets, but deny, except as a popular and misleading manner of speaking, that they have anything in common. The words 'houses,' 'roses,' and 'sunsets' are true of sundry individual entities which are houses and roses and sunsets, and the word 'red' or 'red object' is true of each of sundry individual entities which are red houses, red roses, red sunsets; but there is not, in addition, any entity whatever, individual or otherwise, which is named by the word 'redness', nor, for that matter, by the word 'household,' 'rosehood,' 'sunsethood.' That the houses and roses and sunsets are all of them red may be taken as ultimate and irreducible, and it may be held that McX is no better off, in point of real explanatory power, for all the occult entities which he posits under such names as 'redness.'

One means by which McX might naturally have tried to impose his ontology of universals on us was already removed before we turned to the problem of universals. McX cannot argue that predicates such as 'red' or 'is-red,' which we all concur in using, must be regarded as names each of a single universal entity in order that they be meaningful at all. For we have seen that being a name of something is a much more special feature than being meaningful. He cannot even charge us—at least not by *that* argument—with having posited an attribute of pegasizing by our adoption of the predicate 'pegasizes.'

However, McX hits upon a different strategem. "Let us grant," he says, "this distinction between meaning and naming of which you make so much. Let us even grant that 'is red,' 'pegasizes,' etc., are not names of attributes. Still, you admit they have meanings. But these *meanings*, whether they are *named* or not, are still universals, and I venture to say that some of them might even be the very things that I call attributes, or something to much the same purpose in the end."

For McX, this is an unusually penetrating speech; and the only way I know to counter it is by refusing to admit meanings. However, I feel no reluctance toward refusing to admit meanings, for I do not thereby deny that words and statements are meaningful. McX and I may agree to the letter in our classification of linguistic forms into the meaningful and the meaningless, even though McX construes meaningfulness as the *having* (in some sense of 'having') of some abstract entity which he calls a meaning, whereas I do not. I remain free to maintain that the fact that a given linguistic utterance is meaningful (or *significant*, as I prefer to say so as not to invite hypostasis of meanings as entities) is an ultimate and irreducible matter of fact; or, I may undertake to analyze it in terms directly of what people do in the presence of the linguistic utterance in question and other utterances similar to it.

The useful ways in which people ordinarily talk or seem to talk about meanings boil down to two: the *having* of meanings, which is significance, and *sameness* of meaning, or synonomy. What is called *giving* the meaning of an utterance is simply the uttering of a synonym, couched, ordinarily, in clearer language than the original. If we are allergic to meanings as such, we can speak directly of utterances as significant or insignificant, and as synonymous or heteronymous one with another. The problem of explaining these adjectives 'significant' and 'synonymous' with some degree of clarity and rigor—preferably, as I see it, in terms of behavior—is as difficult as it is important. But the explanatory value of special and irreducible intermediary entities called meanings is surely illusory.

Up to now I have argued that we can use singular terms significantly in sentences without presupposing that there are the entities which those terms purport to name. I have argued further that we can use general terms, for example, predicates, without conceding them to be names of abstract entities. I have argued further that we can view utterances as significant, and as synonymous or heteronymous with one another, without countenancing a realm of entities called meanings. At this point McX begins to wonder whether there is any limit at all to our ontological immunity. Does *nothing* we may say commit us to the assumption of universals or other entities which we may find unwelcome?

I have already suggested a negative answer to this question, in speaking of bound variables, or variables of quantification, in connection with Russell's theory of descriptions. We can very easily involve ourselves in ontological commitments by saying, for example, that *there is something* (bound variable) which red houses and sunsets have in common; or that *there is something* which is a prime number larger than a million. But this is, essentially, the *only* way we can involve ourselves in ontological commitments: by our use of bound variables. The use of alleged names is no criterion, for we can repudiate their namehood at the drop of a hat unless the assumption of a corresponding entity can be spotted in the things we affirm in terms of bound variables. Names are, in fact, altogether immaterial to the ontological issue, for I have shown, in connection with 'Pegasus' and 'pegasize,' that names can be converted to descriptions, and Russell has shown that descriptions can be eliminated. Whatever we say with the help of names can be said in a language which shuns names altogether. To be assumed as an entity is, purely and simply, to be reckoned as the value of a variable. In terms of the categories of traditional grammar, this amounts roughly to saying that to be is to be in the range of reference of a pronoun. Pronouns are the basic media of reference; nouns might better have been named propronouns. The variables of quantification, 'something,' 'nothing,' 'everything,' range over our whole ontology, whatever it may be; and we are convicted of a particular ontological presupposition if, and only if, the alleged presuppositum has to be reckoned among the entities over which our variables range in order to render one of our affirmations true.

We may say, for example, that some dogs are white and not thereby commit ourselves to recognizing either doghood or whiteness as entities. 'Some dogs are white' says that some things that are dogs are white; and, in order that this statement be true, the things over which the bound variable 'something' ranges must include some white dogs, but need not include doghood or whiteness. On the other hand, when we say that some zoölogical species are cross-fertile we are committing ourselves to recognizing as entities the several species themselves, abstract though they are. We remain so committed at least until we devise some way of so paraphrasing the statement as to show that the seeming reference to species on the part of our bound variable was an avoidable manner of speaking.

Classical mathematics, as the example of primes larger than a million clearly illustrates, is up to its neck in commitments to an ontology of abstract entities. Thus it is that the great mediaeval controversy over universals has flared up anew in the modern philosophy of mathematics. The issue is clearer now than of old, because we now have a more explicit standard whereby to decide what ontology a given theory or form of discourse is committed to: a theory is committed to those and only those entities to which the bound variables of the theory must be capable of referring in order that the affirmations made in the theory be true.

Because this standard of ontological presupposition did not emerge clearly in the philosophical tradition, the modern philosophical mathematicians have not on the whole recognized that they were debating the same old problem of universals in a newly clarified form. But the fundamental cleavages among modern points of view on foundations of mathematics do come down pretty explicitly to disagreements as to the range of entities to which the bound variables should be permitted to refer.

The three main mediaeval points of view regarding universals are designated by historians as *realism*, *conceptualism*, and *nominalism*. Essentially these same three doctrines reappear in twentieth-century surveys of the philosophy of mathematics under the new names *logicism*, *intuitionism*, and *formalism*.

*Realism*, as the word is used in connection with the mediaeval controversy over universals, is the Platonic doctrine that universals or abstract entities have being independently of the mind; the mind may discover them but cannot create them. *Logicism*, represented by Frege, Russell, Whitehead, Church, and Carnap, condones the use of bound variables to refer to abstract entities known and unknown, specifiable and unspecifiable, indiscriminately.

*Conceptualism* holds that there are universals but they are mind-made. *Intuitionism*, espoused in modern times in one form or another by Poincaré, Brouwer, Weyl, and others, countenances the use of bound variables to refer to abstract entities only when those entities are capable of being cooked up individually from ingredients specified in advance. As Fraenkel has put it, logicism holds that classes are discovered while intuitionism holds that they are invented—a fair statement indeed of the old opposition between realism and conceptualism. This opposition is no mere quibble; it makes an essential difference in the amount of classical mathematics to which one is willing to subscribe. Logicists, or realists, are able on their assumptions to get Cantor's ascending orders of infinity; intuitionists are compelled to stop with the lowest order of infinity, and, as an indirect consequence, to abandon even some of the classical laws of real numbers. The modern controversy between logicism and intuitionism arose, in fact, from disagreements over infinity.

*Formalism*, associated with the name of Hilbert, echoes intuitionism in deploring the logicist's unbridled recourse to universals. But formalism also finds intuitionism unsatisfactory. This could happen for either of two op-posite reasons. The formalist might, like the logicist, object to the crippling of classical mathematics; or he might, like the *nominalists* of old, object to admitting abstract entities at all, even in the restrained sense of mind-made entities. The upshot is the same: the formalist keeps classical mathematics as a play of insignificant notations. This play of notations can still be of utility—whatever utility it has already shown itself to have as a crutch for physicists and technologists. But utility need not imply significance, in any literal linguistic sense. Nor need the marked success of mathematicians in spinning out theorems, and in finding objective bases for agreement with one another's results, imply significance. For an adequate basis for agree-ment among mathematicians can be found simply in the rules which govern the manipulation of the notations—these syntactical rules being, unlike the notations themselves, quite significant and intelligible.

I have argued that the sort of ontology we adopt can be consequential—notably in connection with mathematics, although this is only an example. Now how are we to adjudicate among rival ontologies? Certainly the answer is not provided by the semantical formula "To be is to be the value of a variable"; this formula serves rather, conversely, in testing the conformity of a given remark or doctrine to a prior ontological standard. We look to bound variables in connection with ontology not in order to know what there is, but in order to know what a given remark or doctrine, ours or someone else's, *says* there is; and this much is quite properly a problem involving language. But what there is is another question.

In debating over what there is, there are still reasons for operating on a semantical plane. One reason is to escape from the predicament noted at the beginning of this essay: the predicament of my not being able to admit that there are things which McX countenances and I do not. So long as I adhere to my ontology, as opposed to McX's, I cannot allow my bound variables to refer to entities which belong to McX's ontology and not to mine. I can, however, consistently describe our disagreement by charac-terizing the statements which McX affirms. Provided merely that my ontology countenances linguistic forms, or at least concrete inscriptions and utterances, I can talk about McX's sentences.

Another reason for withdrawing to a semantical plane is to find com-mon ground on which to argue. Disagreement in ontology involves basic disagreement in conceptual schemes; yet McX and I, despite these basic disagreements, find that our conceptual schemes converge sufficiently in their intermediate and upper ramifications to enable us to communicate successfully on such topics as politics, weather, and, in particular, lan-guage. In so far as our basic controversy over ontology can be translated upward into a semantical controversy about words and what to do with them, the collapse of the controversy into question-begging may be delayed.

It is no wonder, then, that ontological controversy should tend into controversy over language. But we must not jump to the conclusion that what there is depends on words. Translatability of a question into semantical terms is no indication that the question is linguistic. To see Naples is to bear a name which, when prefixed to the words 'sees Naples,' yields a true sentence; still there is nothing linguistic about seeing Naples.

Our acceptance of an ontology is, I think, similar in principle to our acceptance of a scientific theory, say a system of physics: we adopt, at least insofar as we are reasonable, the simplest conceptual scheme into which the disordered fragments of raw experience can be fitted and arranged. Our ontology is determined once we have fixed upon the over-all conceptual scheme which is to accommodate science in the broadest sense; and the considerations which determine a reasonable construction of any part of that conceptual scheme, for example, the biological or the physical part, are not different in kind from the considerations which determine a reasonable construction of the whole. To whatever extent the adoption of any system of scientific theory may be said to be a matter of language, the same—but no more—may be said of the adoption of an ontology.

But simplicity, as a guiding principle in constructing conceptual schemes, is not a clear and unambiguous idea; and it is quite capable of presenting a double or multiple standard. Imagine, for example, that we have devised the most economical set of concepts adequate to the play-by-play reporting of immediate experience. The entities under this scheme—the values of bound variables—are, let us suppose, individual subjective events of sensation or reflection. We should still find, no doubt, that a physicalistic conceptual scheme, purporting to talk about external objects, offers great advantages in simplifying our over-all reports. By bringing together scattered sense events and treating them as perceptions of one object, we reduce the complexity of our stream of experience to a manageable conceptual simplicity. The rule of simplicity is indeed our guiding maxim in assigning sense data to objects: we associate an earlier and a later round sensum with the same so-called penny, or with two different so-called pennies, in obedience to the demands of maximum simplicity in our total world-picture.

Here we have two competing conceptual schemes, a phenomenalistic one and a physicalistic one. Which should prevail? Each has its advantages; each has its special simplicity in its own way. Each, I suggest, deserves to be developed. Each may be said, indeed, to be the more fundamental, though in different senses: the one is epistemologically, the other physically, fundamental.

The physical conceptual scheme simplifies our account of experience because of the way myriad scattered sense events come to be associated with single so-called objects; still there is no likelihood that each sentence about physical objects can actually be translated, however deviously and complexly, into the phenomenalistic language. Physical objects are postulated entities which round out and simplify our account of the flux of experience, just as the introduction of irrational numbers simplifies laws of arithmetic. From the point of view of the conceptual scheme of the elementary arithmetic of rational numbers alone, the broader arithmetic of rational and irrational numbers would have the status of a convenient myth, simpler than the literal truth (namely, the arithmetic of rationals) and yet containing that literal truth as a scattered part. Similarly, from a phenomenalistic point of view, the conceptual scheme of physical objects is a convenient myth, simpler than the literal truth and yet containing that literal truth as a scattered part.

Now what of classes or attributes of physical objects, in turn? A platonistic ontology of this sort is, from the point of view of a strictly physicalistic conceptual scheme, as much a myth as that physicalistic conceptual scheme itself is for phenomenalism. This higher myth is a good and useful one, in turn, in so far as it simplifies our account of physics. Since mathematics is an integral part of this higher myth, the utility of this myth for physical science is evident enough. In speaking of it nevertheless as a myth, I echo that philosophy of mathematics to which I alluded earlier under the name of formalism. But an attitude of formalism may with equal justice be adopted toward the physical conceptual scheme, in turn, by the pure aesthete or phenomenalist.

The analogy between the myth of mathematics and the myth of physics is, in some additional and perhaps fortuitous ways, strikingly close. Consider, for example, the crisis which was precipitated in the foundations of mathematics, at the turn of the century, by the discovery of Russell's paradox and other antinomies of set theory. These contradictions had to be obviated by unintuitive, *ad hoc* devices; our mathematical myth-making became deliberate and evident to all. But what of physics? An antinomy arose between the undular and the corpuscular accounts of light; and if this was not as out-and-out a contradiction as Russell's paradox, I suspect that the reason is that physics is not as out-and-out as mathematics. Again, the second great modern crisis in the foundations of mathematics—precipitated in 1931 by Gödel's proof that there are bound to be undecidable statements in arithmetic—has its companion piece in physics in Heisenberg's indeterminacy principle.

In earlier pages I undertook to show that some common arguments in favor of certain ontologies are fallacious. Further, I advanced an explicit standard whereby to decide what the ontological commitments of a theory are. But the question what ontology actually to adopt still stands open, and the obvious counsel is tolerance and an experimental spirit. Let us by all means see how much of the physicalistic conceptual scheme can be reduced to a phenomenalistic one; still, physics also naturally demands pursuing, irreducible *in toto* though it be. Let us see how, or to what degree, natural science may be rendered independent of platonistic mathematics; but let us also pursue mathematics and delve into its platonistic foundations.

From among the various conceptual schemes best suited to these various pursuits, one—the phenomenalistic—claims epistemological priority. Viewed from within the phenomenalistic conceptual scheme, the ontologies of physical objects and mathematical objects are myths. The quality of myth, however, is relative; relative, in this case, to the epistemological point of view. This point of view is one among various, corresponding to one among our various interests and purposes.

# EMPIRICISM, SEMANTICS, AND ONTOLOGY* †

RUDOLF CARNAP (1891–    ) is Professor Emeritus of Philosophy of the University of California at Los Angeles. He was one of the founders and leading members of the Vienna Circle, and a long-time exponent of logical positivism and logical empiricism. He has made many important contributions to logic and the philosophy of science. Among his many books are *The Logical Syntax of Language, Introduction to Semantics, Meaning and Necessity,* and *Logical Foundations of Probability.*

## 1.  THE PROBLEM OF ABSTRACT ENTITIES

Empiricists are in general rather suspicious with respect to any kind of abstract entities like properties, classes, relations, numbers, propositions, etc. They usually feel much more in sympathy with nominalists than with realists (in the medieval sense). As far as possible they try to avoid any reference to abstract entities and to restrict themselves to what is sometimes called a nominalistic language, i.e., one not containing such references. However, within certain scientific contexts it seems hardly possible to avoid them. In the case of mathematics, some empiricists try to find a way out by treating the whole of mathematics as a mere calculus, a formal system for which no interpretation is given or can be given. Accordingly, the mathematician is said to speak not about numbers, func-

* Reprinted from *Meaning and Necessity* by Rudolf Carnap by permission of The University of Chicago Press. Copyright © 1947 and 1956 by The University of Chicago Press. All rights reserved. Published 1947. Enlarged Edition 1956. Third Impression 1960. Composed and printed by The University of Chicago Press, Illinois, U.S.A.

† I have made here some minor changes in the formulations to the effect that the term "framework" is now used only for the system of linguistic expressions, and not for the system of the entities in question.

tions, and infinite classes, but merely about meaningless symbols and formulas manipulated according to given formal rules. In physics it is more difficult to shun the suspected entities, because the language of physics serves for the communication of reports and predictions and hence cannot be taken as a mere calculus. A physicist who is suspicious of abstract entities may perhaps try to declare a certain part of the language of physics as uninterpreted and uninterpretable, that part which refers to real numbers as space-time coordinates or as values of physical magnitudes, to functions, limits, etc. More probably he will just speak about all these things like anybody else but with an uneasy conscience, like a man who in his everyday life does with qualms many things which are not in accord with the high moral principles he professes on Sundays. Recently the problem of abstract entities has arisen again in connection with semantics, the theory of meaning and truth. Some semanticists say that certain expressions designate certain entities, and among these designated entities they include not only concrete material things but also abstract entities, e.g., properties as designated by predicates and propositions as designated by sentences.[1] Others object strongly to this procedure as violating the basic principles of empiricism and leading back to a metaphysical ontology of the Platonic kind.

It is the purpose of this article to clarify this controversial issue. The nature and implications of the acceptance of a language referring to abstract entities will first be discussed in general; it will be shown that using such a language does not imply embracing a Platonic ontology but is perfectly compatible with empiricism and strictly scientific thinking. Then the special question of the role of abstract entities in semantics will be discussed. It is hoped that the clarification of the issue will be useful to those who would like to accept abstract entities in their work in mathematics, physics, semantics, or any other field; it may help them to overcome nominalistic scruples.

## 2.  LINGUISTIC FRAMEWORKS

Are there properties, classes, numbers, propositions? In order to understand more clearly the nature of these and related problems, it is above all necessary to recognize a fundamental distinction between two kinds of questions concerning the existence or reality of entities. If someone wishes to speak in his language about a new kind of entities, he has to introduce a system of new ways of speaking, subject to new rules; we shall call this procedure the construction of a linguistic *framework* for the new entities in question. And now we must distinguish two kinds of questions of existence: first, questions of the existence of certain entities of the new kind

---

[1] The terms "sentence" and "statement" are here used synonymously for declarative (indicative, propositional) sentences.

*within the framework;* we call them *internal questions;* and second, questions concerning the existence or reality *of the system of entities as a whole,* called *external questions.* Internal questions and possible answers to them are formulated with the help of the new forms of expressions. The answers may be found either by purely logical methods or by empirical methods, depending upon whether the framework is a logical or a factual one. An external question is of a problematic character which is in need of closer examination.

*The world of things.* Let us consider as an example the simplest kind of entities dealt with in the everyday language: the spatio-temporally ordered system of observable things and events. Once we have accepted the thing language with its framework for things, we can raise and answer internal questions, e.g., "Is there a white piece of paper on my desk?", "Did King Arthur actually live?", "Are unicorns and centaurs real or merely imaginary?" and the like. These questions are to be answered by empirical investigations. Results of observations are evaluated according to certain rules as confirming or disconfirming evidence for possible answers. (This evaluation is usually carried out, of course, as a matter of habit rather than a deliberate, rational procedure. But it is possible, in a rational reconstruction, to lay down explicit rules for the evaluation. This is one of the main tasks of a pure, as distinguished from a psychological, epistemology.) The concept of reality occurring in these internal questions is an empirical, scientific, non-metaphysical concept. To recognize something as a real thing or event means to succeed in incorporating it into the system of things at a particular space-time position so that it fits together with the other things recognized as real, according to the rules of the framework.

From these questions we must distinguish the external question of the reality of the thing world itself. In contrast to the former questions, this question is raised neither by the man in the street nor by scientists, but only by philosophers. Realists give an affirmative answer, subjective idealists a negative one, and the controversy goes on for centuries without ever being solved. And it cannot be solved because it is framed in a wrong way. To be real in the scientific sense means to be an element of the system; hence this concept cannot be meaningfully applied to the system itself. Those who raise the question of the reality of the thing world itself have perhaps in mind not a theoretical question as their formulation seems to suggest, but rather a practical question, a matter of a practical decision concerning the structure of our language. We have to make the choice whether or not to accept and use the forms of expression in the framework in question.

In the case of this particular example, there is usually no deliberate choice because we all have accepted the thing language early in our lives as a matter of course. Nevertheless, we may regard it as a matter of decision in this sense: we are free to choose to continue using the thing language or not; in the latter case we could restrict ourselves to a language of sense-data and other "phenomenal" entities, or construct an alternative to the customary thing language with another structure, or, finally, we could refrain from speaking. If someone decides to accept the thing language, there is no objection against saying that he has accepted the world of things. But this must not be interpreted as if it meant his acceptance of a *belief* in the reality of the thing world; there is no such belief or assertion or assumption, because it is not a theoretical question. To accept the thing world means nothing more than to accept a certain form of language, in other words, to accept rules for forming statements and for testing, accepting, or rejecting them. The acceptance of the thing language leads, on the basis of observations made, also to the acceptance, belief, and assertion of certain statements. But the thesis of the reality of the thing world cannot be among these statements, because it cannot be formulated in the thing language or, it seems, in any other theoretical language.

The decision of accepting the thing language, although itself not of a cognitive nature, will nevertheless usually be influenced by theoretical knowledge, just like any other deliberate decision concerning the acceptance of linguistic or other rules. The purposes for which the language is intended to be used, for instance, the purpose of communicating factual knowledge, will determine which factors are relevant for the decision. The efficiency, fruitfulness, and simplicity of the use of the thing language may be among the decisive factors. And the questions concerning these qualities are indeed of a theoretical nature. But these questions cannot be identified with the question of realism. They are not yes-no questions but questions of degree. The thing language in the customary form works indeed with a high degree of efficiency for most purposes of everyday life. This is a matter of fact, based upon the content of our experiences. However, it would be wrong to describe this situation by saying: "The fact of the efficiency of the thing language is confirming evidence for the reality of the thing world"; we should rather say instead: "This fact makes it advisable to accept the thing language."

*The system of numbers.* As an example of a system which is of a logical rather than a factual nature let us take the system of natural numbers. The framework for this system is constructed by introducing into the language new expressions with suitable rules: (1) numerals like "five" and sentence forms like "there are five books on the table"; (2) the general term "number" for the new entities, and sentence forms like "five is a number"; (3) expressions for properties of numbers (e.g., "odd," "prime"), relations (e.g., "greater than"), and functions (e.g., "plus"), and sentence forms like "two plus three is five"; (4) numerical variables ("$m$," "$n$," etc.) and quantifiers for universal sentences ("for every $n$, . . .") and existential sentences ("there is an $n$ such that . . .") with the customary deductive rules.

Here again there are internal questions, e.g., "Is there a prime number greater than a hundred?" Here, however, the answers are found, not by empirical investigation based on observations, but by logical analysis based on the rules for the new expressions. Therefore the answers are here analytic, i.e., logically true.

What is now the nature of the philosophical question concerning the existence or reality of numbers? To begin with, there is the internal question which, together with the affirmative answer, can be formulated in the new terms, say, by "There are numbers" or, more explicitly, "There is an $n$ such that $n$ is a number." This statement follows from the analytic statement "five is a number" and is therefore itself analytic. Moreover, it is rather trivial (in contradistinction to a statement like "There is a prime number greater than a million," which is likewise analytic but far from trivial), because it does not say more than that the new system is not empty; but this is immediately seen from the rule which states that words like "five" are substitutable for the new variables. Therefore nobody who meant the question "Are there numbers?" in the internal sense would either assert or even seriously consider a negative answer. This makes it plausible to assume that those philosophers who treat the question of the existence of numbers as a serious philosophical problem and offer lengthy arguments on either side, do not have in mind the internal question. And, indeed, if we were to ask them: "Do you mean the question as to whether the framework of numbers, *if* we were to accept it, would be found to be empty or not?" they would probably reply: "Not at all; we mean a question *prior* to the acceptance of the new framework." They might try to explain what they mean by saying that it is a question of the ontological status of numbers; the question whether or not numbers have a certain metaphysical characteristic called reality (but a kind of ideal reality, different from the material reality of the thing world) or subsistence or status of "independent entities." Unfortunately, these philosophers have so far not given a formulation of their question in terms of the common scientific language. Therefore our judgment must be that they have not succeeded in giving to the external question and to the possible answers any cognitive content. Unless and until they supply a clear cognitive interpretation, we are justified in our suspicion that their question is a pseudoquestion, that is, one disguised in the form of a theoretical question while in fact it is non-theoretical; in the present case it is the practical problem whether or not to incorporate into the language the new linguistic forms which constitute the framework of numbers.

*The system of propositions.* New variables, "$p$," "$q$," etc., are introduced with a rule to the effect that any (declarative) sentence may be substituted for a variable of this kind; this includes, in addition to the sentences of the original thing language, also all general sentences with variables of any kind which may have been introduced into the language. Further, the general term "proposition" is introduced. "$p$ is a proposition" may be defined by "$p$ or not $p$" (or by any other sentence form yielding only analytic sentences). Therefore, every sentence of the form ". . . is a proposition" (where any sentence may stand in the place of the dots) is analytic. This holds, for example, for the sentence:

(*a*)   "Chicago is large is a proposition."

(We disregard here the fact that the rules of English grammar require not a sentence but a that-clause as the subject of another sentence; accordingly, instead of (*a*) we should have to say "That Chicago is large is a proposition.") Predicates may be admitted whose argument expressions are sentences; these predicates may be either extensional (e.g., the customary truth-functional connectives) or not (e.g., modal predicates like "possible," "necessary," etc.). With the help of the new variables, general sentences may be formed, e.g.,

(*b*)   "For every *p*, either *p* or not-*p*."
(*c*)   "There is a *p* such that *p* is not necessary and not-*p* is not necessary."
(*d*)   "There is a *p* such that *p* is a proposition."

(*c*) and (*d*) are internal assertions of existence. The statement "There are propositions" may be meant in the sense of (*d*); in this case it is analytic (since it follows from (*a*)) and even trivial. If, however, the statement is meant in an external sense, then it is non-cognitive.

It is important to notice that the system of rules for the linguistic expressions of the propositional framework (of which only a few rules have here been briefly indicated) is sufficient for the introduction of the framework. Any further explanations as to the nature of the propositions (i.e., the elements of the system indicated, the values of the variables "*p*," "*q*," etc.) are theoretically unnecessary because, if correct, they follow from the rules. For example, are propositions mental events (as in Russell's theory)? A look at the rules shows us that they are not, because otherwise existential statements would be of the form: "If the mental state of the person in question fulfils such and such conditions, then there is a *p* such that . . . ." The fact that no references to mental conditions occur in existential statements (like (*c*), (*d*), etc.) shows that propositions are not mental entities. Further, a statement of the existence of linguistic entities (e.g., expressions, classes of expressions, etc.) must contain a reference to a language. The fact that no such reference occurs in the existential statements here, shows that propositions are not linguistic entities. The fact that in these statements no reference to a subject (an observer or knower) occurs (nothing like: "There is a *p* which is necessary for Mr. *X*"), shows that the propositions (and their properties, like necessity, etc.) are not subjective. Although characterizations of these or similar kinds are, strictly speaking, unnecessary, they may nevertheless be practically useful. If they are given, they should be understood, not as ingredient parts of the system, but merely as marginal notes with the purpose of supplying to the reader helpful hints or convenient pictorial associations which may make his learning of the use of the expressions easier than the bare system of the rules would do. Such a characterization is analogous to an extra-systematic explanation which a physicist sometimes gives to the beginner. He might, for example, tell him to imagine the atoms of a gas as small balls rushing around with great speed, or the electromagnetic field and its oscillations as quasi-elastic tensions and vibrations in an ether. In fact, however, all that can accurately be said about atoms or the field is implicitly contained in the physical laws of the theories in question.[2]

*The system of thing properties.* The thing language contains words like "red," "hard," "stone," "house," etc., which are used for describing what things are like. Now we may introduce new variables, say "*f*," "*g*," etc., for which those words are substitutable and furthermore the general term "property." New rules are laid down which admit sentences like "Red is a property," "Red is a color," "These two pieces of paper have at least one color in common" (i.e., "There is an *f* such that *f* is a color, and . . ."). The last sentence is an internal assertion. It is of an empirical, factual nature. However, the external statement, the philosophical statement of the reality of properties—a special case of the thesis of the reality of universals—is devoid of cognitive content.

*The systems of integers and rational numbers.* Into a language containing the framework of natural numbers we may introduce first the (positive and negative) integers as relations among natural numbers and then the rational numbers as relations among integers. This involves introducing new types of variables, expressions substitutable for them, and the general terms "integer" and "rational number."

[2] In my book *Meaning and Necessity* (Chicago, 1947) I have developed a semantical method which takes propositions as entities designated by sentences (more specifically, as intensions of sentences). In order to facilitate the understanding of the systematic development, I added some informal, extra-systematic explanations concerning the nature of propositions. I said that the term "proposition" "is used neither for a linguistic expression nor for a subjective, mental occurrence, but rather for something objective that may or may not be exemplified in nature. . . . We apply the term 'proposition' to any entities of a certain logical type, namely, those that may be expressed by (declarative) sentences in a language" (p. 27). After some more detailed discussions concerning the relation between propositions and facts, and the nature of false propositions, I added: "It has been the purpose of the preceding remarks to facilitate the understanding of our conception of propositions. If, however, a reader should find these explanations more puzzling than clarifying, or even unacceptable, he may disregard them" (p. 31) (that is, disregard these extra-systematic explanations, not the whole theory of the propositions as intensions of sentences, as one reviewer understood). In spite of this warning, it seems that some of those readers who were puzzled by the explanations, did not disregard them but thought that by raising objections against them they could refute the theory. This is analogous to the procedure of some laymen who by (correctly) criticizing the ether picture or other visualizations of physical theories, thought they had refuted those theories. Perhaps the discussions in the present paper will help in clarifying the role of the system of linguistic rules for the introduction of a framework for entities on the one hand, and that of extra-systematic explanations concerning the nature of the entities on the other.

*The system of real numbers.* On the basis of the rational numbers, the real numbers may be introduced as classes of a special kind (segments) of rational numbers (according to the method developed by Dedekind and Frege). Here again a new type of variables is introduced, expressions substitutable for them (e.g., "$\sqrt{2}$"), and the general term "real number."

*The spatio-temporal coordinate system for physics.* The new entities are the space-time points. Each is an ordered quadruple of four real numbers, called its coordinates, consisting of three spatial and one temporal coordinates. The physical state of a spatio-temporal point or region is described either with the help of qualitative predicates (e.g., "hot") or by ascribing numbers as values of a physical magnitude (e.g., mass, temperature, and the like). The step from the system of things (which does not contain space-time points but only extended objects with spatial and temporal relations between them) to the physical coordinate system is again a matter of decision. Our choice of certain features, although itself not theoretical, is suggested by theoretical knowledge, either logical or factual. For example, the choice of real numbers rather than rational numbers or integers as coordinates is not much influenced by the facts of experience but mainly due to considerations of mathematical simplicity. The restriction to rational coordinates would not be in conflict with any experimental knowledge we have, because the result of any measurement is a rational number. However, it would prevent the use of ordinary geometry (which says, e.g., that the diagonal of a square with the side 1 has the irrational value $\sqrt{2}$) and thus lead to great complications. On the other hand, the decision to use three rather than two or four spatial coordinates is strongly suggested, but still not forced upon us, by the result of common observations. If certain events allegedly observed in spiritualistic séances, e.g., a ball moving out of a sealed box, were confirmed beyond any reasonable doubt, it might seem advisable to use four spatial coordinates. Internal questions are here, in general, empirical questions to be answered by empirical investigations. On the other hand, the external questions of the reality of physical space and physical time are pseudo-questions. A question like "Are there (really) space-time points?" is ambiguous. It may be meant as an internal question; then the affirmative answer is, of course, analytic and trivial. Or it may be meant in the external sense: "Shall we introduce such and such forms into our language?"; in this case it is not a theoretical but a practical question, a matter of decision rather than assertion, and hence the proposed formulation would be misleading. Or finally, it may be meant in the following sense: "Are our experiences such that the use of the linguistic forms in question will be expedient and fruitful?" This is a theoretical question of a factual, empirical nature. But it concerns a matter of degree; therefore a formulation in the form "real or not?" would be inadequate.

## 3. WHAT DOES ACCEPTANCE OF A KIND OF ENTITIES MEAN?

Let us now summarize the essential characteristics of situations involving the introduction of a new kind of entities, characteristics which are common to the various examples outlined above.

The acceptance of a new kind of entities is represented in the language by the introduction of a framework of new forms of expressions to be used according to a new set of rules. There may be new names for particular entities of the kind in question; but some such names may already occur in the language before the introduction of the new framework. (Thus, for example, the thing language contains certainly words of the type of "blue" and "house" before the framework of properties is introduced; and it may contain words like "ten" in sentences of the form "I have ten fingers" before the framework of numbers is introduced.) The latter fact shows that the occurrence of constants of the type in question—regarded as names of entities of the new kind after the new framework is introduced—is not a sure sign of the acceptance of the new kind of entities. Therefore the introduction of such constants is not to be regarded as an essential step in the introduction of the framework. The two essential steps are rather the following. First, the introduction of a general term, a predicate of higher level, for the new kind of entities, permitting us to say of any particular entity that it belongs to this kind (e.g., "Red is a *property*," "Five is a *number*"). Second, the introduction of variables of the new type. The new entities are values of these variables; the constants (and the closed compound expressions, if any) are substitutable for the variables.[3] With the help of the variables, general sentences concerning the new entities can be formulated.

After the new forms are introduced into the language, it is possible to formulate with their help internal questions and possible answers to them. A question of this kind may be either empirical or logical; accordingly a true answer is either factually true or analytic.

From the internal questions we must clearly distinguish external questions, i.e., philosophical questions concerning the existence or reality of the total system of the new entities. Many philosophers regard a question of this kind as an ontological question which must be raised and answered *before* the introduction of the new language forms. The latter introduction, they believe, is legitimate only if it can be justified by an ontological insight supplying an affirmative answer to the question of reality. In con-

---

[3] W. V. Quine was the first to recognize the importance of the introduction of variables as indicating the acceptance of entities. "The ontology to which one's use of language commits him comprises simply the objects that he treats as falling . . . within the range of values of his variables." "Notes on Existence and Necessity," *Journal of Philosophy*, Vol. 40 (1943), pp. 113–127; compare also his "Designation and Existence," *Journal of Philosophy*, Vol. 36 (1939), pp. 702–709, and "On Universals," *The Journal of Symbolic Logic*, Vol. 12 (1947), pp. 74–84.

trast to this view, we take the position that the introduction of the new ways of speaking does not need any theoretical justification because it does not imply any assertion of reality. We may still speak (and have done so) of "the acceptance of the new entities" since this form of speech is customary; but one must keep in mind that this phrase does not mean for us anything more than acceptance of the new framework, i.e., of the new linguistic forms. Above all, it must not be interpreted as referring to an assumption, belief, or assertion of "the reality of the entities." There is no such assertion. An alleged statement of the reality of the system of entities is a pseudo-statement without cognitive content. To be sure, we have to face at this point an important question; but it is a practical, not a theoretical question; it is the question of whether or not to accept the new linguistic forms. The acceptance cannot be judged as being either true or false because it is not an assertion. It can only be judged as being more or less expedient, fruitful, conducive to the aim for which the language is intended. Judgments of this kind supply the motivation for the decision of accepting or rejecting the kind of entities.[4]

Thus it is clear that the acceptance of a linguistic framework must not be regarded as implying a metaphysical doctrine concerning the reality of the entities in question. It seems to me due to a neglect of this important distinction that some contemporary nominalists label the admission of variables of abstract types as "Platonism." [5] This is, to say the least, an extremely misleading terminology. It leads to the absurd consequence, that the position of everybody who accepts the language of physics with its real number variables (as a language of communication, not merely as a calculus) would be called Platonistic, even if he is a strict empiricist who rejects Platonic metaphysics.

A brief historical remark may here be inserted. The non-cognitive character of the questions which we have called here external questions was recognized and emphasized already by the Vienna Circle under the leader-

---

[4] For a closely related point of view on these questions see the detailed discussions in Herbert Feigl, "Existential Hypotheses," *Philosophy of Science*, 17 (1950), pp. 35–62.

[5] Paul Bernays, "Sur le platonisme dans les mathématiques" (*L'Enseignement math.*, 34 (1935), 52–69). W. V. Quine, see previous footnote and a recent paper "On What There Is," *Review of Metaphysics*, Vol. 2 (1948), pp. 21–38. Quine does not acknowledge the distinction which I emphasize above, because according to his general conception there are no sharp boundary lines between logical and factual truth, between questions of meaning and questions of fact, between the acceptance of a language structure and the acceptance of an assertion formulated in the language. This conception, which seems to deviate considerably from customary ways of thinking, is explained in his article "Semantics and Abstract Objects," *Proceedings* of the American Academy of Arts and Sciences, 80 (1951), 90–96. When Quine in the article "On What There Is," classifies my logistic conception of mathematics (derived from Frege and Russell) as "platonic realism" (p. 33), this is meant (according to a personal communication from him) not as ascribing to me agreement with Plato's metaphysical doctrine of universals, but merely as referring to the fact that I accept a language of mathematics containing variables of higher levels. With respect to the basic attitude to take in choosing a language form (an "ontology" in Quine's terminology, which seems to me misleading), there appears now to be agreement between us: "the obvious counsel is tolerance and an experimental spirit" ("On What There Is," p. 38).

ship of Moritz Schlick, the group from which the movement of logical empiricism originated. Influenced by ideas of Ludwig Wittgenstein, the Circle rejected both the thesis of the reality of the external world and the thesis of its irreality as pseudo-statements; [6] the same was the case for both the thesis of the reality of universals (abstract entities, in our present terminology) and the nominalistic thesis that they are not real and that their alleged names are not names of anything but merely *flatus vocis*. (It is obvious that the apparent negation of a pseudo-statement must also be a pseudo-statement.) It is therefore not correct to classify the members of the Vienna Circle as nominalists, as is sometimes done. However, if we look at the basic anti-metaphysical and pro-scientific attitude of most nominalists (and the same holds for many materialists and realists in the modern sense), disregarding their occasional pseudo-theoretical formulations, then it is, of course, true to say that the Vienna Circle was much closer to those philosophers than to their opponents.

## 4.   ABSTRACT ENTITIES IN SEMANTICS

The problem of the legitimacy and the status of abstract entities has recently again led to controversial discussions in connection with semantics. In a semantical meaning analysis certain expressions in a language are often said to designate (or name or denote or signify or refer to) certain extra-linguistic entities.[7] As long as physical things or events (e.g., Chicago or Caesar's death) are taken as designata (entities designated), no serious doubts arise. But strong objections have been raised, especially by some empiricists, against abstract entities as designata, e.g., against semantical statements of the following kind:

(1)   "The word 'red' designates a property of things";
(2)   "The word 'color' designates a property of properties of things";
(3)   "The word 'five' designates a number";
(4)   "The word 'odd' designates a property of numbers";
(5)   "The sentence 'Chicago is large' designates a proposition."

Those who criticize these statements do not, of course, reject the use of the expressions in question, like "red" or "five"; nor would they deny that

[6] See Carnap, *Scheinprobleme in der Philosophie; das Fremdpsychische und der Realismusstreit*, Berlin, 1928. Moritz Schlick, *Positivismus und Realismus*, reprinted in *Gesammelte Aufsätze*, Wien, 1938.

[7] See *Introduction to Semantics* (Cambridge, Massachusetts, 1942); *Meaning and Necessity* (Chicago, 1947). The distinction I have drawn in the latter book between the method of the name-relation and the method of intension and extension is not essential for our present discussion. The term "designation" is used in the present article in a neutral way; it may be understood as referring to the name-relation or to the intension-relation or to the extension-relation or to any similar relations used in other semantical methods.

these expressions are meaningful. But to be meaningful, they would say, is not the same as having a meaning in the sense of an entity designated. They reject the belief, which they regard as implicitly presupposed by those semantical statements, that to each expression of the types in question (adjectives like "red," numerals like "five," etc.) there is a particular real entity to which the expression stands in the relation of designation. This belief is rejected as incompatible with the basic principles of empiricism or of scientific thinking. Derogatory labels like "Platonic realism," "hypostatization," or " 'Fido'-Fido principle" are attached to it. The latter is the name given by Gilbert Ryle [8] to the criticized belief, which, in his view, arises by a naïve inference of analogy: just as there is an entity well known to me, viz. my dog Fido, which is designated by the name "Fido," thus there must be for every meaningful expression a particular entity to which it stands in the relation of designation or naming, i.e., the relation exemplified by "Fido"-Fido. The belief criticized is thus a case of hypostatization, i.e., of treating as names expressions which are not names. While "Fido" is a name, expressions like "red," "five," etc., are said not to be names, not to designate anything.

Our previous discussion concerning the acceptance of frameworks enables us now to clarify the situation with respect to abstract entities as designata. Let us take as an example the statement:

(*a*)   " 'Five' designates a number."

The formulation of this statement presupposes that our language L contains the forms of expressions which we have called the framework of numbers, in particular, numerical variables and the general term "number." If L contains these forms, the following is an analytic statement in L:

(*b*)   "Five is a number."

Further, to make the statement (*a*) possible, L must contain an expression like "designates" or "is a name of" for the semantical relation of designation. If suitable rules for this term are laid down, the following is likewise analytic:

(*c*)   " 'Five' designates five."

(Generally speaking, any expression of the form " '. . .' designates . . ." is an analytic statement provided the term ". . ." is a constant in an accepted framework. If the latter condition is not fulfilled, the expression is not a statement.) Since (*a*) follows from (*c*) and (*b*), (*a*) is likewise analytic.

Thus it is clear that *if* someone accepts the framework of numbers, then he must acknowledge (*c*) and (*b*) and hence (*a*) as true statements. Gen-

[8] Gilbert Ryle, "Meaning and Necessity," *Philosophy*, 24 (1949), 69–76.

erally speaking, if someone accepts a framework for a certain kind of entities, then he is bound to admit the entities as possible designata. Thus the question of the admissibility of entities of a certain type or of abstract entities in general as designata is reduced to the question of the acceptability of the linguistic framework for those entities. Both the nominalistic critics, who refuse the status of designators or names to expressions like "red," "five," etc., because they deny the existence of abstract entities, and the skeptics, who express doubts concerning the existence and demand evidence for it, treat the question of existence as a theoretical question. They do, of course, not mean the internal question; the affirmative answer to *this* question is analytic and trivial and too obvious for doubt or denial, as we have seen. Their doubts refer rather to the system of entities itself; hence they mean the external question. They believe that only after making sure that there really is a system of entities of the kind in question are we justified in accepting the framework by incorporating the linguistic forms into our language. However, we have seen that the external question is not a theoretical question but rather the practical question whether or not to accept those linguistic forms. This acceptance is not in need of a theoretical justification (except with respect to expediency and fruitfulness), because it does not imply a belief or assertion. Ryle says that the "Fido"-Fido principle is "a grotesque theory." Grotesque or not, Ryle is wrong in calling it a theory. It is rather the practical decision to accept certain frameworks. Maybe Ryle is historically right with respect to those whom he mentions as previous representatives of the principle, viz. John Stuart Mill, Frege, and Russell. If these philosophers regarded the acceptance of a system of entities as a theory, an assertion, they were victims of the same old, metaphysical confusion. But it is certainly wrong to regard *my* semantical method as involving a belief in the reality of abstract entities, since I reject a thesis of this kind as a metaphysical pseudo-statement.

The critics of the use of abstract entities in semantics overlook the fundamental difference between the acceptance of a system of entities and an internal assertion, e.g., an assertion that there are elephants or electrons or prime numbers greater than a million. Whoever makes an internal assertion is certainly obliged to justify it by providing evidence, empirical evidence in the case of electrons, logical proof in the case of the prime numbers. The demand for a theoretical justification, correct in the case of internal assertions, is sometimes wrongly applied to the acceptance of a system of entities. Thus, for example, Ernest Nagel in his review [9] asks for "evidence relevant for affirming with warrant that there are such entities as infinitesimals or propositions." He characterizes the evidence required in these cases—in distinction to the empirical evidence in the case of electrons—as "in the broad sense logical and dialectical." Beyond this no hint is given as to what might be regarded as relevant evidence. Some

[9] Ernest Nagel, "Review of *Meaning and Necessity*," *Journal of Philosophy*, **45** (1948), 467–72.

nominalists regard the acceptance of abstract entities as a kind of super-stition or myth, populating the world with fictitious or at least dubious entities, analogous to the belief in centaurs or demons. This shows again the confusion mentioned, because a superstition or myth is a false (or dubious) internal statement.

Let us take as example the natural numbers as cardinal numbers, i.e., in contexts like "Here are three books." The linguistic forms of the frame-work of numbers, including variables and the general term "number," are generally used in our common language of communication; and it is easy to formulate explicit rules for their use. Thus the logical characteristics of this framework are sufficiently clear (while many internal questions, i.e., arithmetical questions, are, of course, still open). In spite of this, the con-troversy concerning the external question of the ontological reality of the system of numbers continues. Suppose that one philosopher says: "I be-lieve that there are numbers as real entities. This gives me the right to use the linguistic forms of the numerical framework and to make semantical statements about numbers as designata of numerals." His nominalistic opponent replies: "You are wrong; there are no numbers. The numerals may still be used as meaningful expressions. But they are not names, there are no entities designated by them. Therefore the word "number" and numerical variables must not be used (unless a way were found to intro-duce them as merely abbreviating devices, a way of translating them into the nominalistic thing language)." I cannot think of any possible evidence that would be regarded as relevant by both philosophers, and therefore, if actually found, would decide the controversy or at least make one of the opposite theses more probable than the other. (To construe the numbers as classes or properties of the second level, according to the Frege-Russell method, does, of course, not solve the controversy, because the first philosopher would affirm and the second deny the existence of the system of classes or properties of the second level.) Therefore I feel compelled to regard the external question as a pseudo-question, until both parties to the controversy offer a common interpretation of the question as a cognitive question; this would involve an indication of possible evidence regarded as relevant by both sides.

There is a particular kind of misinterpretation of the acceptance of ab-stract entities in various fields of science and in semantics, that needs to be cleared up. Certain early British empiricists (e.g., Berkeley and Hume) denied the existence of abstract entities on the ground that immediate experience presents us only with particulars, not with universals, e.g., with this red patch, but not with Redness or Color-in-General; with this scalene triangle, but not with Scalene Triangularity or Triangularity-in-General. Only entities belonging to a type of which examples were to be found within immediate experience could be accepted as ultimate constituents of reality. Thus, according to this way of thinking, the existence of abstract entities could be asserted only if one could show either that some abstract entities fall within the given, or that abstract entities can be defined in terms of the types of entity which are given. Since these empiricists found no abstract entities within the realm of sense-data, they either denied their existence, or else made a futile attempt to define universals in terms of particulars. Some contemporary philosophers, especially English philosophers following Bertrand Russell, think in basically similar terms. They emphasize a distinction between the data (that which is immediately given in consciousness, e.g., sense-data, immediately past experiences, etc.) and the constructs based on the data. Existence or reality is ascribed only to the data; the constructs are not real entities; the corresponding linguistic expressions are merely ways of speech not actually designating anything (reminiscent of the nominalists' *flatus vocis*). We shall not criticize here this general conception. (As far as it is a principle of accepting certain entities and not accepting others, leaving aside any ontological, phenomenalistic and nominalistic pseudo-statements, there cannot be any theoretical objection to it.) But if this conception leads to the view that other philosophers or scientists who accept abstract entities thereby assert or imply their occurrence as immediate data, then such a view must be rejected as a misinterpretation. References to space-time points, the electromagnetic field, or electrons in physics, to real or complex numbers and their functions in mathematics, to the excitatory potential or unconscious complexes in psychology, to an inflationary trend in economics, and the like, do not imply the assertion that entities of these kinds occur as immediate data. And the same holds for references to abstract entities as designata in semantics. Some of the criticisms by English philosophers against such references give the impression that, probably due to the misinterpretation just indicated, they accuse the semanticist not so much of bad metaphysics (as some nominalists would do) but of bad psychology. The fact that they regard a semantical method involving abstract entities not merely as doubtful and perhaps wrong, but as manifestly absurd, preposterous and grotesque, and that they show a deep horror and indignation against this method, is perhaps to be explained by a misinterpretation of the kind described. In fact, of course, the semanticist does not in the least assert or imply that the abstract entities to which he refers can be experienced as immediately given either by sensation or by a kind of rational intuition. An assertion of this kind would indeed be very dubious psychology. The psychological question as to which kinds of entities do and which do not occur as immediate data is entirely irrelevant for semantics, just as it is for physics, mathematics, economics, etc., with respect to the examples mentioned above.[10]

---

[10] Wilfrid Sellars ("Acquaintance and Description Again", in *Journal of Philos.*, 46 (1949), 496–504; see pp. 502 f.) analyzes clearly the roots of the mistake "of taking the designation relation of semantic theory to be a reconstruction of *being present to an experience*."

## 5.  CONCLUSION

For those who want to develop or use semantical methods, the decisive question is not the alleged ontological question of the existence of abstract entities but rather the question whether the use of abstract linguistic forms or, in technical terms, the use of variables beyond those for things (or phenomenal data), is expedient and fruitful for the purposes for which semantical analyses are made, viz. the analysis, interpretation, clarification, or construction of languages of communication, especially languages of science. This question is here neither decided nor even discussed. It is not a question simply of yes or no, but a matter of degree. Among those philosophers who have carried out semantical analyses and thought about suitable tools for this work, beginning with Plato and Aristotle and, in a more technical way on the basis of modern logic, with C. S. Peirce and Frege, a great majority accepted abstract entities. This does, of course, not prove the case. After all, semantics in the technical sense is still in the initial phases of its development, and we must be prepared for possible fundamental changes in methods. Let us therefore admit that the nominalistic critics may possibly be right. But if so, they will have to offer better arguments than they have so far. Appeal to ontological insight will not carry much weight. The critics will have to show that it is possible to construct a semantical method which avoids all references to abstract entities and achieves by simpler means essentially the same results as the other methods.

The acceptance or rejection of abstract linguistic forms, just as the acceptance or rejection of any other linguistic forms in any branch of science, will finally be decided by their efficiency as instruments, the ratio of the results achieved to the amount and complexity of the efforts required. To decree dogmatic prohibitions of certain linguistic forms instead of testing them by their success or failure in practical use, is worse than futile; it is positively harmful because it may obstruct scientific progress. The history of science shows examples of such prohibitions based on prejudices deriving from religious, mythological, metaphysical, or other irrational sources, which slowed up the developments for shorter or longer periods of time. Let us learn from the lessons of history. Let us grant to those who work in any special field of investigation the freedom to use any form of expression which seems useful to them; the work in the field will sooner or later lead to the elimination of those forms which have no useful function. *Let us be cautious in making assertions and critical in examining them, but tolerant in permitting linguistic forms.*

# THE NEED FOR ABSTRACT ENTITIES
# IN SEMANTIC ANALYSIS*

ALONZO CHURCH (1903–      ) of Princeton University has been
one of the major contributors to symbolic logic in this
century. He has been editor of *The Journal of Symbolic Logic*
since it began publication in 1936. Among his major
publications are A *Bibliography of Symbolic Logic, The
Calculi of Lambda-Conversion,* and *Introduction to
Mathematical Logic.*

We distinguish between a *logistic system* and a *formalized language* on the basis that the former is an abstractly formulated calculus for which no interpretation is fixed, and thus has a syntax but no semantics; but the latter is a logistic system together with an assignment of meanings to its expressions.

As primitive basis of a logistic system it suffices to give, in familiar fashion: (1) The list of primitive symbols or *vocabulary* of the system (together usually with a classification of the primitive symbols into categories, which will be used in stating the formation rules and rules of inference). (2) The *formation rules,* determining which finite sequences of primitive symbols are to be *well-formed* expressions, determining certain categories of well-formed expressions—among which we shall assume that at least the category of *sentence* is included—, and determining (in case *variables* are included among the primitive symbols) which occurrences of variables in a well-formed expression are *free* occurrences and which are *bound* occurrences.[1] (3) The transformation rules or *rules of inference,* by which from the *assertion* of certain sentences (the *premisses,* finite in number) a certain sentence (the *conclusion*) may be *inferred.* (4) Certain asserted sentences, the *axioms.*

In order to obtain a formalized language it is necessary to add, to these *syntactical rules* of the logistic system, *semantical rules* assigning meanings (in some sense) to the well-formed expressions of the system.[2] The character of the semantical rules will depend on the theory of meaning adopted, and this in turn must be justified by the purpose which it is to serve.

---

* Reprinted by kind permission of author, publisher, and Kraus Reprint Corporation, from *American Academy of Arts and Sciences Proceedings,* Vol. 80, 1951, pp. 100–112.

[1] For convenience of the present brief exposition we make the simplifying assumption that sentences are without free variables, and that only sentences are asserted.

[2] The possibility that the meaningful expressions may be a proper subclass of the well-formed expressions must not ultimately be excluded. But again for the present sketch it will be convenient to treat the two classes as identical—the simplest and most usual case. Compare, however, footnote 13.

Let us take it as our purpose to provide an abstract theory of the actual use of language for human communication—not a factual or historical report of what has been observed to take place, but a norm to which we may regard every-day linguistic behavior as an imprecise approximation, in the same way that e.g., elementary (applied) geometry is a norm to which we may regard as imprecise approximations the practical activity of the land-surveyor in laying out a plot of ground, or of the construction foreman in seeing that building plans are followed. We must demand of such a theory that it have a place for all observably informative kinds of communication—including such notoriously troublesome cases as belief statements, modal statements, conditions contrary to fact—or at least that it provide a (theoretically) workable substitute for them. And solutions must be available for puzzles about meaning which may arise, such as the so-called "paradox of analysis."

There exist more than one theory of meaning showing some promise of fulfilling these requirements, at least so far as the formulation and development have presently been carried. But the theory of Frege seems to recommend itself above others for its relative simplicity, naturalness, and explanatory power—or, as I would advocate, Frege's theory as modified by elimination of his somewhat problematical notion of a function (and in particular of a *Begriff*) as *ungesättigt*, and by some other changes which bring it closer to present logistic practice without loss of such essentials as the distinction of sense and denotation.

This modified Fregean theory may be roughly characterized by the tendency to minimize the category of *syncategorematic* notations—i.e., notations to which no meaning at all is ascribed in isolation but which may combine with one or more meaningful expressions to form a meaningful expression [3]—and to reduce the categories of meaningful expressions to two, (proper) *names* and *forms*, for each of which two kinds of meaning are distinguished in a parallel way.

A name, or a *constant* (as we shall also say, imitating mathematical terminology), has first its *denotation*, or that of which it is a name.[4] And each name has also a *sense*—which is perhaps more properly to be called its meaning, since it is held that complete understanding of a language involves the ability to recognize the sense of any name in the language, but does not demand any knowledge beyond this of the denotations of names.

---

[3] Such notations can be reduced to at most two, namely the notation (consisting, say, of juxtaposition between parentheses) which is used in application of a singulary function to its argument, and the abstraction operator λ. By the methods of the Schönfinkel-Curry combinatory logic it may even be possible further to eliminate the abstraction operator, and along with it the use of variables altogether. But this final reduction is not contemplated here—nor even necessarily the simpler reduction to two syncategorematic notations.

[4] The complicating possibility is here ignored of *denotationless names*, or names which have a sense but no denotation. For though it may be held that these do occur in the natural languages, it is possible, as Frege showed, to construct a formalized language in such a way as to avoid them.

(Declarative) *sentences,* in particular, are taken as a kind of names, the denotation being the *truth-value* of the sentence, *truth* or *falsehood,* and the sense being the *proposition* which the sentence expresses.

A name is said to *denote* its denotation and to *express* its sense, and the sense is said to be *a concept of* the denotation. The abstract entities which serve as senses of names let us call *concepts*—although this use of the word 'concept' has no analogue in the writings of Frege, and must be carefully distinguished from Frege's use of 'Begriff.' Thus anything which is or is capable of being the sense of some name in some language, actual or possible, is a concept.[5] The terms *individual concept, function concept,* and the like are then to mean a concept which is a concept of an individual, of a function, etc. A *class concept* may be identified with a *property,* and a *truth-value concept* (as already indicated) with a proposition.

Names are to be meaningful expressions without free variables, and expressions which are analogous to names except that they contain free variables, we call forms (a rather wide extension of the ordinary mathematical usage, here adopted for lack of a better term).[6] Each variable has a *range,* which is the class of admissible *values* of the variable.[7] And analogous to the denotation of a name, a form has a *value* for every system of admissible values of its free variables.[8]

The assignment of a value to a variable, though it is not a syntactical operation, corresponds in a certain way to the syntactical operation of substituting a constant for the variable. The denotation of the substituted constant represents the value of the variable.[9] And the sense of the substituted constant may be taken as representing a *sense-value* of the variable. Thus every variable has, besides its range, also a *sense-range,* which is the class of admissible sense-values of the variable. And analogous to the sense of a name, a form has a *sense-value* for every system of admissible sense-values of its free variables.[10]

---

[5] This is meant only as a preliminary rough description. In logical order, the notion of a concept must be postulated and that of a possible language defined by means of it.

[6] Frege's term in German is *Marke.*—The form or *Marke* must of course not be confused with its associated abstract entity, the *function.* The function differs from the form in that it is not a linguistic entity, and belongs to no particular language. Indeed the same function may be associated with different forms; and if there is more than one free variable the same form may have several associated functions. But in some languages it is possible from the form to construct a name (or names) of the associated function (or functions) by means of an abstraction operator.

[7] The idea of allowing variables of different ranges is not Fregean, except in the case of functions in Frege's sense (i.e., as *ungesättigt*), the different categories of which appear as ranges for different variables. The introduction of *Gegenstandsbuchstaben* with restricted ranges is one of the modifications here advocated in Frege's theory.

[8] Exceptions to this are familiar in common mathematical notation. E.g. the form $x / y$ has no value for the system of values 0,0 of $x$, $y$. However, the semantics of a language is much simplified if a value is assigned to a form for every system of values of the free variables which are admissible in the sense that each value belongs to the range of the corresponding variable. And for purposes of the present exposition we assume that this has been done. (Compare footnote 4.)

[9] Even if the language contains no constant denoting the value in question, it is possible to consider an extension of the language obtained by adjoining such a constant.

[10] The notion of a sense-value of a form is not introduced by Frege, at least not

The following principles are assumed.[11] (i) Every concept is a concept of at most one thing. (ii) Every constant has a unique concept as its sense. (iii) Every variable has a non-empty class of concepts as its sense-range. (iv) For any assignment of sense-values, one to each of the free variables of a given form, if each sense-value is admissible in the sense that it belongs to the sense-range of the corresponding variable, the form has a unique concept as its sense-value. (v) The denotation of a constant· is that of which its sense is a concept. (vi) The range of a variable is the class of those things of which the members of the sense-range are concepts. (vii) If S, $s_1, s_2, \ldots, s_m$ are concepts of A, $a_1, a_2, \ldots, a_m$ respectively, and if S is the sense-value of a form F for the system of sense-values $s_1, s_2, \ldots, s_m$ of its free variables $x_1, x_2, \ldots, x_m$, then the value of F for the system of values $a_1, a_2, \ldots a_m$ of $x_1, x_2, \ldots, x_m$ is A. (viii) If C′ is obtained from a constant C by replacing a particular occurrence of a constant c by a constant c′ that has the same sense as c, then C′ is a constant having the same sense as C.[12] (ix) If C′ is obtained from a constant C by replacing a

explicitly, but it can be argued that it is necessarily implicit in his theory. For Frege's question, "How can a=b if true ever differ in meaning from a=a?" can be asked as well for forms a and b as for constants, and leads to the distinction of value and sense-value of a form just as it does to the distinction of denotation and sense of a constant. Even in a language like that of *Principia Mathematica*, having no forms other than propositional forms, a parallel argument can be used to show that from the equivalence of two propositional forms A and B the identity in meaning of A and B in all respects is not to be inferred. For otherwise how could A ≡ B if true (i.e., true for all values of the variables) ever differ in meaning from A ≡ A?

[11] For purposes of the preliminary sketch, the meta-language is left unformalized, and such questions are ignored as whether the meta-language shall conform to the theory of types or to some alternative such as transfinite type theory or axiomatic set theory. Because of the extreme generality which is attempted in laying down these principles, it is clear that there may be some difficulty in rendering them precise (in their full attempted generality) by restatement in a formalized meta-language. But it should be possible to state the semantical rules of a particular object language so as to conform, so that the principles are clarified to this extent by illustration.

It is not meant that the list of principles is necessarily complete or in final form, but rather a tentative list is here proposed for study and possible amendment. Moreover it is not meant that it may not be possible to formulate a language not conforming to the principles, but only that a satisfactory general theory may result by making conformity to these principles a part of the definition of a formalized language (compare footnote 12).

[12] In the case of some logistic systems which have been proposed (e.g., by Hilbert and Bernays), if semantical rules are to be added, in conformity with the theory here described and with the informally intended interpretation of the system, it is found to be impossible to satisfy (viii), (x), and (xiv), because of restriction imposed on the bound variables which may appear in a constant or form used in a particular context. But it would seem that modifications in the logistic system necessary to remove the restriction may reasonably be considered non-essential, and that in this sense (viii), (x), (xiv) may still be maintained.

In regard to all of the principles it should be understood that non-essential modifications in existing logistic systems may be required to make them conform. In particular the principles have been formulated in a way which does not contemplate the distinction in typographical style between free and bound variables that appears in systems of Frege and of Hilbert-Bernays.

In (x) and (xi), the condition that f′ have the same free variables as f can in many cases be weakened to the condition that every free variable of f′ occur also as a free variable of f.

particular occurrence of a constant c by a constant c′ that has the same denotation as c, then C′ is a constant having the same denotation as C.[13] (x) If C′ is obtained from a constant C by replacing a particular occurrence of a form f by a form f′ that has the same free variables as f, and if, for every admissible system of sense-values of their free variables, f and f′ have the same sense-value, then C′ is a constant having the same sense as C.[12] (xi) If C′ is obtained from a constant C by replacing a particular occurrence of a form f by a form f′ that has the same free variables as f, and if, for every system of values of their free variables which are admissible in the sense that each value belongs to the range of the corresponding variable, f and f′ have the same value, then C′ is a constant having the same denotation as C.[13] (xii) If $x_1$, $x_2$, . . . , $x_m$ are all the distinct variables occurring (necessarily as bound variables) in a constant C, if $y_1$, $y_2$, . . . , $y_m$ are distinct variables having the same sense-ranges as $x_1$, $x_2$, . . . , $x_m$ respectively, and if C′ is obtained from C by substituting $y_1$, $y_2$, . . . , $y_m$ throughout for $x_1$, $x_2$, . . . , $x_m$ respectively, then C′ is a constant having the same sense as C. (xiii) If $x_1$, $x_2$, . . . , $x_m$ are the distinct variables occurring in a constant C, if $y_1$, $y_2$, . . . , $y_m$ are distinct variables having the same ranges as $x_1$, $x_2$, . . . , $x_m$ respectively, and if C′ is obtained from C by substituting $y_1$, $y_2$, . . . , $y_m$ throughout for $x_1$, $x_2$, . . . , $x_m$ respectively, then C′ is a constant having the same denotation as C. (xiv) The result of substituting constants for all the free variables of a form is a constant, if the sense of each substituted constant belongs to the sense-range of the corresponding variable.[12] (xv) The sense of a constant C thus obtained by substituting constants $c_1$, $c_2$, . . . , $c_m$ for the free variables $x_1$, $x_2$, . . . , $x_m$ of a form F is the same as the sense-value of F when the senses of $c_1$, $c_2$, . . . , $c_m$ are assigned as the sense-values of $x_1$, $x_2$, . . . , $x_m$.

To these must still be added principles which are similar to (viii)–(xv), except that substitution is made in forms instead of constants, or that forms and variables as well as constants are substituted for the free variables of a form. Instead of stating these here, it may be sufficient to remark that they follow if arbitrary extensions of the language are allowed by adjoining (as primitive symbols) constants which have as their senses any concepts that belong to sense-ranges of variables in the language, if the foregoing

[13] Possibly (ix) and (xi) should be weakened to require only that if C′ is well-formed then it is a constant having the same denotation as C. Since there is in general no syntactical criterion by which to ascertain whether two constants c and c′ have the same denotation, or whether two forms have always the same values, there is the possibility that the stronger forms of (ix) and (xi) might lead to difficulty in some cases. However, (ix) as here stated has the effect of preserving fully the rule of substitutivity of equality —where the equality sign is so interpreted that [$c_1 = c_2$] is a sentence denoting truth if and only if $c_1$ and $c_2$ are constants having the same denotation—and if in some formalized languages, (ix) and (xi) should prove to be inconsistent with the requirement that every well-formed expression be meaningful (footnote 2), it may be preferable to abandon the latter. Indeed the preservation of the rule of substitutivity of equality may be regarded as an important advantage of a Fregean theory of meaning over some of the alternatives that suggest themselves.

principles are assumed to hold also for such extensions of the language, and if there is assumed further: (xvi) Let an expression F contain the variables $x_1$, $x_2$, . . . , $x_m$; and suppose that in every extension of the language of the kind just described and for every substitution of constants $c_1$, $c_2$, . . . , $c_m$ for the variables $x_1$, $x_2$, . . . , $x_m$ respectively, if the sense of each constant belongs to the sense-range of the corresponding variable, F becomes a constant; then F is a form having $x_1$, $x_2$, . . . , $x_m$ as its free variables.

To those who find forbidding the array of abstract entities and principles concerning them which is here proposed, I would say that the problems which give rise to the proposal are difficult and a simpler theory is not known to be possible.[14]

To those who object to the introduction of abstract entities at all I would say that I believe that there are more important criteria by which a theory should be judged. The extreme demand for a simple prohibition of abstract entities under all circumstances perhaps arises from a desire to maintain the connection between theory and observation. But the pref-

[14] At the present stage it cannot be said with assurance that a modification of Frege's theory will ultimately prove to be the best or the simplest. Alternative theories demanding study are: the theory of Russell, which relies on the elimination of names by contextual definition to an extent sufficient to render the distinction of sense and denotation unnecessary; the modification of Russell's theory, briefly suggested by Smullyan (in *The Journal of Symbolic Logic*, vol. 13 (1948), pp. 31–37), according to which descriptive phrases are to be considered as actually contained in the logistic system rather than being (in the phrase of Whitehead and Russell) "mere typographical conveniences," but are to differ from names in that they retain their need for scope indicators; and finally, the theory of Carnap's *Meaning and Necessity*.

Though the Russell theory has an element of simplicity in avoiding the distinction of two kinds of meaning, it leads to complications of its own of a different sort, in connection with the matter of scope of descriptions. The same should be said of Smullyan's proposed modification of the theory. And the distinctions of scope become especially important in modal statements, where they cannot be eliminated by the convention of always taking the minimum scope, as Smullyan has shown (loc. cit.).

Moreover, in its present form it would seem that the Russell theory requires some supplementation. For example, 'I am thinking of Pegasus,' 'Ponce de Leon searched for the fountain of youth,' 'Barbara Villiers was less chaste than Diana' cannot be analyzed as '$(Ec)$ [x is a Pegasus $\equiv_x x{=}c$] [I am thinking of c],' '$(Ec)$ [x is a fountain of youth $\equiv_x x{=}c$] [Ponce de Leon searched for c],' '$(Ec)$ [x is a Diana $\equiv_x x{=}c$] [Barbara Villiers was less chaste than c]' respectively—if only because of the (probable or possible) difference of truth-value between the given statements and their proposed analyses. On a Fregean theory of meaning the given statements might be analyzed as being about the individual concepts of Pegasus, of the fountain of youth, and of Diana rather than about some certain winged horse, some certain fountain, and some certain goddess. For the Russell theory it might be suggested to analyze them as being about the property of being a Pegasus, the property of being a fountain of youth, and the property of being a Diana. This analysis in terms of properties would also be possible on a Fregean theory, though perhaps slightly less natural. On a theory of the Russell type the difficulty arises that names of properties seem to be required, and on pain of readmitting Frege's puzzle about equality (which leads to the distinction of sense and denotation in connection with names of any kind), such names of properties either must be analyzed away by contextual definition—it is not clear how—or must be so severely restricted that two names of the same property cannot occur unless trivially synonymous.

erence of (say) *seeing* over *understanding* as a method of observation seems to me capricious. For just as an opaque body may be seen, so a concept may be understood or grasped. And the parallel between the two cases is indeed rather close. In both cases the observation is not direct but through intermediaries—light, lens of eye or optical instrument, and retina in the case of the visible body, linguistic expressions in the case of the concept. And in both cases there are or may be tenable theories according to which the entity in question, opaque body or concept, is not assumed, but only those things which would otherwise be called its effects.

The variety of entities (whether abstract or concrete) which a theory assumes is indeed one among other criteria by which it may be judged. If multiplication of entities is found beyond the needs of the workability, simplicity, and generality of the theory, then the razor shall be applied.[15] The theory of meaning here outlined I hold exempt from such treatment no more than any other, but I do advocate its study.

Let us return now to our initial question, as to the character of the semantical rules which are to be added to the syntactical rules of a logistic system in order to define a particular formalized language.

On the foregoing theory of meaning the semantical rules must include at least the following: (5) *Rules of sense,* by which a sense is determined for each well-formed expression without free variables (all such expressions thus becoming names). (6) *Rules of sense-range,* assigning to each variable a sense-range. (7) *Rules of sense-value,* by which a sense-value is determined for every well-formed expression containing free variables and every admissible system of sense-values of its free variables (all such expressions thus becoming forms).

[15] Here a warning is necessary against spurious economies, since not every subtraction from the entities which a theory assumes is a reduction in the variety of entities.

For example, in the simple theory of types it is well known that the individuals may be dispensed with if classes and relations of all types are retained; or one may abandon also classes and relations of the lowest type, retaining only those of higher type. In fact any finite number of levels at the bottom of the hierarchy of types may be deleted. But this is no reduction in the variety of entities, because the truncated hierarchy of types, by appropriate deletions of entities in each type, can be made isomorphic to the original hierarchy—and indeed the continued adequacy of the truncated hierarchy to the original purposes depends on this isomorphism.

Similarly the idea may suggest itself to admit the distinction of sense and denotation at the $n$th level and above in the hierarchy of types, but below the $n$th level to deny this distinction and to adopt instead Russell's device of contextual elimination of names. The entities assumed would thus include only the usual extensional entities below the $n$th level, but at the $n$th level and above they would include also concepts, concepts of concepts, and so on. However, this is no reduction in the variety of entities assumed, as compared to the theory which assumes at all levels in the hierarchy of types not only the extensional entities but also concepts of them, concepts of concepts of them, and so on. For the entities assumed by the former theory are reduced again to isomorphism with those assumed by the latter, if all entities below the $n$th level are deleted and appropriate deletions are made in every type at the $n$th level and above.

Some one may object that the notion of isomorphism is irrelevant which is here introduced, and insist that any subtraction from the entities assumed by a theory must be considered a simplification. But to such objector I would reply that his proposal leads (in the cases just named, and others) to perpetual oscillation between two theories $T_1$ and $T_2$, $T_1$ being reduced to $T_2$ and $T_2$ to $T_1$ by successive "simplifications" *ad infinitum.*

In the case of both syntactical and semantical rules there is a distinction to be drawn between *primitive* and *derived* rules, the primitive rules being those which are stated in giving the primitive basis of the formalized language, and the derived rules being rules of similar kind which follow as consequences of the primitive rules. Thus besides primitive rules of inference there are also derived rules of inference, besides primitive rules of sense also derived rules of sense, and so on. (But instead of "derived axioms" it is usual to say *theorems.*)

A statement of the denotation of a name, the range of a variable, or the value of a form does not necessarily belong to the semantics of a language. For example, that 'the number of planets' denotes the number nine is a fact as much of astronomy as it is of the semantics of the English language, and can be described only as belonging to a discipline broad enough to include both semantics and astronomy. On the other hand, a statement that 'the number of planets' denotes the number of planets is a purely semantical statement about the English language. And indeed it would seem that a statement of this kind may be considered as purely semantical only if it is a consequence of the rules of sense, sense-range, and sense-value, together with the syntactical rules and the general principles of meaning (i)–(xvi).

Thus as derived semantical rules rather than primitive, there will be also: (8) *Rules of denotation,* by which a denotation is determined for each name. (9) *Rules of range,* assigning to each variable a range. (10) *Rules of value,* by which a value is determined for every form and for every admissible system of values of its free variables.

By stating (8), (9), and (10) as primitive rules, without (5), (6), and (7) there results what may be called the *extensional part* of the semantics of a language. The remaining *intensional part* of the semantics does not follow from the extensional part. For the sense of a name is not uniquely determined by its denotation, and thus a particular rule of denotation does not of itself have as a consequence the corresponding rule of sense.

On the other hand, because the meta-linguistic phrase which is used in the rule of denotation must itself have a sense, there is a certain sense (though not that of logical consequence) in which the rule of denotation, by being given as a primitive rule of denotation, uniquely indicates the corresponding rule of sense. Since the like is true of the rules of range and rules of value, it is permissible to say that we have fixed an *interpretation* of a given logistic system, and thus a formalized language, if we have stated only the extensional part of the semantics.[16]

Although all the foregoing account has been concerned with the case of a formalized language, I would go on to say that in my opinion there is no difference in principle between this case and that of one of the natural languages. In particular, it must not be thought that a formalized language

[16] As is done in the . . . revised edition of my *Introduction to Mathematical Logic,* Part I.

depends for its meaning or its justification (in any sense in which a natural language does not) upon some prior natural language, say English, through some system of translation of its sentences into English—or, more plausibly, through the statement of its syntactical and semantical rules in English. For speaking in principle, and leaving all questions of practicality aside, the logician must declare it a mere historical accident that you and I learned from birth to speak English rather than a language with less irregular, and logically simpler, syntactical rules, similar to those of one of the familiar logistic systems in use today—or that we learned in school the content of conventional English grammars and dictionaries rather than a more precise statement of a system of syntactical and semantical rules of the kind which has been described in this present sketch. The difference of a formalized language from a natural language lies not in any matter of principle, but in the degree of completeness that has been attained in the laying down of explicit syntactical and semantical rules and the extent to which vaguenesses and uncertainties have been removed from them.

For this reason the English language itself may be used as a convenient though makeshift illustration of a language for which syntactical and semantical rules are to be given. Of course only a few illustrative examples of such rules can be given in brief space. And even for this it is necessary to avoid carefully the use of examples involving English constructions that raise special difficulties or show too great logical irregularities, and to evade the manifold equivocacy of English words by selecting and giving attention to just one meaning of each word mentioned. It must also not be asked whether the rules given as examples are among the "true" rules of the English language or are "really" a part of what is implied in an understanding of English; for the laying down of rules for a natural language, because of the need to fill gaps and to decide doubtful points, is as much a process of legislation as of reporting.

With these understandings, and with no attempt made to distinguish between primitive and derived rules, following are some examples of syntactical and semantical rules of English according to the program which has been outlined.[17]

(1)   Vocabulary: 'equals' 'five' 'four' 'if' 'is' 'nine' 'number' 'of' 'planet' 'planets' 'plus' 'round' 'the' 'then' 'the world'—besides the bare list of primitive symbols (words) there must be statements regarding their classification into categories and systematic relations among them, e.g., that 'planet' is a common noun,[18] that 'planets' is the

---

[17] For convenience, English is used also as the meta-language, although this gives a false appearance of triviality or obviousness to some of the semantical rules. Since the purpose is only illustrative, the danger of semantical antinomies is ignored.

[18] For present illustrative purposes the question may be avoided whether common nouns in English, in the singular, shall be considered to be variables (e.g., 'planet' or 'a planet' as a variable having planets as its range), or to be class names (e.g., 'planet' as a proper name of the class of planets), or to have "no status at all in a logical grammar" (see Quine's *Methods of Logic*, p. 207), or perhaps to vary from one of these uses to another according to context.

plural of 'planet,' [19] that 'the world' is a proper noun, that 'round' is
an adjective.

(2)  Formation Rules: If A is the plural of a common noun, then 'the'
⌢'number'⌢'of'⌢A is a singular term. A proper noun standing
alone is a singular term. If A and B are singular terms, then A⌢
'equals'⌢B is a sentence. If A is a singular term and B is an adjective,
then A⌢'is'⌢B is a sentence.[20] If A and B are sentences, then 'if'
⌢A⌢'then'⌢B is a sentence.—Here singular terms and sentences
are to be understood as categories of well-formed expressions; a more
complete list of formation rules would no doubt introduce many
more such.

(3)  Rules of Inference: Where A and B are sentences, from 'if'⌢A⌢
'then'⌢B and A to infer B. Where A and B are singular terms and
C is an adjective, from A⌢'equals'⌢B and B⌢'is'⌢C to infer A⌢
'is'⌢C.

(4)  Axioms-Theorems: 'if the world is round, then the world is round';
'four plus five equals nine.'

(5)  Rules of Sense: 'round' expresses the property of roundness. 'the
world' expresses the (individual) concept of the world. 'the world
is round' expresses the proposition that the world is round.

(8)  Rules of Denotation: 'round' denotes the class of round things. 'the
world' denotes the world. 'the world is round' denotes the truth-
value thereof that the world is round.[21]

On a Fregean theory of meaning, rules of truth in Tarski's form—e.g.,
" 'the world is round' is true if and only if the world is round"—
follow from the rules of denotation for sentences. For that a sentence is true is taken to be the same as that it denotes truth.

---

[19] Or possibly 'planet' and 's' could be regarded as two primitive symbols, by making a
minor change in existing English so that all common nouns form the plural by adding 's.'

[20] If any of you finds unacceptable the conclusion that therefore 'the number of
planets is round' is a sentence, he may try to alter the rules to suit, perhaps by distinguishing different types of terms. This is an example of a doubtful point, on the decision
of which there may well be differences of opinion. The advocate of a set-theoretic language may decide one way and the advocate of type theory another, but it is hard to
say that either decision is the "true" decision for the English language as it is.

[21] But of course it would be wrong to include as a rule of denotation: 'the world is
round' denotes truth. For this depends on a fact of geography extraneous to semantics
(namely that the world is round).

# A WORLD OF INDIVIDUALS*

Nelson Goodman (1906–    ) has written extensively on
logic, philosophy of language, and philosophy of science.
Among his books are *The Structure of Appearance* and
*Fact, Fiction and Forecast.*

## 1.   INDIVIDUALS AND CLASSES

For me, as a nominalist, the world is a world of individuals.
But this simple statement, I have learned from bitter experience, can be
misunderstood in numberless ways. Some misunderstandings have arisen
from inadequacies in my own explanations. Other misunderstandings have
arisen from inadequate attention to those explanations. Conflicting arguments in bewildering variety have been brought forward to show that
nominalism is bad. This paper is one more attempt to make clear what I
mean by nominalism and why I think nominalism is good.

A certain amount of trouble can be blamed on emotions attaching to
the word "individual." One writer [1] calls it an 'honorific' word; and I am
often criticized for applying the term "individual" to something or other
that is unworthy of it. Use of a different word, even a coined one, might
have been advisable in order to forestall such complaints. Nevertheless, I
am prepared to defend the choice of the term "individual" as entirely in
accord with a common practice of adapting ordinary language to technical
purposes. In some cases, what I take as an individual may indeed lack
many characteristics usually associated with the term "individual," and
may not count as an individual according to common usage. But the situation with respect to the term "class" is exactly parallel. According to the
layman's prelogical usage, children in a schoolroom make up a class, and
so do people at a given social level, but Plato and this sheet of paper and
the Taj Mahal do not. The term "set" in ordinary usage is perhaps even
more restricted than the term "class." Yet by the logician's usage any things
whatever make up a class or set. The contention that a genuine whole or
individual cannot consist of widely scattered and very unlike parts misses
the point as completely as would the contention that a genuine class
cannot consist of widely scattered and very unlike members. In the case of
"individual" as in the case of "class," a technical usage is explicated with
the help of a calculus, and the divergence from ordinary usage is expressly
noted. A class for Boole need not have social cohesion; and an individual
for me need not have personal integration.

---

* Reprinted by the kind permission of the author and publisher from *The Problem
of Universals* (Notre Dame, Ind.: Notre Dame University Press, 1956).
[1] Victor Lowe on p. 125 of "Professor Goodman's Concept of an Individual" in the
*Philosophical Review*, vol. 62 (1953), pp. 117–126.

Confusion of another kind has resulted from the incautious opening sentence of my joint article [2] with Quine. Although the statement "We do not believe in abstract entities" was intended more as a headline than as final doctrine, and although some reservations concerning it were almost immediately indicated,[3] it has been fair game for critics ever since. Neither of us would write that sentence today, but neither of us would so change it as to affect anything beyond the first paragraph of the article in question. Quine has recently written that he would "now prefer to treat that sentence as a hypothetical statement of conditions for the construction in hand."[4] My own change would be not from the categorical to the hypothetical, but from the vaguely general to the more specific. I do not look upon abstractness as either a necessary or a sufficient test of incomprehensibility; and indeed the line between what is ordinarily called "abstract" and what is ordinarily called "concrete" seems to me vague and capricious. Nominalism for me consists specifically in the refusal to recognize classes.

What has not always been noticed is that essentially this revision is made in my book,[5] published four years later than the joint article. A key principle in this later formulation is that the nominalist rejects classes as incomprehensible, but may take anything whatever as an individual. Some misguided criticism would have been obviated ¡had enough attention been paid to this statement; but I suspect that some of my critics feel they do me a kindness by not taking it seriously. Further explanation may help.

Nominalism as I conceive it (and I am not here speaking for Quine) does not involve excluding abstract entities, spirits, intimations of immortality, or anything of the sort; but requires only that whatever is admitted as an entity at all be construed as an individual. A given philosopher, nominalist or not, may impose very stringent requirements upon what he will admit as an entity; but these requirements, however sound they may be and however intimately associated with traditional nominalism, are quite independent of nominalism in my sense. The nominalism I have described demands only that all entities admitted, no matter what they are, be treated as individuals. Just what this means, I shall explain in the following sections; but for the moment we may suppose that to treat entities as individuals for a system is to take them as values of the variables of lowest type in the system.

Incidentally, several of my critics have confused themselves by lumping together, without due attention to context, passages from different parts

---

[2] "Steps Towards a Constructive Nominalism," *Journal of Symbolic Logic*, vol. 12 (1947), pp. 105–122.

[3] See the third paragraph and the second footnote of the joint article.

[4] *From a Logical Point of View*, Harvard University Press, 1953, pp. 173–4.

[5] *The Structure of Appearance*, Harvard University Press, 1951, see especially p. 35. Incidentally (as explained in the book and later in the present article) since any nominalistic system is readily translated into a platonistic one, acceptance of most of the book by no means depends upon an acceptance of nominalism. This has been explicitly acknowledged by most of my critics.

of my book. In Chapter VI, I discuss the choice of elements for a certain constructional system; but this does not turn upon the propriety of construing certain entities as individuals. Whatever we are willing to recognize as an entity at all may be construed as an individual. But in building a system, we must consider carefully what entities we are willing to recognize at all—or better, what terms we are willing to interpret as denoting and what terms we want to interpret syncategorematically. Important as the question is, nominalism does not decide it. I have never suggested that nominalism is enough to make a system acceptable. I have suggested only that platonism is enough to make it inacceptable. But more of this later.

Now, however, is nominalism consequential at all? If the nominalist is free to construe anything he pleases as an individual, can't he even construe a class as an individual?

Whatever can be construed as a class can indeed be construed as an individual, and yet a class cannot be construed as an individual. If this seems paradoxical, it can perhaps be clarified by means of an analogy. Suppose that in a certain game a player is to begin by dealing each card from his hand onto the table at either his left or his right; he may put any card on either side and may move a card from side to side if he likes. Then while it is quite true that he is free to put any card on either side, he can never get a left-hand card on the right-hand side; for a card is a left-hand card or a right-hand card according as it lies on his left or his right. Similarly, a table is an individual, or the class of its legs and top, or the class of its molecule-classes of atoms, according to the way it is construed in a system. And whether the Great Dipper is an individual or a class of stars depends upon the system we are using. We can construe anything as an individual (and aside from nominalistic scruples we can construe anything as a class); but we can no more construe a class as an individual than we can get a left-hand card on the right-hand side.

## 2.   THE PRINCIPLE OF NOMINALISM

In brief, while the nominalist may construe anything as an individual, he refuses to construe anything as a class. But just what is the principle of this refusal? In my book I said that, roughly speaking, the nominalist sticks at a distinction of entities without a distinction of content; and some of my critics have overlooked the more explicit formulation that soon followed. The nominalist denies that two different entities can be made up of the same entities. Let us suppose, for example, that a nominalist and a platonist start with the same minimal, atomic elements [6] for their systems; merely for comparative purposes take the number of

---

[6] An atomic element—or atom—of a system is simply an element of the system but contains no lesser elements of the system. Depending on the system, an electron or a molecule or a planet might be taken as an atom.

these atoms as 5. The nominalist admits also all wholes or individual sums comprised of these, and so has a universe of $2^5$-1, or 31, entities. He cannot concoct any more; for whatever individuals among the 31 are added together, the result is another individual among those 31. Our platonist, we may suppose, admits no sums of atoms but admits all classes of them. This, not counting the null and unit classes, gives him also 31 entities. But he further admits all classes of classes of atoms; and by this single step he welcomes into his universe $2^{31}$-1, or over two billion, additional entities. And he has no thought of stopping there. He also admits all classes of classes of classes of atoms, and so on *ad infinitum*, climbing up through an explosively expanding universe towards a prodigiously teeming Platonic Heaven. He gets all these extra entities out of his original five by a magical process that enables him to make two or more distinct entities from exactly the same entities. And it is just here that the nominalist draws the line.

In the nominalist's world, if we start from any two distinct entities and break each of them down as far as we like (by taking parts, parts of parts, and so on), we always arrive at some entity that is contained in one but not the other of our two original entities. In the platonist's world, on the contrary, there are at least two different entities that we can so break down (by taking members, members of members, and so on) as to arrive at exactly the same entities. For instance, suppose $K$ has two members: the class of $a$ and $b$, and the class of $c$ and $d$; and suppose $L$ has two members: the class of $a$ and $c$, and the class of $b$ and $d$. Then although $K$ and $L$ are different classes, they alike break down into $a$, $b$, $c$, and $d$. Again $K$ breaks down into the same entities as does the class having $K$ and $L$ as its members. These are clear cases of what the nominalist objects to as a distinction of entities without distinction of content.

This discloses the relationship between nominalism and extensionalism, which spring from a common aversion to the unwonted multiplication of entities. Extensionalism precludes the composition of more than one entity out of exactly the same entities by membership; nominalism goes further, precluding the composition of more than one entity out of the same entities by any chains of membership. For the extensionalist, two entities are identical if they break down into the same members; for the nominalist, two entities are identical if they break down in any way into the same entities. The extensionalist's restriction upon the generation of entities is a special case of the nominalist's more thoroughgoing restriction.

Nominalism describes the world as composed of individuals. To explain nominalism we need to explain not what individuals are but rather what constitutes describing the world as composed of them. So to describe the world is to describe it as made up of entities no two of which break down into exactly the same entities. What this means I have just explained, but a somewhat more technical formulation may be helpful.

Suppose we have two constructional systems, having one or more (but not necessarily the same or even the same number of) atoms. Entities other than atoms are generated in system **I** as classes, and in system **II** as sum-individuals. Let us now obliterate all purely notational differences between the two systems. We may suppose from the start that each system uses but one style of variable.[7] Then let us remove all remaining tell-tale signs from system **I** other than "$\epsilon$" by expansion in terms of "$\epsilon$," and similarly let us remove all peculiar signs of system **II** other than "$\ll$" by expansion in terms of "$\ll$." Finally, let us put "$R$" in for every occurrence of "$\epsilon$" "$\epsilon/\epsilon$," "$\epsilon/\epsilon/\epsilon$," etc. in system **I**, and for every occurrence of "$\ll$" in system **II**. No purely notational distinction between the two systems remains; and "$R$" in each is irreflexive, asymmetric, and transitive. Will anything now reveal which system is which?

For each system, $x$ is an atom if and only if nothing stands in the relation $R$ to $x$[8]; and $x$ is an atom of $y$ (symbol: "$Axy$") if and only if $x$ is an atom and is identical with or bears the relation $R$ to $y$. Now in a nominalistic but not in a platonistic system, entities are the same if their atoms are the same. Thus the disguised systems will be distinguishable from each other by the fact that the nominalistic system satisfies, while the platonistic system violates, the principle:

$$(x)\ (Axy \equiv Axz) \supset y = z.[9]$$

Obviously the disguised **I** will violate this principle if the system acknowledges more than $2^n-1$ entities, where $n$ is the number of its atoms; or again, if **I** acknowledges any unit-classes, since the unit-class and its member will have the same atoms. But even if **I** is a platonistic system so restricted as to be distinguished on neither of these two scores, it will still be detectable in its disguised version through violation of the stated principle. And if **I** admits no two such classes, then indeed it is not platonistic at all, regardless of its notation.

This, I think, disposes of the charge that the distinction between nominalism and platonism is a mere matter of notation,[10] and also clarifies the nominalist's dictum: "No distinction of entities without distinction of content." For a nominalistic system, no two distinct things have the same atoms; only from different atoms can different things be generated; all non-identities between things are reducible to non-identities between their atoms.

The further question must be raised whether the distinction between nominalism and platonism can be made *purely* formal? In the case we

[7] The aim is to take systems as nearly alike as possible, in order to isolate the critical difference.

[8] Any null class of system **I** will thus appear simply as one of the atoms of the disguised version of **I**, and thus leave no revealing trace.

[9] Both systems will satisfy the converse principle; under nominalism and platonism alike, if $x$ and $y$ are identical they have the same atoms.

[10] E.g. by Wang on p. 416 of "What is an Individual?" in the *Philosophical Review*, vol. 62 (1953), pp. 413–420.

have just considered, the problem was how to determine whether a given system is nominalistic or platonistic when we know that a given one of its relations is either $\epsilon$ * or $\ll$. Suppose now that we are confronted with a system without knowing anything about the interpretation of its predicates; or better, suppose we are given only the arrow-diagrams of the relations of the system. Can we determine whether the system is nominalistic or platonistic? The answer is *no*. We need to know either which elements are atoms of the system or—what amounts to the same thing—which relation is the 'generating' relation [11] of the system. Take, for example, the following diagram for a system with a single relation:

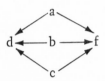

If we know that *a*, *b*, and *c* are the atoms of the system, or that the relation mapped is a generating one, then we know that the system is platonistic—since the distinct elements *d* and *f* then have exactly the same atoms. On the other hand, if we know that *a*, *b*, *c*, *d*, and *f* are all atoms of the system, then we know that the system is nominalistic. But if we do not know what the atoms are or whether the relation is a generating relation, we cannot tell whether the system is platonistic or nominalistic. Notice, though, that without such knowledge, *neither* can we tell whether a system is *extensional* or not. The system diagrammed is extensional if the relation is that of child to parent but surely not extensional if the relation is that of member to class.[12] Lest anyone gleefully welcome the apparent opportunity to dismiss both "nominalistic" and "extensional" as not purely formal characterizations of systems, I hasten to point out that no characterization of systems is purely formal in the sense implied. For if we are given just an arrow-diagram, without any interpretative information whatever, then we do not even know that the arrows represent relationships or that the letters represent elements. We can tell nothing at all about the system in question or even that there *is* a system in question; the diagram might be a hex sign or a complex character serving as the proper name of a single element. A classification of symbolic systems becomes significant only when at least some restrictions are imposed upon the interpretation of the symbols. The criterion for nominalism is formal to the same rather high degree as the usual criterion for extensionality.

[11] Given the atoms of the system, a *generating* relation is one such that if and only if *x* is a non-atomic element of the system will there be some element *y* that stands in that relation to *x*. The *generating relation G* of a system is the relation that obtains between two elements *x* and *y* of the system if and only if *x* and *y* are connected by a chain in which each linked pair belongs to a generative relation of the system.

[12] The system diagrammed, in fact, is extensional only if it is nominalistic, although obviously this is not true of all systems. Every system, of course, is nominalistic only if it is extensional.

What I have tried to do so far is to explain my version of nominalism. In outline, I have said that the nominalist insists on the world being described as composed of individuals, that to describe the world as composed of individuals is to describe it as made up of entities no two of which have the same content, and that this in turn is to describe it by means of a system for which no two distinct entities have exactly the same atoms.

Now, by way of justifying and defending the nominalism thus explained, I want to consider a number of objections to it.

## 3.  ANSWERS TO OBJECTIONS

(i) *Objection:* The nominalism described is not really nominalism in the traditional sense.

*Answer:* Doubtless a good many different theses are equally legitimate descendants of earlier nominalism. I claim no more than that the principle I have set forth is one reasonable formulation of the traditional injunction against undue multiplication of entities. And I willingly submit this claim to Father Bochenski for adjudication. If he rules against me, he deprives me of nothing but a label that incites opposition.

(ii) *Objection:* The principle of nominalism set forth is false as a statement, and groundless as a stipulation; for we know from everyday experience that different things often *are* made out of the same material, or the same particles, at different times.

*Answer:* The catch here is the phrase "at different times." Of course, different figures are often made out of the same lump of clay at different times; and of course, the same atoms often combine into different articles at different times. Likewise, different rooms are, so to speak, often made out of the same building at different places; and the same roads sometimes make up different crossings at different places. Admittedly, it is (spatially) different parts of the building or of the roads that are comprised in the two different rooms or the two different crossings; but so likewise, it is (temporally) different parts of the clay or the atoms that are comprised in the different figures or the different articles. We are at liberty to disregard the temporal or any other dimension we please; but if we were to rule out the spatial divisibility of buildings, or of roads, then we would not very consistently speak of the building, or a road, at different places. Similarly, if we rule out temporal divisibility, then we cannot very consistently speak of the clay, or of the atoms, *at different times.* The common experience of (different temporal parts of) the same clay making up different figures no more discredits the principle of nominalism than does the common experience of (different spatial parts of) the same building making up different rooms.

A variation on this objection points to ordered pairs like *Washington, Lincoln* and *Lincoln, Washington* as clearly illustrating the composition of different entities out of the same individuals.[13] To be pertinent, of course, this objection must not rest on any appeal to the logician's usual manner of defining these ordered pairs as distinct classes of classes; for the legitimacy of such multiple generation of classes out of the same individuals is just what is in question. Rather the argument must be that, regardless of how ordered pairs are defined in any formal system, we have here an everyday instance of distinct things being composed of the same things. But surely this claim is not true. Normally we no more conclude that we describe different composite entities when we name two people in different order than we conclude that a house from top to bottom and the house from bottom to top are different entities, or that the capital of Massachusetts and the largest city in New England are different things. We do not take the varied histories of the Battle of Bull Run as recounting different occurrences. In daily life a multiplicity of descriptions is no evidence for a corresponding multiplicity of things described.

Thus I find in common experience nothing discordant with the principle of nominalism.

(iii) *Objection:* Observance of the stated principle of nominalism is no sufficient guarantee of soundness or sense in a philosophical system; for trash of almost any kind can still be brought in on the ground floor as admitted atoms of the system.

*Answer:* Granted. Nominalism no more guarantees philosophical soundness than the refusal to eat poison guarantees physical well-being. Many additional rules must be observed if we are to achieve either philosophical or mental health. Indeed, in some cases a moderately platonistic system with a wholesome atomic ontology may be a lesser evil than a nominalistic system that takes monstrous vacuities as its atoms—just as a very tiny dose of poison may be less harmful than a bullet in the head.

Nominalism is a necessary rather than a sufficient condition for an acceptable philosophic system. To build well we must also exercise the most scrupulous care in choosing our raw materials. A given philosopher's choice of atoms may very likely be guided by attitudes or principles that are associated with nominalism by temperament or tradition; but such associated principles are independent of nominalism as I have defined it. Nominalism does not protect us from starting with ridiculous atoms. It does protect us from manufacturing gimcracks out of sound atoms by the popular devices of platonism. Nominalism, in other words, is a restrictive rule of processing that won't select our raw materials or help us make good things out of bad materials but will help keep us from making bad things out of good materials.

---

[13] *Cf.* p. 110 of C. G. Hempel's article "Reflections on Nelson Goodman's *The Structure of Appearance*," in the *Philosophical Review*, vol. 62 (1953), pp. 108–116.

(iv) *Objection:* To keep the rule of nominalism by generating wholes, rather than classes, of individuals costs as much as it pays; for it often means forcing the imagination to accept as individuals some scattered or heterogeneous conglomerations that are never in practice recognized as single units and are surely incomprehensible if classes are.[14]

*Answer:* This is perhaps the most chronic complaint against nominalism: that a progressively and in the end hopelessly strained analogy is involved in extending the application of such terms as "part," "whole," and "individual" beyond the realm of well-demarcated spatio-temporally continuous lumps. Yet as I have suggested earlier, I think this objection can be flatly and finally answered. The terminology of a system is irrelevant to the classification of the system as nominalistic or platonistic by the criterion I have explained. So long as a system admits no two distinct entities having exactly the same atoms, it is nominalistic no matter whether its generating relation is called "$\epsilon*$" or "$\ll$" or just "$R$," and no matter whether the values of its variables are called "classes" or "individuals" or just "entities." The words and symbols used in a system do not make it platonistic; it becomes platonistic only when it admits different entities having just the same atoms.

Thus a nominalistic system cannot put any burden on the imagination that a platonistic system does not. For the nominalist's apparatus is simply part of the platonist's apparatus. A nominalistic system can be mapped into a platonistic one. A nominalistic system is a platonistic system curtailed in a specific way.

Whatever new charges may be brought against nominalism, this bestloved of all objections now deserves to be laid to rest.

(v) *Objection:* Nominalism is trivial for a finitist and pointless for a non-finitist, since any system with a finite ontology can easily be made nominalistic while a system with an infinite ontology is repugnant to any nominalist.

*Answer:* Take the last point first. The nominalist is unlikely to be a non-finitist only in much the way a bricklayer is unlikely to be a ballet dancer. The two things are at most incongruous, not incompatible. Obviously, by the stated criterion for nominalism, some systems with infinite ontologies are nominalistic, and some systems with finite ontologies are platonistic.

But now, Hao Wang argues,[15] any finitistic platonistic system can be easily nominalized. He does not suppose that this can be done by any immediately obvious method, but refers to an ingenious device invented by Quine.[16] Now for the moment let us suppose that this device is entirely

---

[14] This objection is urged, for example, by Lowe in the article cited in footnote 1 above; and is also put forth by Quine on p. 559 of his review of *The Structure of Appearance*, in the *Journal of Philosophy*, vol. 48 (1951), pp. 556–563.

[15] See the article cited in footnote 10 above.

[16] In Quine's article "On Universals" in the *Journal of Symbolic Logic*, vol. 12 (1947), pp. 74–84.

successful. Does this mean that the nominalistic program is thereby rendered pointless and trivial? On the contrary it means that an important part of the nominalistic program has been accomplished. The nominalist, after all, is looking for a nominalistic translation of everything that seems to him worth saving. The more he succeeds in finding ways of supplanting platonistic constructions by nominalistic ones, the fewer will be the cases where platonistic apparatus need be eschewed; for we can use without qualms whatever we know how to eliminate. When Wang in effect says: "So you see these occurrences of platonism are harmless after all," he completely discounts the fact that only the nominalist's efforts removed the sting. One might as well say that the program for eradicating smallpox in the United States is trivial because there is no smallpox around. In one sense, of course, any completed program is trivial—in just the sense that the goal of any program is to trivialize itself.

Unfortunately, however, the nominalistic program has not been so fully accomplished for all finite systems. Quine, after presenting his device, explicitly points out its fatal defects. The device can never be used in a system with an ontology embracing the entire universe; for more inscriptions will be needed to write out even a single universally quantified statement than there are things in the universe. Quine offers his device as an interesting but unsuccessful attempt, and drops it forthwith.

Thus Wang is wrong about the facts concerning Quine's device; and even if the facts were as Wang supposes, they would not support the conclusion he tries to draw.

(vi) *Objection*: Nominalism is impossible.

*Answer*: This neatly complements the charge of triviality just discussed. Call a program impossible until it is completed, and call it trivial afterwards, and you have a well-rounded defense against it. In the formal sciences we have proofs that certain problems cannot be solved—for example, the trisection of angles with straight-edge and compass alone. But nothing even resembling proof is available for the impossibility of nominalism. And parts of the program that were once confidently cited as impossible have recently been accomplished; in particular the nominalistic and even finitistic treatment of most of classical mathematics, including general definitions for "proof" and "theorem." [17]

Even if full realization of the nominalistic program ultimately does turn out to be impossible, the efforts expended on it may not be unfruitful. The impossibility of trisecting the angle with straight-edge and compass hardly detracts from the value of Euclidean geometry, or leads us to conclude that Euclid was too frugal in his choice of tools.

In the end, the nominalist may not be quite able to live within his means, but he is going to keep on trying as long as he can. Before he

[17] In the joint article "Steps Towards a Constructive Nominalism," cited in footnote 2 above.

resorts to larceny he wants to make very sure that, and how much, he needs to steal.

(vii) *Objection:* Nominalism would hamper the development of mathematics and the other sciences by depriving them of methods they have used and are using to achieve some of their most important results.[18]

*Answer:* Not at all. The nominalist does not presume to restrict the scientist. The scientist may use platonistic class constructions, complex numbers, divination by inspection of entrails, or any claptrappery that he thinks may help him get the results he wants. But what he produces then becomes raw material for the philosopher, whose task is to make sense of all this: to clarify, simplify, explain, interpret in understandable terms. The practical scientist does the business but the philosopher keeps the books. Nominalism is a restraint that a philosopher imposes upon himself, just because he feels he cannot otherwise make real sense of what is put before him. He must digest what is fed him before he can assimilate it; but he does not expect it all to be pre-digested.

All the same, the advantages to the scientist of abundant and intricate apparatus are easily overestimated. Paucity of means often conduces to clarity and progress in science as well as in philosophy. Some scientists indeed—for example, certain workers in structural linguistics [19]—have even imposed the full restriction of nominalism upon themselves in order to avoid confusion and self-deception. The policy of 'no holds barred' may be exhilarating, but it can sometimes result in a terrible tangle.

(viii) *Objection:* Nominalism is bigoted. In adopting or rejecting systematic apparatus or a system-form, we ought to be governed not by a supposed insight into its intrinsic merits and defects but solely by the results we are enabled to achieve. Language and system-forms are instruments, and instruments are to be judged by how well they work. The philosopher must not handicap himself by prejudiced or dogmatic repudiations of anything that will serve his purpose.

*Answer:* This point is strongly urged by Carnap [20] and seems also to have been responsible for Quine's somewhat tentative defection from nominalism. But surely the nominalist does not want to exclude anything that will serve the purpose of philosophy. His critics seem to conceive of that purpose as consisting of correct prediction and the control of nature. These are certainly among the major concerns of daily life, technology, and science; but they do not constitute the primary goal of philosophy— nor, I think, of science in its more philosophical aspects. Obviously a system that predicted future events correctly but reported past events errone-

---

[18] E.g. see p. 40 of Carnap's "Empiricism, Semantics and Ontology" in the *Revue Internationale de Philosophie*, vol. 4 (1950), pp. 20–40. (Reprinted in *Semantics and the Philosophy of Language*, ed. Linsky, University of Illinois Press, 1952, pp. 208–228.)

[19] In particular, Zellig Harris and Noam Chomsky. See, for instance, the latter's "Systems of Syntactic Analysis" in the *Journal of Symbolic Logic*, vol. 18 (1953), pp. 242–256.

[20] In the article cited in footnote 18 above.

ously would be quickly dropped by any theoretical scientist or philosopher in his right mind. But even a true and detailed account of facts past, present, and future will leave the philosopher's work undone. As I suggested a moment ago, his task is to interrelate, systematize, interpret, explain. He is driven not by practical needs but by an impractical desire to understand. He, too, will judge a system by how well it works; but a system works for him only to the extent that it clarifies. The nominalist shuns platonistic devices precisely because he feels that their use would defeat rather than serve the purpose of philosophy. A clear story cannot be told in unintelligible language.

The nominalist cannot demonstrate the need for the restrictions he imposes upon himself. He adopts the principle of nominalism in much the same spirit that he and others adopt the principle of extensionality or that logical philosophers in general adopt the law of contradiction. None of these is amenable to proof; all are stipulated as prerequisites of soundness in a philosophic system. They are usually adopted because a philosopher's conscience gives him no choice in the matter. This does not mean that he need deny that he might some time change his mind. If the neopragmatist pushes me hard enough, I will even concede that I might some day give up the law of contradiction in the interest of getting better results—although if I should give up the law I am puzzled about what the difference would then be between getting results and not getting results. But I make this concession only if the pragmatist concede in return that we might some day even give up his Law of Getting Results. Or does he want to exempt this as constituting the essence of the human mind?

Carnap protests eloquently against what he considers narrowmindedness in philosophy, concluding with the exhortation: "*Let us be cautious in making assertions and critical in examining them but tolerant in permitting linguistic forms*"; and Quine agrees that "the obvious counsel is tolerance and an experimental spirit." [21] Reluctant as I am to cast a shadow on all this sweetness and light, there are limits to my tolerance of tolerance. I admire the statesman tolerant of divergent political opinions, and the person tolerant of racial and educational differences; but I do not admire the accountant who is tolerant about his addition, the logician who is tolerant about his proofs, or the musician who is tolerant about his tone. In every activity, satisfactory performance requires meticulous care in some matters; and in philosophy, one of these matters is the choice of systematic apparatus or 'linguistic form'. Thus in place of Carnap's exhortation, I propose another: "*Let us, as philosophers, be utterly fastidious in choosing linguistic forms.*"

What choices fastidiousness will dictate varies with the individual philosopher. But if that were good reason for indifference, then variations in taste and belief would be good reason for indifference about quality in art and about truth in science.

---

[21] *From a Logical Point of View* (see footnote 4 above), p. 19.

## 4.  AU REVOIR

I have explained my version of nominalism, and dealt with objections to the effect that it is not nominalism at all, that it is false or groundless, that it is too weak, that it is too strong, that it is trivial, that it is impossible, that it cripples the sciences, and that it is bigoted. Yet I by no means suppose that I have answered all the criticisms that will be or even all that have been made. Nominalism generates few entities but it arouses endless objections. The nominalist is looked upon as an intellectual vandal; and all the good neighbors rush to protect the family heirlooms against him. But the nominalist can go about his business undismayed; for his position is virtually unassailable. Every device he uses, every step he takes, is acceptable to his opponents; he makes no move that is not entirely legitimate by platonistic standards. When the nominalist and the platonist say *au revoir*, only the nominalist can be counted on to comply with the familiar parting admonition they may exchange: "Don't do anything I wouldn't do."

## SUGGESTIONS FOR FURTHER READING
## ON LOGIC AND ONTOLOGY

BOCHENSKI, I. M., A. CHURCH, N. GOODMAN.  *The Problem of Universals.* Notre Dame, Ind.: University of Notre Dame Press, 1956.

CARTWRIGHT, R. L.  "Negative Existentials," *The Journal of Philosophy*, Vol. 57 (1960), pp. 629–639. Reprinted in *Philosophy and Ordinary Language*, C. E. Caton, ed. Urbana, Ill.: University of Illinois Press, 1963.

GÖDEL, K.  "Russell's Mathematical Logic," *The Philosophy of Bertrand Russell*, P. A. Schilpp, ed. Evanston, Ill.: Northwestern University Press, 1946.

GOODMAN, N., and W. V. O. QUINE.  "Steps Toward a Constructive Nominalism," *The Journal of Symbolic Logic*, Vol. 12 (1947), pp. 105–122.

HENKIN, L.  "Some Notes on Nominalism," *The Journal of Symbolic Logic*, Vol. 18 (1953), pp. 19–29.

LEONARD, H. S.  "The Logic of Existence," *Philosophical Studies*, Vol. 7 (1956), pp. 49–64.

MYHILL, J.    "Two Ways of Ontology in Modern Logic," *The Review of Metaphysics*, Vol. 5 (1952), pp. 639–655.

NAGEL, E.  "Logic Without Ontology," *Naturalism and the Human Spirit*, Y. H. Krikorian, ed. New York: Columbia University Press, 1944.

QUINE, W. V. O.  "On Universals," *The Journal of Symbolic Logic*, Vol. 12 (1947), pp. 74–84.

SELLARS, W.  "Grammar and Existence: A Preface to Ontology," *Mind*, Vol. 69 (1960). Reprinted in *Science, Perception and Reality*, New York: Humanities Press, 1963, pp. 247–281.

# *Part*
## 6 LOGIC AND ORDINARY LANGUAGE

## *Introduction*

Symbolic logic is today a well-established academic discipline in its own right, taught in mathematics departments, in philosophy departments, in special programs, and even in some law schools. It has applications in pure mathematics, in electrical engineering, in programming computers, in the social sciences, and in linguistics. No one disputes its developments, its applications, or its successes. But some philosophers have disputed the claim that symbolic logic has serious applications within philosophy itself, or even any significance for philosophy.

Ryle's essay on "Formal and Informal Logic" considers a variety of arguments purporting to show that general philosophy not only gets along very well without making use of formal or symbolic logic, but that it uses another kind of logic more appropriate to its proper concerns. Several of these arguments are criticized and discarded by Ryle, but the conclusion is maintained. Some of Ryle's observations are undoubtedly correct and well worth making: for example, that some inferences depend upon terms other than logical constants, and that the logical constants of ordinary language are by no means identical with the logical constants expressed by the special symbols of symbolic logic.

The two selections from Strawson's *Introduction to Logical Theory* show in some detail how a philosopher of ordinary language approaches logic. In his first chapter Strawson locates logical appraisal among other kinds of appraisal, such as moral or aesthetic, and attempts to explain it in terms of *inconsistency*. In his discussion he has interesting and important things to say about problems of definition and explanation. In his eighth chapter Strawson, like Ryle, is concerned with differences between two kinds of logic: formal logic, on the one hand, and the logic of ordinary language, on the other. Again, what he has to say is stimulating and provocative.

Quine, in his brilliant review of Strawson's book, clarifies further the issues between symbolic logicians and philosophers of ordinary language. He points out the obscurities in some ordinary language terms that seem to be accepted uncritically, and warns of the dangers of hypostatization. Quine suggests that Strawson's "dim view of the scope of applicability of formal logic" is perhaps attributable to confusion over tensed and tenseless verbs. An extremely valuable part of Quine's essay is his description of "the formal logician's job" as an integral part of the ongoing scientific enterprise.

Geach, in his short essay, points out the enormous disparity between Strawson's treatments of symbolic logic and the traditional pseudo-Aristotelian logic. His documentation of the difference is conclusive, and although he does not attempt to explain it, Geach points out a very serious danger that is involved. It is that

*Many readers will vaguely think Strawson has proved that the traditional system with all its faults is philosophically less misleading than the new-fangled one. Those Colleges of Unreason where the pseudo-Aristotelian logic is presented as the only genuine logic, and those lecturers who would like to teach the philosophy of logic without having to learn any modern logic, may well thus have been supplied with a pretext for supine ignorance.*

# FORMAL AND INFORMAL LOGIC*

Gilbert Ryle (1900–    ) is Waynflete Professor of Logic and
Metaphysics at Oxford University. He has written extensively
on theory of knowledge, metaphysics, philosophy of language,
and philosophy of mind. Among his books are *The Concept
of Mind* and *Dilemmas*.

Since Aristotle, there has existed a branch of inquiries, often
entitled 'Formal Logic,' which has always adhered more or less closely to
general philosophical inquiries. It is not easy to describe this liaison between Formal Logic and philosophy. The systematic presentation of the
rules of syllogistic inference is a very different sort of activity from, say,
the elucidation of the concept of pleasure. The Aristotle who inaugurated
the former is the same thinker as the Aristotle who considerably developed
the latter, yet the kinds of thinking in which he was involved are very
widely different. The technical problems in the theory of the syllogism
have a strong resemblance to the problems of Euclidean geometry; the
ideals of systematization and rigorous proof are at work, questions of
switches and shades of significance are barred, false moves are demonstrable
fallacies. The problems in, say, the theory of pleasure or perception or
moral responsibility are not like this. Aristotle debates with Plato and
Socrates, and the issues become better defined as the debate progresses,
but the debate does not take the shape of a chain of theorems, nor do the
arguments used in that debate admit of notational codification. Whether
a given philosophical argument is valid or fallacious is, in general, itself a
debatable question. Simple inspection cannot decide. More often it is a
question of whether the argument has much, little or no force. Yet
different though Formal Logic is from philosophy, the operations characteristic of Formal Logic exercise a detectable, if minor, control over the
operations characteristic of philosophy. For good or for ill, the ways in which
Aristotle debates the notion of *pleasure*, the *soul* or the *continuum* reflect
lessons which he had taught himself in his logical inquiries. Nor is
Aristotle peculiar in this. With a negligible number of exceptions, every
philosopher of genius and nearly every philosopher of even high talent
from Aristotle to the present day has given himself some schooling in some
parts of Formal Logic, and his subsequent philosophical reasonings have
exhibited the effects upon him of this self-schooling, including sometimes
his revolts against it.

In some respects the following analogy holds. Fighting in battles is

* From *Dilemmas* by Gilbert Ryle. The Tarner Lectures, 1953, pp. 111–120. Copyright 1954 by The Syndics of the Cambridge University Press. Reprinted by permission
of the author and the Cambridge University Press.

markedly unlike parade-ground drill. The best conducted drill-evolutions would be the worst possible battle-movements, and the most favourable terrain for a rearguard action would entirely forbid what the barrack-square is made for. None the less the efficient and resourceful fighter is also the well-drilled soldier. The ways in which he takes advantage of the irregularities of the ground show the marks of the schooling he had received on the asphalt. He can improvise operations in the dark and at the risk of his life now, partly because he had learned before to do highly stereotyped and formalized things in broad daylight and in conditions of unmitigated tedium. It is not the stereotyped motions of drill, but its standards of perfection of control which are transmitted from the parade-ground to the battlefield.

Aristotelian Formal Logic gave weapon-drill in only a limited variety of rather short-range inference-weapons. The supplementations given by the Megarian and Stoic logicians were, unfortunately, only slightly and belatedly influential. It was left to the nineteenth and twentieth centuries to generalize and systematize the discipline. In particular, the discipline was then in considerable measure mathematicized, and mathematicized in two separate ways. First, the new builders of Formal Logic, being themselves mathematicians, knew how to give mathematical shape, mathematical rigour and mathematical notations to this branch of abstract theory. Secondly, since their interest in Formal Logic derived from dissatisfaction with the logical foundations of mathematics itself, Formal Logic came to be not only mathematical in style but also mathematical in subject-matter; to be employed, that is, primarily in order to fix the logical powers of the terms or concepts on which hinged the proofs of propositions in pure mathematics.

Formal or Symbolic Logic has grown up into a science or discipline of such scope, such rigour and such fertility that it is now out of all danger of surviving only as the nursery-governess of philosophy. Indeed, philosophers are now complacent if they and their pupils are capable of doing their schoolroom sums in the subject, and gratified and flattered if original logicians are willing to join them, from time to time, in their own expeditions over the moors.

Now, perhaps, I can indicate in a very provisional way the nature of the dispute which has already begun between Formal Logic and general philosophy. Some properly zealous, if sometimes gratuitously jealous Formal Logicians are now beginning to say to the philosopher 'It is time that you stopped trying to solve your problems by your old-fashioned exercises in improvisation and trial-and-error. Your problems are, as you say yourself, logical problems, and we have now got the procedures for solving logical problems. Where you grope, we calculate. Where you haggle, we employ the cash-register. Where you ponder imponderable pros and cons, we work out the correct logical change.'

The natural response of the offended and also jealous philosopher is this. 'Yes, you have invented or hit upon a private game, with fewer pieces but more squares than are provided by chess. You have converted the words "logic" and "logical" to your private ends, and now you invite us to cease exploring the moors in order to become conductors on your trams. And for what? For nothing, apparently, but the proliferation of truistic formulae. No philosophical problem of any interest to anyone has yet been solved by reducing it to the shape or size that suits some slot in your slot-machine. Your cash-register is indeed quite impeccable and totally neutral, and for that reason it cannot be appealed to for aid in the settlement of any bargaining-disputes. There was the notion, once projected by Leibniz and later championed by Russell, that philosophers would soon be so equipped and drilled that they would be able to decide their issues by calculation. But now we have learned, what we should have foreseen, that questions which can be decided by calculation are different, *toto caelo* different, from the problems that perplex. There is one person to whom it is impertinence to give the advice that he should keep one foot on the kerb—and that is the pathfinder. Kerbs cannot exist where the road is unmade, and roads cannot be made where the route has not been found.'

You can guess for yourselves the abusive nouns which are now liable to be interchanged. 'Muddler-through,' 'romantic,' 'anti-scientist,' 'hunch-rider,' 'litterateur' and of course 'Platonist' come from the one side; from the other side there come 'Formalist,' 'computer,' 'reductionist,' 'pseudo-scientist' and, of course, 'Platonist.'

As might be anticipated, neither party is right, though both are more nearly right than the appeasers who try to blend the operations of the one party with the operations of the other. The drill-sergeant is wrong who thinks that soldiering consists in going through the motions tabulated in the drill-book. The *franc-tireur* is wrong who thinks that soldiering consists in outbursts of amateur gunmanship. But neither is so wrong as the scenario-writer who represents fighting soldiers as heroes going berserk in close column of platoons.

Let us examine, rather more closely, the actual work, as distinct from the intermittent promises of Formal Logicians. Aristotle, it is nearly enough correct to say, examined certain ranges of inferences, namely those which pivot on the notions of *all, some,* and *not.* He saw that from two premises like 'some men are blue-eyed' and 'some men are red-haired' it does not follow that any men are both blue-eyed and red-haired, or, of course, that none are. On the other hand from 'all men or mortal' and 'all philosophers are men' it does follow that all philosophers are mortal. There are rules governing the employment of *all, some* and *not* such that all inferences pivoting on two or all three of these concepts, arranged in certain ways, are valid, while all inferences pivoting on them arranged in certain other ways are invalid. These rules are perfectly general, anyhow in this sense, the differences of concrete subject-matter make no difference to the validity or fallaciousness of the inferences. The quantifier-words 'all' and 'some' can be followed indifferently by 'men,' 'cows,' 'gods' or what you will, without affecting our decision that the inference holds or does not hold. What determines whether a proposed syllogism is valid or fallacious is the work given to 'all,' 'some' and 'not,' irrespective of the concrete topics of its premisses and conclusion. So, for brevity, we can say that Aristotle was investigating the logical powers of certain topic-neutral concepts, namely those of *all, some* and *not*. These are sometimes listed among what are nowadays called the 'logical constants.'

In a similar way the Megarian and Stoic logicians began the investigation of the logical powers of the equally topic-neutral concepts of *and, or,* and *if;* they concentrated on certain propositional conjunctions or connectives, where Aristotle had concentrated on certain quantifiers. They were studying the legitimacy and illegitimacy of possible arguments in so far as they hinged on these particuar topic-neutral conjunctions.

These studies yielded a modest degree of codification of the inference-patterns that were examined, and even a semi-Euclideanization of the rules of these inferences. Certain crucial fallacy-patterns were classified. So it was natural, though, as we now know, quite mistaken to suppose that any piece of valid reasoning whatsoever was, by some device or other of rewording, reducible to one of the already scheduled patterns, and every piece of fallacious reasoning reducible to one of the already registered howlers. Some terms like 'all,' 'some' and 'not,' and perhaps also 'and,' 'or' and 'if' do carry inferences; the rest, it was mistakenly supposed, do not.

Part of what characterizes the terms which do, on this view, carry inferences is that these terms or 'logical constants' are indifferent to subject-matter or are topic-neutral; so part of what characterizes all the other terms which were supposed not to carry inferences is that they are not topic-neutral. Inferences are valid or invalid in virtue of their forms, and to say this, it was supposed, was to say that they were valid or invalid because of the ways in which certain topic-neutral or purely formal expressions occurred in certain positions and arrangements in their premisses and conclusions. This temptingly crisp doctrine, whose obituary notice has yet to be written, might easily suggest the following demarcation of Formal Logic from philosophy. Formal Logic, it might be said, maps the inference-powers of the topic-neutral expressions or logical constants on which our arguments pivot; philosophy has to do with the topical or subject-matter concepts which provide the fat and the lean, but not the joints or the tendons of discourse. The philosopher examines such notions as *pleasure, colour, the future,* and *responsibility,* while the Formal Logician examines such notions as *all, some, not, if* and *or.*

But this way of making the division quickly breaks down. To begin with, topic-neutrality is not enough to qualify an expression as a logical constant. European languages, ancient and modern, and especially the largely uninflected languages, are rich in topic-neutral expressions, most of which have, for very good reasons, received no attention at all from Formal Logicians. We may call English expressions 'topic-neutral' if a foreigner who understood them, but only them, could get no clue at all from an English paragraph containing them what that paragraph was about. Such expressions can or must occur in any paragraph about any topic, abstract or concrete, biographical or legal, philosophical or scientific. They are not dedicated to this topic as distinct from that. They are like coins which enable one to bargain for any commodity or service whatsoever. You cannot tell from the coins in the customer's hand what he is going to buy. In this way 'not,' 'and,' 'all,' 'some,' 'a,' 'the,' 'is,' 'is a member of,' etc., certainly are topic-neutral, but so are 'several,' 'most,' few,' 'three,' 'half,' 'although,' 'because,' 'perhaps,' 'may,' as well as hosts of other conjunctions, particles, prepositions, pronouns, adverbs, etc. Some expressions seem to be nearly but not quite topic-neutral. The temporal conjunctions 'while,' 'after' and 'before,' and the spatial conjunction 'where' could be used not in all, but only in nearly all sorts of discourse. Our foreigner could tell from the occurrence of temporal conjunctions in the paragraph that no purely geometrical matter was being discussed.

But not only do Formal Logicians very properly ignore the great majority of topic-neutral expressions, as not being in their beat; they also, very properly, bestow their professional attentions upon the logical powers of certain classes of expressions which are by no means topic-neutral. Relational expressions like 'north of,' 'taller than' and 'encompasses' are pivots of strict inferences, and it has proved necessary and feasible to divide such expressions up into families according to the sorts of inferences which they do and do not carry. 'Taller-than,' for example, is transitive, in the sense that if A is taller than B, and B than C, then A is taller than C. But 'next to' and 'mother of' are not transitive. A can be next to B and B to C without A being next to C; and Sarah cannot be the mother of the child of her own daughter. This does not prevent us from discovering rigorous parities of reasoning between, for example, inferences hinging on 'north of' and inferences hinging on 'encompasses.' But the feature of parity cannot always be detached for separate examination by publication of some elided topic-neutral expression. Sometimes it can. 'Fatter than' works, in some directions, like 'hotter than,' and what is common to the two can be brought out by the rewording 'more fat than' and 'more hot than,' where the expression 'more so and so than' is a detachable topic-neutral expression.

So we should say, perhaps, with considerable loss of crispness and misleadingness, that Formal Logic is a certain sort of study of parities of reasoning or certain special kinds of parities of reasoning; and that it is convenient, when possible, to exhibit these parities by operations with topic-neutral expressions detached from any particular topical contexts; but that this is not essential and is not always possible. Not all strict inferences pivot on the recognized logical constants, and not all topic-neutral expressions qualify for treatment as logical constants.

A further amendment is required. I have spoken as if our ordinary 'and,' 'or,' 'if,' 'all,' 'some' and so on are identical with the logical constants with which the Formal Logician operates. But this is not true. The logician's 'and,' 'not,' 'all,' 'some' and the rest are not our familiar civilian terms; they are conscript terms, in uniform and under military discipline, with memories, indeed, of their previous more free and easy civilian lives, though they are not living those lives now. Two instances are enough. If you hear on good authority that she took arsenic and fell ill you will reject the rumour that she fell ill and took arsenic. This familiar use of 'and' carries with it the temporal notion expressed by 'and subsequently' and even the causal notion expressed by 'and in consequence.' The logicians' conscript 'and' does only its appointed duty—a duty in which 'she took arsenic and fell ill' is an absolute paraphrase of 'she fell ill and took arsenic.' This might be called the minimal force of 'and.' In some cases the overlap between the military duties and the civilian work and play of an expression is even slighter. What corresponds in the glossary of Formal Logic to the civilian word 'if' is an expression which plays only a very small, though certainly cardinal part of the role or roles of that civilian word.

This point that Formal Logic operates (1) only with some, and not with all topic-neutral expressions, and (2) only with artificial extracts from the selected few topic-neutral expressions of ordinary discourse is sometimes used by philosophers as a criticism of the programme of Formal Logic. Where the philosopher concerns himself with full-blooded concepts like that of *pleasure* or *memory*, the Formal Logician concerns himself only with meatless concepts like those of *not* and *some*; and even these have to be filed down to reduced size and unnatural shape before the Formal Logician will deign to inspect them. Moreover, the philosopher investigates concepts which, in one way or another, generate genuine perplexities. He investigates the concepts, say, of *seeing* and not that of, say, *perspiring*, since the former is charged with paradoxes where the latter is not. But, the criticism goes, the Formal Logician investigates the inference-carrying labours of concepts which engender no paradoxes whatsoever; what he finds out about *and* and *not* are only elaborations of what every child has completely mastered in his early talking years.

I mention this allegation here because it makes the right opening for me. It is quite false that doing Formal Logic is doing gratuitous and profitless philosophy upon philosophically transparent concepts. It is quite false, equally, that the philosopher is doing makeshift and amateurish Formal Logic upon wrongly chosen because non-logical concepts. The battlefield is not a makeshift parade-ground; and the parade-ground is not a sham battlefield.

None the less, there remains a very important way in which the adjective 'logical' is properly used to characterize both the inquiries which belong to Formal Logic and the inquiries which belong to philosophy. The Formal Logician really is working out the logic of *and, not, all, some,* etc., and the philosopher really is exploring the logic of the concepts of *pleasure, seeing, chance,* etc., even though the work of the one is greatly unlike the work of the other in procedure and in objectives. Neither is doing what the other is doing, much less is either doing improperly what the other is doing properly. Yet we are not punning when we say, for example, that the considerations which are decisive for both are 'logical' considerations, any more than we are punning if we say that the choice of drill-evolutions and the choice of battle-evolutions are both decided by 'military' considerations. How can this be?

I find the following partial parallel of some assistance. Trading begins with barter of goods for goods, and, by means of fixed places and times for markets, such barter-dealings can reach a fairly high degree of systematization. Though the relative exchange-values of different sorts of goods vary with times and places, some measure of stabilization can be achieved by tacit or explicit convention. There is, however, even at this stage, a strong pressure upon traders to use just a few kinds of consumable goods not only for consumption, but also, at least for a short time, as a sort of informal currency. Dried fishes, cigarettes or iron bars, though wanted for use, come also to be wanted because any other trader can be relied on to accept them, whether he himself wants to use them or not, because they will always be exchangeable anywhere for consumable goods. So long as they are reasonably imperishable, easy to store and handle, easy to count or weigh, and certain to be wanted some day by someone for consumption purposes, they are negotiable as exchange-tokens. From this stage to the stage of operating with a conventional currency or legal tender is a relatively short step. Though no one, perhaps, can be expected to want to use metal discs for any consumption purpose, everyone can be expected to want to use them for exchange-purposes. They might be described as auxiliary goods, goods which are of little or no utility in themselves, but of great utility for getting and disposing of other goods which are wanted for themselves.

For future purposes we should notice another kind of auxiliary goods. Baskets, pitchers, sacks, brown paper and string are, to exaggerate a little, of no use in themselves, but only for the collection and housing of goods which we do want for themselves. But clearly the way in which baskets and string are auxiliary to marketing and storing is different from the way in which coins are auxiliary. A basket or keg is only being actually useful to us when we are in possession of goods for it to contain. A coin is useful to us in another way. While we possess the coin, we do not possess what we shall buy with it. But still there is a certain similarity between them. A coin is commodity-neutral, for I can buy any sort of commodity with it. A sack or a piece of string is, in lower degree, commodity-neutral. You cannot tell from the fact that I go to market with a sack or some string precisely what kinds of goods I shall bring back with its aid. It would be useful for any of a fairly wide range of goods, though not, of course, for all kinds of goods.

Linguistic dealings between men have some of the features of market-dealings between men. There is a comparable pressure upon language to evolve idioms, which may or may not be separate words, to subserve in stabilized ways different kinds of constantly recurring linguistic negotiations. We need and therefore we get a variety of topic-neutral words, inflections, constructions, etc., some of which function rather like baskets, pitchers, string and wrapping-paper, while others function rather like the dried fishes, cigarettes or iron bars and, later on, rather like the coins and currency notes, part or the whole of whose utility is to serve as instruments of exchange. . . .

# LOGICAL THEORY*

PETER FREDERICK STRAWSON (1919–     ). See page 105.

## FROM CHAPTER 1: LOGICAL APPRAISAL

1. When a man says or writes something, there are many different ways in which his performance may be judged. Among other things, we may question his truthfulness or criticize his style, we may assess the morality of what he says, or we may appraise its logic; though not all these types of assessment are appropriate to all kinds of utterance. The words 'logical' and 'illogical' are themselves among the words of logical appraisal. If you call a discourse logical, you are in some degree commending it. If you call it illogical, you are, so far, condemning it. Words and phrases which go with 'logical' are 'consistent,' 'cogent,' 'valid,' 'it follows'; words and phrases which go with 'illogical' are 'inconsistent,' 'self-contradictory,' 'invalid,' 'a *non sequitur.*' Part of our problem is to see what sort of appraisal these words are used for, to what kind of standards we appeal in using them. It is easy to see that these are not moral or aesthetic standards; that logical criticism is not, say, a kind of literary criticism. A slightly more difficult distinction is that between the criticism we offer when we declare a man's remarks to be untrue and the criticism we offer when we declare them to be inconsistent. In the first case we criticize his remarks on the ground that they fail to square with the facts; in the second case we criti-

---

* Reprinted by permission of the author, John Wiley & Sons, Inc., and Methuen & Co., Ltd., from P. F. Strawson, *Introduction to Logical Theory* (New York: John Wiley & Sons, Inc., 1952), pp. 1–7, 211–217.

cize them on the ground that they fail to square with one another. The charge of untruth refers beyond the words and sentences the man uses to that in the world about which he talks. We deny his assertion, and, in doing so, make a counter-assertion of our own about the subject of his discourse. We contradict him. But the charge of inconsistency does not in this way refer to anything outside the statements that the man makes. We simply consider the way his statements hang together. Just from considering the sentences themselves, as they are used, we can, perhaps, see that not all the statements he makes can be true together. It is not that we contradict him, and in doing so, make a counter-assertion about the subject of his remarks; we assert that he has contradicted himself, and, in doing this, we make no appeal to the facts and express no opinion about them. It is this kind of internal criticism that is appraisal of the logic of a piece of discourse.

## I. *Inconsistency*

2. Words of logical appraisal have connected meanings. To be clear about the meaning of one such word is to be clear about the meanings of the others. For example, in a proof or argument, one statement (the conclusion) is said to follow logically from, or to be logically implied by, others (the premises), if the argument is valid; and an argument is valid only if it would be inconsistent (or self-contradictory) to assert the premises while denying the conclusion; or, in other words, only if the truth of the premises is inconsistent with the falsity of the conclusion. A deductive argument is a sort of threat, which takes the form: if you accept these premises as true, then you must accept this conclusion as true as well, on pain of self-contradiction. From among the various concepts of logical appraisal, I shall select this notion of inconsistency or self-contradiction for detailed discussion. Other choices could have been made, but there are reasons, which will emerge as we go on, for making this choice.

3. What is inconsistency? It is better to approach this question indirectly, by asking a series of others. One might ask first: Why bother to avoid inconsistency? What is wrong with contradicting yourself? There is nothing morally wrong about it. It may not even be entirely pointless. Suppose a man sets out to walk to a certain place, but, when he gets half-way there, turns round and comes back again. This may not be pointless. He may, after all, have wanted only exercise. But, from the point of view of a change of position, it is as if he had never set out. And so a man who contradicts himself may have succeeded in exercising his vocal chords. But from the point of view of imparting information, of communicating facts (or falsehoods) it is as if he had never opened his mouth. He utters words, but does not say anything. Or he might be compared with a man who makes as if to give something away and then takes it back again. He arouses expectations which he does not fulfil; and this may have been his purpose. Similarly, it may have been the purpose of a man who contradicts himself just to create puzzlement. The point is that the *standard* purpose of

speech, the intention to communicate something, is frustrated by self-contradiction. Contradicting oneself is like writing something down and then erasing it, or putting a line through it. A contradiction cancels itself and leaves nothing. Consequently one cannot explain what a contradiction is just by indicating, as one might be tempted to do, a certain form of words. One might be tempted to say that a contradiction was anything of the form 'X is the case and X is not the case.' But this will not do. If someone asks you whether you were pleased by something, you may reply: 'Well, I was and I wasn't,' and you will communicate perfectly well. Or there might be a convention that when one said anything of this form, the second part of the sentence was to be neglected. Then the minimum requirement for such a contradiction would be to say, first, 'X is the case and X is not the case' and, after that, 'X is not the case and X is the case.' Nevertheless, the temptation to explain a contradiction as anything of this form is, we shall see, not without point.

4. The next two questions to ask are more difficult. They are: (a) when we use these words of logical appraisal, what is it exactly that we are appraising? and (b) how does logical appraisal become possible? That is, we shall ask: what is it exactly that we declare to be inconsistent? and: what makes inconsistency possible? I have spoken of *statements* as being inconsistent with each other; and there is a temptation to think that in this context we mean by a statement the same thing as a sentence of a certain kind; or, perhaps, the meaning of such a sentence. But suppose I write on the blackboard the following two pairs of sentences: (i) 'I am under six foot tall' and 'I am over six foot tall'; (ii) 'The conductor is a bachelor' and 'The conductor is married.' In writing the sentences on the blackboard, I have, of course, not contradicted myself; for I may have written them there with a purely illustrative intention, in giving an English lesson. Someone might say: Nevertheless, the sentences in each pair *are* inconsistent with each other. But what would this mean? Would it mean that if they were ever uttered with the intention of making a statement, an inconsistency would result? But suppose the first two sentences were uttered by different people, or by the same person at an interval of years; and that the second two sentences were uttered in different omnibuses, or in the same omnibus, but on different days. Then there would be no inconsistency. Earlier, I paraphrased 'seeing that two statements are inconsistent' as 'seeing that they cannot both be true together.' And it is clear that that of which we can say that it is true or false is also that of which we can say that it is consistent or inconsistent with another of its kind. What these examples show is that we cannot identify that which is true or false (the statement) with the sentence used in making it; for the same sentence may be used to make quite different statements, some of them true and some of them false. And this does not arise from any ambiguity in the sentence. The sentence may have a single meaning which is precisely what, as in these cases, allows it to be used to make quite different statements.

So it will not do to identify the statement either with the sentence or with the meaning of the sentence. A particular statement is identified, not only by reference to the words used, but also by reference to the circumstances in which they are used, and, sometimes, to the identity of the person using them. No one would be tempted to say that the sentence 'I am over six foot tall' was inconsistent with the sentence 'You are under six foot tall.' But plainly they can be used, in certain circumstances, to make statements which are inconsistent with each other; i.e., in the case where the second sentence is addressed to the man by whom the first sentence is uttered.

It is easy to see why one is tempted to think of the sentence 'I am over six foot tall' as being inconsistent with the sentence 'I am under six foot tall.' One thinks of both sentences as being uttered, in the same breath, by the same person. In this case we should ordinarily regard that person as having contradicted himself, i.e., we should regard him as having said something and then unsaid it; and so as having said nothing. The important assumption is that the two expressions 'over six foot tall' and 'under six foot tall' are applied to the same person at the same time. Let us give the name 'incompatible predicates' to any pair of expressions the application of which to the same person or thing at the same time results in an inconsistency. Thus we can say that one of the ways in which it is possible to say something inconsistent is by applying incompatible predicates to the same person or thing at the same time.

5. But must a language have incompatible predicates in it? And what makes predicates incompatible? I want to answer the first question by saying, not that a language must have incompatible predicates in it; only that it is very natural that it should. And I want to answer the second question by saying that it is we, the makers of language, who make predicates incompatible. One of the main purposes for which we use language is to report events and to describe things and persons. Such reports and descriptions are like answers to questions of the form: what was it like? what is it (he, she) like? We describe something, say what it is like, by applying to it words that we are also prepared to apply to other things. But not to all other things. A word that we are prepared to apply to everything without exception (such as certain words in current use in popular, and especially military, speech) would be useless for the purposes of description. For when we say what a thing is like, we not only compare it with other things, we also distinguish it from other things. (These are not two activities, but two aspects of the same activity.) Somewhere, then, a boundary must be drawn, limiting the applicability of a word used in describing things; and it is we who decide where the boundaries are to be drawn.

This metaphor of drawing boundaries is in some ways misleading. I do not mean by it that we often make conscious decisions of this kind (though we sometimes do); nor that our boundary-drawing is a quite arbitrary matter; nor that the boundaries are fixed and definite; nor that the decisions we make when we make them, are purely verbal decisions. The boundaries are more like areas of indeterminate ownership than frontier-lines. We show ourselves to be near such a boundary, and we show also its indeterminacy, when, in reply to such a question as 'Was it red?' we give such an answer as 'Well, I suppose you could call it red.' We show ourselves on the point of making a boundary-decision when, with all the facts before us, we hesitate over the application of a certain word. Does such and such an act constitute an act of aggression or not? This case shows, too, how our decision is not a purely verbal matter; for important consequences may follow from our deciding that it is, or is not, an act of aggression. What makes our decisions, for a word already in use, non-arbitrary, is this: that our normal purpose will be defeated if the comparison implicit in the use of the word is too unnatural, if the similarity is too tenuous.

We may say: two predicates are incompatible when they lie on different sides of a boundary we have drawn: 'under six foot tall' and 'over six foot tall'; 'red' and 'orange'; 'aggressive' and 'pacific.' But this needs some explanation. Suppose you draw a closed figure on a piece of paper and then someone indicates a point on the ceiling and says: 'Does this point lie inside or outside the boundaries of the figure?' Of course, one might answer by imagining the boundaries of the figure extended in another dimension, up to the ceiling. But you might refuse to answer the question, by saying that you were drawing the boundary line only in the plane of the paper. Whatever lay outside the line in the plane of the paper was excluded from the figure. Things lying in a different plane were not excluded from it, but neither were they included in it. The figure has a certain plane of exclusiveness. And so with a word: it has a certain range of incompatibilities. 'Under six foot tall' is incompatible with 'over six foot tall'; but neither is incompatible with 'aggressive.' The last expression has a different incompatibility-range from the other two. There may sometimes be objections of a logical kind to applying expressions with different incompatibility-ranges to the same thing; but these will not be the objection that inconsistency will result from doing so.

When we apply a predicate to something, we implicitly exclude from application to that thing the predicates which lie outside the boundaries of the predicate we apply, but in the same incompatibility-range. By this I mean that if we go on to apply to the thing, in the same breath, one of the predicates which lie outside those boundaries, we shall be taken to have contradicted ourselves and said nothing. (This might be taken as a definition of 'incompatible predicates'.) But there is a qualification to be made here. Just as we might reply to the query 'Were you pleased?' with the words 'Well, I was and I wasn't' without inconsistency, so we might apply to the same thing, in the same breath, two predicates, which would ordinarily be regarded as incompatible, without contradicting ourselves. If we do this, we invite the question 'What do you mean?'; and if we can explain what we mean, or show the point of saying what we say, then we have not contradicted ourselves. But if there is no way of doing this, we are inconsistent. Thus we might say, in answer to a question, 'He is both over six foot tall and under six foot tall,' and then explain that he has a disease which makes him stoop, but that if he were cured and were able to stand upright, he would top the six-foot mark. This shows again that one cannot fully explain what self-contradiction is, just by reference to groupings of words.

## FROM CHAPTER 8: TWO KINDS OF LOGIC

### I. *Formal Logic: Applications and Limitations*

1. Language is used for a variety of purposes. The normal use of some sentences is to give orders; of others, to ask questions; of yet others, to take oaths, to convey greetings, to make apologies, or to give thanks. When sentences are used in any of these ways it makes no sense to inquire whether what is said is true or false. But the normal use of an indefinitely large number of sentences is to say things to which this inquiry is appropriate. Such sentences as these I have called, by an easily understood brachylogy, 'statement-making sentences.' To know the meaning of a sentence of this kind is to know under what conditions someone who used it would be making a true statement; to *explain* the meaning is to *say* what these conditions are. One way of giving a partial account of these conditions is to say what some of the entailments of the sentence are. For to say that one sentence entails another is to say that a statement made by the use of the first is true only if the corresponding statement made by the use of the second is true; and to say that one sentence entails and is entailed by another is to say that a statement made by the use of the first is true if, and only if, the corresponding statement made by the use of the second is true. This might make us think that to give the two-way entailments (the logical equivalents) of a statement-making sentence is all that can be done, in the way of *saying*, to give its meaning. And since the meaning of sentences can sometimes be explained simply by talking, we may think that, in such cases, this is all that ever *need* be done; that where talking can explain, this is the only kind of talking we can do and the only kind we need do.

To think this is to make a mistake, though a common one. Let us return to the point that to explain the meaning of a statement-making sentence is to say under what conditions someone who used it would be making a true statement: and let us call this 'giving the rules of use' of the sentence. We have just noticed the temptation to think that the only kind of rules involved are entailment-rules. I want to show, first, that this view is false, and, second, that the fact of its falsity imposes an unavoidable limitation on the scope and application of formal logic. The limitation in question is not one to be deplored or to be welcomed. It is one to be noticed; for the failure to notice it leads to logical mythology.

It is a fact I have remarked upon before, that the questions, whom a sentence is uttered by, and where and when it is uttered, may be relevant to the question of whether a true statement is made by its utterance. The same sentence in different mouths may be used to make one true, and one false, statement ('My cat is dead'); the same sentence in the same mouth at different times may be used to make one true, and one false, statement ('My cat is dead'); and so on. (Not only is this true of the majority of the statement-making sentences we use in ordinary speech. It is also an unavoidable feature of any language we might construct to serve the same general purposes. But I shall not try to prove this; for it is with ordinary discourse that I am concerned.) Since this is so, the assertion that a sentence S entails a sentence S' cannot be generally taken to mean that if any statement made by the use of the first is true, then any statement made by the use of the second would be true. It must rather be taken to mean the following: If, at some time, at some place, in the mouth of some speaker, the utterance of S results or would result in a true statement, then the utterance of S' at that time, at that place, in the mouth of that speaker, would result in a true statement. So the entailments of S may tell us to what *kind* of situation S may be correctly applied; they do not give general instructions enabling us to determine whether, in the mouth of a certain speaker, at a certain time, at a certain place, S is being applied to a situation of that kind. Such general instructions can be given; but not by entailment-rules. Entailment-rules, as the above schematic formulation shows, abstract from the time and place of the utterance and the identity of the utterer: so they cannot tell the whole story about the conditions under which a sentence is used to make a true statement, unless the sentence is one of which it is true that, if its utterance by anyone, at any time, at any place results in a true statement, then its utterance by anyone else, at any other time, at any other place, results in a true statement.

Entailment-rules, then, must be supplemented by rules of another kind. We may call these 'referring rules.' Referring rules take account of what entailment-rules abstract from, viz., the time and place of the utterance and the identity of the utterer. Examples of referring rules are: the word 'I' is correctly used by a speaker to refer to himself; the word 'you' is correctly used to refer to the person or persons whom the speaker is addressing; one of the correct uses of the present tense is for the description of states of affairs contemporaneous with the describing of them; the past tense is correctly used to indicate that the situation or event reported is temporally prior to the report. Elucidation of some or all of the uses of such words as 'the,' 'a,' 'over there,' 'he,' 'they,' 'now,' 'here,' 'this,' 'those' are elucidations of referring rules; so are some discussions of the uses of the many tenses of verbs. Consideration of these and other examples shows that the description I gave of the factors taken account of by referring rules (viz., time and place of utterance, and identity of the speaker) must be generously interpreted. These factors embrace many distinguishable features of

what, in a wide sense of the word, might be called the *context* of an utterance. A referring rule lays down a *contextual requirement* for the correct
employment of an expression. But the fact that the contextual requirement
is satisfied is not a part of what is *asserted* by the use of a sentence containing an expression governed (in this use) by a referring rule: it is, rather,
presupposed by the use of the expression. . . . Thus, if someone says, 'He
will die in the course of the next two months,' it is linguistically out-
rageous to reply, 'No, he won't' *and then give as one's reason* 'He's dead
already.' If the event has already taken place, the question whether it will
take place within the next two months or not is a question which does not
arise. 'He's dead already' disputes the presupposition that his death lies in
the future, that he is not dead already. But it does not *contradict* the
original statement, since to do this would be to admit its presuppositions;
and hence does not contradict anything entailed by the original statement.
The fact that the fulfilment of the contextual requirement is not part of
what is asserted by the use of a sentence containing an expression governed by a referring rule thus involves and is involved by the distinction
between referring rules and entailment-rules.

2. Formal logic is concerned with the meanings of sentences only in so
far as these can be given by entailment-rules. Indeed, its concern is far
more limited than this suggests, for only a relatively small subclass of
highly general entailment-rules are of interest to the logician. Hence formal
logic systematically ignores the referring element in ordinary speech. This
fact helps to explain the preoccupation of formal logic with certain types
of sentence; and helps to explain also the popularity among logicians of
certain collateral doctrines. . . . From the logician's point of view, the
ideal type of sentence is one of which the meaning is entirely given by
entailment-rules; that is, it is one from which the referring element is
absent altogether; that is, roughly, it is one of which it is true that if its
utterance at any time, at any place, by any speaker, results in a true statement, then its utterance at any other time, at any other place, by any other
speaker, results in a true statement. Almost the only types of contingent
sentence (i.e., sentence the utterance of which would result in a contingent
statement) which seem able fully to realize this ideal are positively and
negatively existential sentences, of which some forms are studied by the
predicative calculus, or sentences compounded of these. That sentences
of this sort may realize the ideal is easily seen. For the main, though not
the only, referring elements, of sentences which contain such elements,
are of two types: (1) the time-indications, relative to the moment of
utterance of the sentence, which are given by the tenses of verbs; (2) the
logical subjects, i.e., the separate words or phrases used to pick out the
object or objects, person or persons, &c., which are being referred to.
Neither of these elements need be present in a sentence exemplifying one
of the positively or negatively existential forms studied in the calculus.
For (1), . . . '$(\exists x)$' must be interpreted as, if not temporally ambiguous,

either timeless or omnitemporal; and (2) since such a sentence is existential, it need contain no expression which functions as a logical subject. Of course, in so far as we attempt to cast ordinary empirical statements into one of these forms, we may find one or both of these types of referring element in the subordinate clauses of the resulting existential sentence. But the logician is concerned with the form; and here he seems to have found a form which *can* be exemplified by sentences entirely free from referring elements.

A qualification must be added here. It is not quite true that the only contingent sentences which answer to this ideal of independence of context of utterance are those sentences which are entirely free from referring elements. For law-sentences in general answer to this ideal; and therefore subject–predicate law-sentences answer to it; for although they contain a referring element of the second type, the reference is to an open class, and is therefore independent of contextual conditions.

All necessary statements may be said to answer, though in a different way, to the ideal of independence of context. For sentences embodying necessary statements are merely the analogues of higher-order sentences stating entailments, or else other logical relations which can be re-expressed as entailments. Their use is not to describe or report or forecast. They embody entailment-rules, and, like them, abstract from contextual conditions. So one does not in making them refer to any part of the world, or to any stretch or moment of the world's history; and the present tense, in which they are generally, though not necessarily, framed, is, not the omnitemporal, but the timeless present. We have already seen that, with certain safeguards, the symbolism of modern logic may be used in writing some of them.

I shall return later to the consideration of the sentences which do answer to the logician's ideal. But first I want once more to stress the obvious fact that the vast majority of the statement-making sentences we ever have, or might have, occasion to use in ordinary speech do not answer to it. For in this contrast between the logically ideal type of sentence and the types we mostly employ is the final explanation of many facts which I have mentioned in earlier chapters; particularly in the last three. For example, it explains how it is that many features of the use of ordinary speech which are sufficiently general to deserve consideration under such a title as 'The Logic of Language' are necessarily omitted from consideration under the narrower title 'Formal Logic.' Here I may instance such features as the uses of 'a' and 'the'; the presupposition-relation between certain subject–predicate statements and certain existence-statements; the functions of the various grammatical tenses. Second, it explains the *acharnement* with which differing types of subject–predicate statements are assimilated to negatively and/or positively existential forms, with the result that both their general character and the differences between them are obscured. This is a natural consequence; for the formal logician is reluctant to admit, or even envisage the possibility, that his analytical equipment is inadequate for the dissection of most ordinary types of empirical statement. Third, it explains the myth of the logically proper name and reveals the full importance of the myth. The logically proper name is envisaged as a type of referring expression which shall be free from the unideal characteristics which all referring expressions possess. If there did exist a class of expressions the meaning of each of which was identical with a single object, then of course the use of any expression of that class to refer to the appropriate object would be independent of contextual conditions. A contingent sentence of the form '$fx$,' where the predicate replacing '$f$' was omnitemporal and the individual expression replacing '$x$' was an expression of this class, would have the ideal characteristic that, if its utterance at any time, at any place, in the mouth of any speaker, resulted in a true statement, then its utterance at any other time, at any other place, in the mouth of any other speaker, would result in a true statement. Now the whole structure of quantificational logic, with its apparatus of individual variables, seems, or has seemed to most of its exponents, to require, for its application to ordinary empirical speech to be possible, that there should exist individual referring expressions which could appear as values of the individual variables. That is to say, the whole structure has seemed to presuppose the existence of simple predicative sentences of the form '$fx$.' The belief in logically proper names made it possible to assume both that there were such sentences and that they were of the logically ideal type; and thus helped to preserve the illusion that formal logic was an adequate instrument for the dissection of ordinary speech. In fact, there *are* such sentences, but they are *not* of the logically ideal type. Finally, the preoccupation with the ideal type of sentence explains the persistent neglect of the distinction between sentence and statement. For, in the case of sentences of the ideal type, the distinction really *is* unimportant. Such a sentence whenever it is used, is used to make one and the same statement; the contextual conditions of its use are irrelevant to the truth or falsity of that statement. To this type of sentence the otherwise bogus trichotomy 'true, false, or meaningless' may be harmlessly applied. . . .

# MR. STRAWSON ON LOGICAL THEORY*

WILLARD VAN ORMAN QUINE (1908–    ). See page 165.

A philosopher of ordinary language has brought his limpid vernacular to bear on formal logic.[1] Step by unhurried step he explains the terms of logical appraisal and what the logician's business is, and sets the logician's artifacts over against the speech of natural man. '⊃' emerges at page 34, the truth tables at page 68, the quantifiers at page 131, and the syllogism at page 158. The intervening and ensuing space is given over not to theorems and proofs and decision procedures (except for some sketchy examples), but to interpretation and criticism. A ninth chapter, the last, is an excellent little philosophical essay on induction.

The division of the present review into sections will correspond to the structure not of the book, but of the critical reflexions which the book has stimulated in this reader.

## 1. ENTAILMENT, ANALYTICITY, AND COMPANY

First Mr. Strawson undertakes to explain, in an ordinary-language setting, the notions of inconsistency and entailment. The devices at his disposal are analogy and example; and even the method of example offers difficulties, since he is at pains to withhold the stigma of inconsistency from speech fads like "Well, I do and I don't."

Engineers have been known to work wonders with the differential calculus without ever having been given an account of its foundations more intelligible than the notion of an actual infinitesimal; and there are philosophers who have, through use and custom, grown to feel equally at home with the notion of entailment which so pervades G. E. Moore's philosophical analyses. There are philosophers of ordinary language who have grown so inured to the philosophical terms 'entails' and 'inconsistent' as to look upon them, perhaps, as ordinary language. But the reader without such benefits of use and custom is apt to feel, even after Mr. Strawson's painstaking discussion of the notions of inconsistency and entailment, somewhat the kind of insecurity over these notions that many engineers must have felt, when callow, over derivatives and differentials. At the risk of seeming unteachable, I go on record as one such reader.

---

* Reprinted by kind permission of the author and publisher, from *Mind*, Vol. 63, 1953, pp. 433–451.
[1] P. F. Strawson, *Introduction to Logical Theory*. 1952. Pp. x + 266. London: Methuen & Co. New York: John Wiley & Sons.

Turning away from Mr. Strawson's book for a bit, let us seek perspective on the general problem. The terms 'entail' and 'inconsistent' belong to a group other members of which are 'analytic' and 'synonymous.' Because of the easy interdefinability of these terms, one of them suffices to represent the group; and a handy choice is 'analytic.' In recent classical philosophy the usual gesture toward explaining 'analytic' amounts to something like this: a statement is analytic if it is true by virtue solely of meanings of words and independently of matters of fact. It can be objected, in a somewhat formalistic and unsympathetic spirit, that the boundary which this definition draws is vague or that the definiens is as much in need of clarification as the definiendum. This is an easy level of polemic in philosophy, and no serious philosophical effort is proof against it. But misgivings over the notion of analyticity are warranted also at a deeper level, where a sincere attempt has been made to guess the unspoken *Weltanschauung* from which the motivation and plausibility of a division of statements into analytic and synthetic arise. My guess is that that *Weltanschauung* is a more or less attenuated holdover of phenomenalistic reductionism.

A philosopher may have rejected phenomenalism in the full reductionistic sense, in favour of admitting that statements for the most part are laden with an irreducibly extra-phenomenal burden over and above their phenomenal import. But he may continue to hold (*a*) that the statements do still possess their phenomenal import, what there is of it, as separate statements one by one; or he may hold rather (*b*) that the statements are tied to the testimony of the senses only in a systematic or holistic way which defies any statement-by-statement distribution of sensory certificates. If he holds so much as the vestige (*a*) of phenomenalistic reductionism, then he will find it natural to accept in principle a division between analytic and synthetic truths, the former being those in which the phenomenal content is null. If on the other hand his position is (*b*), he may be expected to find no way of putting some truths into empirical quarantine and judging the remainder free of infection. For him the contribution which linguistic meaning makes to knowledge and the contribution which sensory evidence makes to knowledge are too inextricably intertwined to admit of a sentence-by-sentence separation.

My own position is (*b*). I do grant that any given sensory event seems more relevant to some statements than to others; also that some statements seem less directly touched than others by sensory events in general; but I think these variations can be accounted for as sporadic surface effects, without prejudice to (*b*) as underlying principle.[2] My misgivings over the notion of analyticity are thus misgivings in principle. But those also who espouse the notion espouse it mainly in principle, granting freely that the boundary between the analytic and synthetic can be troublesome and indecisive in application.

[2] See my "Two dogmas of empiricism," *Philosophical Review*, vol. lx (1951), pp. 20–43, especially pp. 40 ff.

The purpose of the foregoing excursion is not to invoke my philosophy in criticism of another man's book. There are rather three other points. One is that misgivings over analyticity and related notions are not just a cavilling over fuzzy boundaries. A second is that these notions are too bound up with a debatable philosophical position to be well suited to the very prominent roles which Mr. Strawson assigns to them in his project of clarifying elementary logic from the standpoint of ordinary language. A third is that I should think Mr. Strawson himself, with his stress on the realities of common-sense language, would incline rather to (b) than to (a).

He frequently shows awareness that there are difficulties in applying analyticity and related notions. On page 5 he writes:

> What makes predicates incompatible? . . . It is we, the makers of a language, who make predicates incompatible. . . . A boundary must be drawn, limiting the applicability of a word used in describing things; and it is we who decide where the boundaries are to be drawn.
>
> This metaphor of drawing boundaries is in some ways misleading. I do not mean by it that we often make conscious decisions of this kind . . . nor that the decisions we make when we make them, are purely verbal decisions.

On page 91 he writes:

> What we are suffering from here is perhaps a crudity in our notion of entailment.

On page 231 he writes:

> We may very often hesitate to say whether a given sentence is analytic or synthetic; and the imprecision of this distinction as applied to ordinary speech, reflects an imprecision in the application of the notion of entailment to ordinary speech.

The laudable observation last quoted might well have caused a philosopher of ordinary language to wonder about his use of the notion of analyticity as a keystone. But, as I have urged in earlier pages, the notion has yet a more serious fault than vagueness.

## 2.   LOGICAL TRUTH

If the author has chosen too soft and friable a keystone in analyticity, then it is fair to ask what he could have used in its place. Insofar as he uses the notion of analyticity in defining the province of logic, my answer is as follows: he could have used, instead, the notion of truth and the notion of logical vocabulary. Given these, the business of formal logic is describable as that of finding statement forms which are *logical*, in the sense of containing no constants beyond the logical vocabulary, and (extensionally) *valid*, in the sense that all statements exemplifying the form in question are true. Statements exemplifying such forms may be called *logically true*. Here there is no hint of a doctrine as to the epistemological grounds of logical truth; no affirmation or denial of conventionalism (whatever that would be), nor any effort to separate the analytic from the synthetic.

Mr. Strawson observes (pp. 40 ff.), and rightly (if for the moment we set aside any misgivings over the notion of analyticity), that not all analytic statements are instances of logical forms all of whose instances are analytic. As examples to the contrary he cites statements of the non-logical form:

$$x \text{ is a younger son} \supset x \text{ is a brother.}[3]$$

However, he recognizes that instances of the latter kind are not supposed to be provided for by rules of logic. The forms which the logician wants as theorems are, by Mr. Strawson's own account, just those logical forms all of whose instances are analytic. This account matches that in my preceding paragraph, except that it has 'analytic' instead of 'true.' In net resultant scope these two accounts of logic differ little if any. They may differ in that certain logical forms whose validity depends on the size of the universe would qualify as theorems for my logic book and not for his; but I should need to understand analyticity better to be sure even of this.

I have urged, above, that Mr. Strawson's characterization of the scope of logic in terms of the notion of analyticity be dropped in favour of a characterization in terms of the notions of logical vocabulary and truth. Logical vocabulary is specified only, I suppose, by enumeration. If this element of apparent arbitrariness is a shortcoming, it is a shortcoming also in Mr. Strawson's characterization; for this also depends on the notion of logical vocabulary, via logical form. He may still feel that he brings out the essential nature of logic more fully than my characterization would do, in that the logical truths turn out for him to be some (though not all) of the analytic statements. However, one who rejects the notion of analyticity is less averse than others to finding that the boundaries of logic, like those of biochemistry and other disciplines, are to some degree capricious.

The notion of analyticity, as used in Mr. Strawson's characterization of logic, gave way to the notion of truth in my alternative characterization. The notion of truth is also of course one of which Mr. Strawson avails himself frequently in the course of his book. Possibly he considers the notion intelligible only as a sum of analyticity and empirical truth; if so, reluctance to do without the notion of analyticity is the more understandable. But in fact the inclusive notion of truth is a far less dubious

[3] For further discussion of this contrast see my "Two dogmas," cited earlier.

starting point than that of analyticity; for we understand under what circumstances to say of *any* given statement that it is true, just as clearly as we understand the statement itself.

The group of notions to which that of analyticity gives rise, *viz.* entailment, inconsistency, and synonymy, are paralleled by a group of notions issuing from logical truth in the sense defined a few paragraphs back. Thus, just as one statement entails another, if the corresponding conditional ('$\supset$') is analytic, so for me one statement (logically) implies another if that conditional is logically true. Just as a statement is inconsistent for Mr. Strawson if its negation is analytic, so for me it is inconsistent, or logically false, if its negation is logically true. It is noteworthy, for my strictures against the notion of analyticity, that much of Mr. Strawson's use of analyticity and entailment in the course of his logical expositions strongly resembles my use of logical truth and implication in *Methods of Logic*. On the other hand there also are long and inconclusive passages in Mr. Strawson's book which would drop out if the recommended shift were made.

## 3.   WORDS INTO SYMBOLS. TRUTH-VALUE GAPS

Logic, under either of the accounts contrasted above, is *formal* logic in a narrow sense which excludes those preparatory operations, in applied logic, whereby sentences of ordinary language are fitted to logical forms by interpretation and paraphrase. Mr. Strawson stresses the magnitude of these applicational manoeuvres, and in this I am in full agreement. The considerations involved in them deserve attention in logic texts, and have been given attention in some; rarely, however, with the sympathetic care and subtlety which Mr. Strawson bestows on them.

One conspicuous divergence between language as used and language as depicted in logical forms is the correspondence of many idioms on the one hand to few on the other. Reduction of the rich variety of more or less interchangeable grammatical constructions and logical locutions of ordinary language to a conveniently standardized minimum is imperative for algorithmic purposes; for the power and simplicity of an algorithm, or indeed of any theory, depend on there being many occurrences of few elements rather than few occurrences of many.

Further divergence between language as used and language as reflected in logical forms remains after reductions of the kind just alluded to have been completed; for, the surviving logical particles have uses in ordinary language which diverge from the laws formulated by logicians. The well-known failure of the ordinary statement operators 'or,' 'if-then,' 'and,' and 'not' to conform in all cases to the precepts of truth-functional logic is well expounded by Mr. Strawson. Because 'and' and 'not' deviate less radically than the others, I have found it pedagogically helpful (in *Ele-*

*mentary Logic*) to treat the translation of ordinary language into logical form, at the truth-functional level, as funneled through 'and' and 'not'; and Mr. Strawson follows suit.

Such failures of correspondence are not, of course, confined to the truth-functional level. They recur with 'every' and 'some,' in relation to the logic of quantification. Mr. Strawson also develops these details with much sensitivity.

Another conspicuous way in which ordinary language diverges from language as reflected in logical forms is in the existence of what I have called truth-value gaps. One illustration in my *Methods of Logic* is the conditional, under ordinary usage in the indicative mood. Ordinarily the conditional is not thought of as true or false at all, but rather the consequent is thought of as conditionally true or false given the antecedent. Another example, *op. cit.*, is provided by the singular description; if the object which it purports to describe does not exist, then commonly the contexts of the description are accorded no truth values under ordinary usage. "The question of their truth," as Mr. Strawson phrases it in his able exposition of the topic, "does not arise."

Mr. Strawson exploits this idea in a detailed defence of the traditional syllogistic logic apropos of the famous question, raised by Leibniz and others, of existential import. Mr. Strawson's method is to construe the categorical forms, for purposes of traditional logic, in such a way that where a term is empty of extension the question of the truth of the containing categorical statement does not arise. He argues plausibly that this view does considerable justice to ordinary language. His is, I expect, the best way of defending the traditional syllogistic.

A substantial offshoot of Mr. Strawson's reflexions on truth-value gaps is a theory, expounded earlier in an article by Strawson [4] and reminiscent also of Aquinas and Geach,[5] in which a distinction is made between the referential and the predicative role of a singular term. This distinction, little heeded in logical literature, is important for an appreciation of ordinary language; and, as Mr. Strawson well brings out, it reveals a marked failure on the part of Russell's theory of descriptions to correspond to the ordinary use of 'the.'

Normally, if the role of a singular term in a given statement is referential, the question of the truth of the statement does not arise in case the purported object of the term is found not to exist. Since modern formal logic closes all such truth-value gaps, it is not to be wondered that there is nothing in modern logic to correspond to the referential role, in Mr. Strawson's sense, of terms. Mr. Strawson is at pains to point out that proper names, so-called by formal logicians, are therefore far from corresponding to the singular terms of ordinary language.

[4] P. F. Strawson, "On referring," *Mind*, vol. lix (1950), pp. 320–344.
[5] P. T. Geach, "Subject and predicate," *ibid.*, pp. 461–482.

On this point he thinks to find modern logic in a difficulty. For, he writes (p. 216):

> Now the whole structure of quantificational logic, with its apparatus of individual variables, seems, or has seemed to most of its exponents, to require, for its application to ordinary speech to be possible at all, that there should exist individual referring expressions that could appear as values of the individual variables.

It is therefore important to emphasize, in contrariety to what the above quotation suggests, that anything even remotely analogous to proper names or singular terms is systematically eliminable from modern logic altogether, both in theory and in application.[6]

Granted the value of the distinction between referential and predicative roles as a means of capturing the genius of ordinary language, it would be a mistake to infer that modern logic errs in not keeping the idiosyncrasy of ordinary language which that distinction brings out. We shall recur to the general question of the function of formal logic in § 5, below. Meanwhile let us rest with this analogy: Weierstrass did not define the infinitesimal, but showed rather how to get on without it.


## 4.   INSTABILITY OF TRUTH VALUE. TENSE

Another important respect in which language as used diverges from language as reflected in logical forms is the variation of truth value from occurrence to occurrence of a single sentence. Such variation can result from the use of indices ('I,' 'here,' 'now') or tensed verbs; also it can result from casual ambiguities, variously resolved by varying contexts and situations. Formal logic, on the other hand, developing arguments as it does in which a schematic letter '$p$' keeps recurring, is misapplied unless the sentence represented by '$p$' is thought of as keeping a fixed truth value at all points in the argument.

In describing these matters, Mr. Strawson adopts a double terminology: 'sentence' versus 'statement.' One and the same sentence can be used in ordinary language to make any of various statements, whereas a sentence to which formal logic is applied must be thought of as making one fixed statement and no other. In appealing thus to "statements," not as a kind of sentence but as acts performed by uttering sentences, or perhaps contents conveyed by sentences, Mr. Strawson gains a certain expository ease and also runs a certain risk. The risk is that of hypostatizing obscure entities, akin perhaps to "propositions" or "meanings" or "facts" or "states of affairs," and reading into them an explanatory value which is not there.

Terminological questions aside, the variation of truth values in ordinary

---

[6] Cf. *Methods of Logic*, pp. 215–224.

language and the insistence on fixed truth values for purposes of formal logic are points which are no less important than they are familiar. Mr. Strawson overstates the consequent limitation on the uses of formal logic, however, when he writes (p. 223):

(1) that when we inquire what use can be made of the symbolic apparatus of logic we find that for certain general reasons it seems best adapted to the role of systematically exhibiting the logical relationships between sentences which answer to the ideal of independence of contextual conditions;

(2) that the actually occurring sentences of this type are analytic sentences and law-sentences.

Formal logic would be a pretty idle luxury if its applicability were limited thus severely. In explanation of why formal logic is not really thus limited, let me quote myself (*Methods of Logic*, p. 43):

Insofar as the interpretation of ambiguous expressions depends on circumstances of the argument as a whole—speaker, hearer, scene, date, and underlying problem and purpose—the fallacy of equivocation is not to be feared; for, those background circumstances may be expected to influence the interpretation of an ambiguous expression uniformly wherever the expression recurs in the course of the argument. . . .

The fallacy of equivocation arises rather when the interpretation of the ambiguous expression is influenced in varying ways by immediate contexts, . . . so that the expression undergoes changes of meaning within the limits of the argument. In such cases we have to rephrase . . . to the extent of resolving such part of the ambiguity as might, if left standing, end up by being resolved in different ways by different immediate contexts within the proposed logical argument.

Mr. Strawson's dim view of the scope of applicability of formal logic is perhaps attributable in part to the fact that he gets into trouble over tensed and tenseless verbs on pages 150 f.:

For example, we might try writing the sentence 'There was at least one woman among the survivors' in the form '$(\exists x)$ ($x$ is a woman. $x$ was among the survivors).' But to say 'There *is* at least one person who is a woman and was among the survivors' is at least to suggest that the person is alive at the time the sentence is uttered. . . . Changing the second 'is' to 'was' will not help; it will merely prompt the question 'What became of her then? Has she changed her sex?' Nor can the difficulty be evaded by declaring '$(\exists x)$' in this sentence to be timeless; it is not true that when we speak of persons and incidents the question of time-reference does not arise.

Mr. Strawson's error occurs where he says "Nor can the difficulty be evaded . . . ." The only tenable attitude toward quantifiers and other notations of modern logic is to construe them always, in all contexts, as timeless. This does not mean that the values of 'x' may not themselves be thing-events, four-dimensional beings in space-time; it means only that date is to be treated on a par with location, colour, specific gravity, etc.— hence not as a qualification on '∃', but merely as one of sundry attributes of the thing-events which are values of 'x.' When 'x' ranges rather over numbers, Mr. Strawson appreciates that '(∃x)' is best read 'There [is] in the number series a number x such that,' with tenseless '[is]'; but he does not appreciate that '(∃x)' is likewise to be read 'There [is] in space-time a thing-event x such that' when 'x' ranges over the four-dimensional denizens of the ages and galaxies of space-time. Any value of 'x' in this latter or spatio-temporal universe of discourse will in fact have a time, just as any value of 'x' in the former or numerical universe of discourse will in fact have a highest prime factor; but the '[is]' or '∃' itself speaks no more of time than of prime factors.

The way to render Mr. Strawson's example is '(∃x) (x [is] a woman . x was among the survivors),' with tenseless '[is]' and, as always, tenseless '∃.' The 'was' here involves reference presumably to some time or occasion implicit in the missing context; if we suppose it given by some constant 'D' (e.g., 'The sinking of the Lusitania'), then the whole amounts to '(∃x) (x [is] a woman . x [is] among the survivors of D),' tenseless throughout.

The above example is not odd, but typical. The four-dimensional view of space-time is part and parcel of the use of modern formal logic, and in particular the use of quantification theory, in application to temporal affairs. It may be felt to be a criticism of modern logic that it calls for so drastic a departure from the time-slanted Indo-European language structure. But the better way of looking at the matter is to recognize both in the four-dimensional approach, with its notable technical advantages, and in quantification theory, with its notable technical advantages, two interrelated contributions to scientific method.

It would be hard to exaggerate the importance of recognizing the tenselessness of quantification over temporal entities. The precept has been followed as a matter of course by anyone who has been serious about applying modern logic to temporal entities.[7] I see no reason to expect a coherent application of quantification theory to temporal matters on any other basis.

Earlier I suggested that Mr. Strawson's failure to appreciate the tenselessness of quantification over temporal entities might be a factor in his underestimation of the scope of modern logic. I should like to go further and say that I do not see how, failing to appreciate the tenselessness of quantification over temporal entities, one could reasonably take modern logic very seriously. From having perhaps wondered at Mr. Strawson's doubts over logic, one comes to wonder rather at his forebearance.

---

[7] Examples: Carnap, *Der logische Aufbau der Welt*; Woodger, *The Axiomatic Method in Biology*; Woodger, *Biology and Language*.

## 5.  THE PLACE OF FORMAL LOGIC

Reduction of ordinary language to logical form is, as noted in § 3 above, a reduction in at least two ways: reduction of the variety of idioms and grammatical constructions, and reduction of each surviving idiom to one fixed and convenient interpretation. That fixed interpretation is bound to be, moreover, a pretty Pickwickian one, as is evident from §§ 3-4 above. Now Mr. Strawson represents this Procrustean activity somewhat as a hobby:

> Logicians like to present a tidy system of interconnected rules. The neatness of a system might suffer if it had too many constants in it (p. 49).
> And it is this ideal of systematization which has most profoundly influenced the modern development of logic; so profoundly that the original conception of simply codifying the most general principles we appeal to in making our logical appraisals has pretty well been lost sight of. . . . The formal logician, in relation to ordinary language, might be compared with a man ostensibly mapping a piece of country of which the main contours are highly irregular and shifting. But the man is passionately addicted to geometry. . . . Naturally his maps will never quite fit (pp. 57 f.).

The pleasures of science are not to be denied, but the tendency to equate those pleasures with the pleasures of games can be seriously misleading. There are those, certainly, who have approached mathematics and logic in the same spirit in which they approach chess; but my suspicion, undissipated still by the fashionable tendency to cite quaternions as a case to the contrary, is that those playful spirits have been less productive of important results than those whose pleasure in science is the pleasure of working toward fundamentals. There is no deciding whether ibn-Tahir and al-Khwarizmi devised Arabic numeration and algebraic notation in a gaming spirit, but at any rate the motivation of the Procrustean treatment of ordinary language at the hands of logicians has been rather that of achieving theoretical insights comparable to those which Arabic numeration and algebra made possible. That their hope has not been forlorn is attested by such discoveries as Gödel's of the impossibility of a complete system of number theory, and Church's of the impossibility of a decision procedure for quantification theory.

Nor need one set one's sights so high; even the humdrum spinning out of elementary logical principles in modern logic brings insights, concerning the general relation of premiss to conclusion in actual science and common sense, which are denied to men who scruple to disturb a particle of natural language in its full philological concreteness. The naturalist who observes nature only with his hands clasped behind him may gain poetic inspiration, and he may even contribute a little something to taxonomy; but he is not to be looked to for a basic contribution to scientific theory.

The ancillary activity of analyzing and paraphrasing scientific sentences of ordinary language, so as to abstract out their logical form and explore the formal consequences, is comparable in principle to the activity of the physicist who re-works and re-thinks his data and hypotheses into a stereo-typed mathematical form so as to be able to bring the techniques of tensor analysis or differential equations to bear upon them. It is an important activity, and deserving of all the space and acumen which Mr. Strawson expends upon it. My only quarrel is with the notion, hinted now and again, that it is somehow wrong to have to undertake this activity, and that for-mal logicians have been generally seduced by hobbyism into making mistakes about language—as if Frenchmen betrayed ignorance of French when they depart from the pattern of 'soixante-dix-neuf' and 'quatre-vingts' by writing '79' and '80.'

The long and perceptive passages in which Mr. Strawson traces out something like a logic of ordinary language have all the interest and value of an able philological inquiry. But it is a mistake to think of Mr. Strawson as doing here, realistically, a job which the dream-beset formal logician had been trying to do in his unrealistic way. Actually the formal logician's job is very different, and may be schematized as follows. To begin with let us picture formal logic as one phase of the activity of a hypothetical individual who is also physicist, mathematician, et al. Now this overdrawn individual is interested in ordinary language, let us suppose, only as a means of getting on with physics, mathematics, and the rest of science; and he is happy to depart from ordinary language whenever he finds a more convenient device of extraordinary language which is equally adequate to his need of the moment in formulating and developing his physics, mathe-matics, or the like. He drops 'if-then' in favour of '⊃' without ever enter-taining the mistaken idea that they are synonymous; he makes the change only because he finds that the purposes for which he had been *needing* 'if-then', in connexion with his particular scientific work, happen to be satisfactorily manageable also by a somewhat different use of '⊃' and other devices. He makes this and other shifts with a view to streamlining his scientific work, maximizing his algorithmic facility, and maximizing his understanding of what he is doing. He does not care how inadequate his logical notation is as a reflexion of the vernacular, as long as it can be made to serve all the particular needs for which he, in his scientific programme, would have otherwise to depend on that part of the vernacular. He does not even need to paraphrase the vernacular into his logical notation, for he has learned to think directly in his logical notation, or even (which is the beauty of the thing) to let it think for him.

Not that this logical language is independent of ordinary language. It has its roots in ordinary language, and these roots are not to be severed. Everyone, even to our hypothetical logician-scientist and his pupils' pupils, grows up in ordinary language, and can learn the logician-scientist's technical jargon, from '⊃' to $\frac{'dy'}{dx}$ to 'neutrino,' only by learning how, in principle at least, to paraphrase it into ordinary language. But for this purpose no extensive analysis of the logic of ordinary language is required. It is enough that we show how to reduce the logical notations to a few primitive notations (say '∼,' '.,' 'ε,' and universal quantification) and then explain just *these* in ordinary language, availing ourselves of ample paraphrases and scholia as needed for precision. These explanations would be such as to exclude, explicitly, any unwanted vagaries of the 'not,' 'and,' 'is,' and 'every' of ordinary language; such also as to provide for the tenselessness, the eternal invariance of truth-value, which classical logical theory presupposes in the statements to which it is applied (*cf.* § 4 above).

Let it not be inferred from the above account that formal logic is a scientific tool without philosophical relevance; nor let it be supposed that its philosophical relevance must consist in a point-by-point application to the recorded speech behaviour of the man in the street. Philosophy is in large part concerned with the theoretical, non-genetic underpinnings of scientific theory; with what science could get along with, could be reconstructed by means of, as distinct from what science has historically made use of. If certain problems of ontology, say, or modality, or causality, or contrary-to-fact conditionals, which arise in ordinary language, turn out not to arise in science as reconstituted with the help of formal logic, then those philosophical problems have in an important sense been solved: they have been shown not to be implicated in any necessary foundation of science. Such solutions are good to just the extent that (*a*) philosophy of science is philosophy enough and (*b*) the refashioned logical underpinnings of science do not engender new philosophical problems of their own.

One example of such elimination of philosophical perplexities is Frege's "definition" of number. Another is the avoidance, by means of quantification theory, of the misleading substantive 'nothing.' Another is the recourse to '⊃' and quantification to avoid the vernacular 'if-then,' with the problems of cause and modality to which it gives rise. And the classic case is Russell's theory of descriptions. Mr. Strawson (to get back to him after an absence of a page and a half) ably shows the failure of Russell's theory of descriptions as an analysis of the vernacular usage of the singular 'the,' but he shows no appreciation of the value of Russell's theory as a means of getting on in science without use of any real equivalent of the vernacular 'the.' Russell's '(ɿx)' is to the vernacular 'the x such that' as '⊃' is to the vernacular 'if-then'; in neither case do we have a *translation*, but in both cases we have an important means of *avoidance* for scientific purposes. And in both cases we therefore have solutions of philosophical problems, in one important sense of this phrase.

## 6.  PERPLEXITY OVER TRANSITIVITY

Mr. Strawson compares (pp. 40–46) the forms of inference:

(1)   all $f$'s are $g$ and $x$ is an $f$ $\therefore$ $x$ is a $g$,
(2)   $x$ is a younger son $\therefore$ $x$ has a brother,
(3)   $xRy$ and $yRz$ $\therefore$ $xRz$.

He observes that all inferences of forms (1) and (2) are valid (indeed analytically so), whereas only some inferences of the form (3) are valid. In particular those inferences of the form (3) are valid (analytically so) which have, *e.g.*, the more special forms:

(4)   $x$ is congruent with $y$ and $y$ is congruent with $z$
      $\therefore$ $x$ is congruent with $z$,
(5)   $x$ is an ancestor of $y$ and $y$ is an ancestor of $z$
      $\therefore$ $x$ is an ancestor of $z$,
(6)   $x$ is faster than $y$ and $y$ is faster than $z$
      $\therefore$ $x$ is faster than $z$.

He observes further that the forms (1) and (3) are logical (*cf.* § 2, above), while the forms (2), (4), (5), and (6) are not. So far all is in order. But then he continues his discussion with a perplexing air of perplexity over (3). "Some logicians," he writes, "have felt that all those words which, substituted for '$R$' [in (3)], would yield valid inference patterns *ought* to have some common verbal feature." He goes on to urge, rightly, that those logicians (whoever they may be) are mistaken. But he recurs to (3) in extended passages later in the book (pp. 53–55, 203, 207–208, 210); and the reader gets a sense of there still being a puzzle in the author's mind, both from the disproportionate use of space and from two particular subsequent passages.

   In one of these passages (pp. 207 f.) he cites "transitively relational inference" as an example of what the traditional formal logic could not do. "Attempts," he continues, ". . . to maintain the reducibility of, *e.g.*, transitively relational inferences to syllogistic form have a certain interest. . . . The cruder kind of attempt merely introduces the principle . . . as a further premise, to be added to those of the original inference." But what more than this can modern logic do for "transitively relational inference"? (3) is not a law of any logic, as the author himself has stressed in other pages. *Any* logic will need to bolster (3) with an appropriate further premiss of the form:

(7)   $xRy \cdot yRz \cdot \supset xRz$,

except in those special examples whose transitivity happens to be logically demonstrable. This remark is indeed a flat tautology.

In the other passage (p. 204) he classifies as transitive those relational predicates which, if substituted in (7), yield *analytic* formulae. But standard usage requires only, for "transitivity," that (7) come out *true* for all x, y, and z. This discrepancy may suggest a clue to the author's very special concern over transitivity: is it traceable to a notion that whenever (7) holds for all x, y, and z it holds analytically? And if he thinks this, does he think it because (7) is a logical formula? But this would be a mistake. Transitivity is indeed a logical trait, in that (7) is a logical formula. Likewise nullity is a logical trait, in that '$(x) \sim fx$' is a logical formula; but the possession of nullity (or fulfilment of '$(x) \sim fx$') by the predicate of griffinhood is a matter of empirical zoology. The fulfilment of (7), for all x, y, and z, by a given predicate can be equally accidental. Example: Take '$xRy$' in (7) as '$x$ and $y$ are residents of the western Azores and live within ten miles of each other.' (Here the relevant facts are that the western Azores are eleven miles apart and the longer of them is ten miles long.)

For the mistaken ideas which I have attributed to Mr. Strawson in the psychological speculations of the foregoing paragraph, he is not responsible beyond having led me to speculate. There are passages, *e.g.* in the lower part of page 54 and the next page, where his views on transitivity seem quite in order; yet the extensive further passages make one wonder. Actually the matter of transitivity need not have occupied him much beyond the observations noted in the first paragraph of the present section of this review. (7) is on a par, in logical status, with '$\sim fx$' or '$(x) \sim fx$' (as lately noted), and (3) is on a par with:

(8)  $fx \therefore gx.$

They are on a par in the sense of being logical and non-valid and having some valid cases. Some cases of (3) are analytically valid, *e.g.* (4)-(6) and others not; some cases of (8) are analytically valid, *e.g.* (2) and others not. For some choices of '$R$', moreover, (3) is not analytically valid but still leads from true premisses always to true conclusions; witness the Azores example. Correspondingly, of course, for (8).

## 7.  FURTHER CRITICAL OBSERVATIONS

The direct value of the book is very considerable, and lies in the realm of logical analysis of ordinary language. The book also has additional value in an ironically negative way: the very misconceptions which I have been warring against in this review are philosophically significant enough so that it is important to have got them out into the open, particularly as they are probably not peculiar to Mr. Strawson. Finally it is scarcely to be denied that various proponents of modern logic have laboured from time to time under misconceptions of their own; and some of those Mr. Strawson usefully sets right.

The value of the book in this last respect would have been enhanced if the author had made references to the literature. The anonymity of his "formal logicians say" engenders an air of *Strawson v. Strawman*. The discipline of documenting his adversary might also have operated now and again as a corrective, by leading him to wonder whether formal logicians do think quite the way he supposed they did, on certain points, after all. The almost total absence of citations has also other disadvantages, apart from the polemical point. Finding so much in the book that is familiar but unattributed, a less than omnivorous reader is in danger of supposing that the unfamiliar parts are old too, thus giving the author less than his due. Perhaps the ultimate in non-citation occurs on page 99, where it is said that Whitehead and Russell's fifth truth-functional axiom is superfluous; mere mention of Bernays would have enabled the curious reader to look up the proof, with help say of Church's *Bibliography*.

The remainder of this review will be given over to a series of miscellaneous points of criticism, each of which can be covered in briefer space than those belaboured in the foregoing sections.

There is a recurrent notion among philosophers that a predicate can be significantly denied only of things that are somehow homogeneous in point of category with the things to which the predicate applies; or that the complement of a class comprises just those things, other than members of the class, which are somehow of the same category as members of the class. This point of view turns up on pages 6, 112, and elsewhere. It is part and parcel of the doctrine that 'This stone is thinking about Vienna' (Carnap's example) is meaningless rather than false. This attitude is no doubt encouraged by Russell's theory of types, to which, by the way, Mr. Strawson seems to think modern logic is firmly committed (*cf.* p. 227). It is well, in opposition to this attitude, to note three points: the obscurity of the notion of category involved, the needlessness for formal logic of any such strictures on negation and complement, and the considerable theoretical simplifications that are gained by lifting such bans. This is not to deny the importance for linguistics of what the linguists call substitution classes, and at points Mr. Strawson has essentially that notion in mind (*cf.* p. 226); but the needs and purposes of linguistics are very different from those of formal logic.

On page 16, the author writes: "To say of two statements that they are contradictories is to say that they are inconsistent with each other and that no statement is inconsistent with both of them." But this is unsatisfactory where S is by itself inconsistent, and hence inconsistent with every statement; for then every statement would qualify as a contradictory of S by the quoted definition, and thus contradictories of S would fail of mutual equivalence. The definition of "contraries," on the same page, is subject to a similar difficulty. My criticism depends indeed on assuming that a self-inconsistent $S$ counts as a statement, but I think I am authorized in this by the foot of page 8.

A related difficulty occurs on page 87, where 'if' is being contrasted with '⊃': "As an example of a law which holds for 'if,' but not for '⊃,' we may give the analytic formula '$\sim$ [(if $p$, then $q$) . (if $p$, then not $q$)].'" But how does this supposedly analytic formula fare when '$p$' is taken as '$q . \sim q$'? Presumably 'if $q . \sim q$ then $q$' holds, as a case of 'if $q . r$ then $q$'; and similarly for 'if $q . \sim q$ then $\sim q$.' Maybe the author's defence would be that my instance is one where, for ordinary 'if,' the question of truth "does not arise" (*cf.* § 3 of this review); if so, then the passage needs expanding.

Whether or not the above two paragraphs bring out two genuine cases of failure to allow for an always-false component, at any rate just such an oversight does unequivocally occur on page 204. An assertion on that page hinges on incompatibility of:

$$(x)(y)(z)(fxy . fyz . \supset fxz), \qquad (x)(y)(z)(fxy . fyz . \supset \sim fxz),^8$$

whereas actually both of these formulae come out true if $(x)(y) \sim fxy$.

On page 17, line 18, 'both' should be read 'each of' to avoid ambiguity.

In the italicized definition of 'truth-functional' on page 66, the words *"and only"* should be dropped. If they add anything, what they add is wrong; for we can often know the truth of a truth-functional compound without knowing the truth value of any component. A similar remark applies to "solely" in the middle of page 69.

On page 66, and again on page 216 (quoted in § 3 above), the idiom 'value of a variable' is used, contrary to custom, to refer to substitutable constant expressions rather than to the objects in the universe of discourse over which a quantification ranges. The latter, more orthodox usage occurs at the foot of page 112. On page 66 the "variables" are unquantifiable statement letters; so in this case it would be more natural not to think of them as taking "values" at all, but to speak of them as standing for (*i.e.* in place of) sentences.

Mr. Strawson is good on '⊃' and 'if-then.' He rightly observes the divergences between the two, and stresses that '$p \supset q$' is more accurately read as 'not ($p$ and not $q$)' than 'if $p$ then $q$.' He also shows awareness that such correspondence as '⊃' does bear to 'if-then' is better than its correspondence to 'implies.' But both ideas languish. Pages 218 ff. would seem less strange and more obvious if he would there revive the reading 'not ($p$ and not $q$).' Again the terminology 'material implication and equivalence,' which he rightly deplores on page 94 but continues to use, could easily have been omitted from the book altogether in favour of the less objectionable terminology 'material conditional and biconditional,' whose currency in the literature is encouragingly on the increase.

---

[8] Here and elsewhere, even in quotation, I depart slightly from the author's dot conventions.

On page 106, "or doctors" should be changed twice to "and doctors." The reason is that the logical sum of classes is represented rather by 'and' than 'or' in ordinary language, as the author has correctly noted on the preceding page.

In the small print of page 124 the author speculates on the possibility of a mechanical routine for testing validity of truth functions of formulae of Boolean class algebra, without remarking that the literature contains various.[9] Mostly these techniques, as published, are geared to the notation of monadic quantification theory, but they are easily adapted to the other notation. Actually the author is speculating on the possibility of a test of a somewhat special form; still the reader should be informed that tests are at hand.

On page 140, 'Nobody loves without somebody else suffering' is wrongly rendered '$(x)(\exists y)[\sim(x=y) \cdot fx \cdot \supset gy]$.' It should be '$(x)(\exists y)[fx \supset \cdot \sim (x=y) \cdot gy]$.' Mr. Strawson's formula is a logical truism, provable thus: $x = x$; therefore

$$\sim(x=x) \cdot fx \cdot \supset gx; \text{ therefore } (\exists y)[\sim(x=y) \cdot fx \cdot \supset gy].$$

On page 149, where the author explains Russell's theory of descriptions, the paraphrase which he gives of 'the King of England smiled' is redundant: '$x$ is King of England' can be deleted, for it follows from the ensuing quantification. Or, if he wants to keep the redundant clause for perspicuity, he might as well weaken '$\equiv$' to '$\supset$' in the ensuing quantification. The same criticism applies to page 185 and again to page 186.

[9] For one and reference to others see *Methods of Logic*, p. 116 and preceding pages.

# MR. STRAWSON ON SYMBOLIC
# AND TRADITIONAL LOGIC*

PETER T. GEACH (1921–    ) of Birmingham University has written extensively on logic and its history, philosophy of language, and philosophy of mind. Among his books are *Reference and Generality* and *Mental Acts*.

Some readers of Mr. Strawson's *Introduction to Logical Theory* may have been struck, as I have, by a systematic difference between his treatment of the modern (truth-functional and quantificational) logic and

* Reprinted by kind permission of the author and publisher, from *Mind*, Vol. 72, 1963, pp. 125–128.

of the traditional pseudo-Aristotelian logic. (It looks as though Strawson would let the traditional logicians steal the horse, but not let the modern logicians look over the hedge, as regards departures from ordinary language.) I shall not try to explain this difference, nor shall I draw any conclusion from it as regards Strawson's general attitude in logical theory; I shall merely establish that it is a fact.

(1) How far do the logical constants of a formal system correspond to the use of certain expressions in ordinary language? In answering this question, Strawson painstakingly brings out divergences between truth-functional connectives and the nearest ordinary-language analogues (pp. 79–93). Even in "the identification of 'and' with '.' there is already a considerable distortion of the facts" (p. 79); and even for cases where only a very stupid pupil would try to transcribe 'and' into symbols with '.', we are warned that such transcription would be illegitimate (*cf.* the examples on p. 80).

On the other hand, the only divergence that Strawson recognises between the uses of 'all' and 'some' in the traditional 'all S is P' and 'some S is (not) P' and the ordinary-language uses of the same words is that " 'some,' in its most common employment as a separate word, carries an implication of plurality" (pp. 177 f.) (I am not sure what this "implication of plurality" is: whether, *e.g.*, for the example 'some metal is lighter than water' the implication would be that there is more than one metal, or that there is more than one metal lighter than water; a back-reference to p. 165 f. suggests the latter interpretation. And, as often happens for philosophers' assertions about the common use of words, one may feel tempted to dispute the assertion; but I resist the temptation.)

Now in fact there are other divergences. It would admittedly be odd to say '(not) all John's children are asleep' if John had no children; and accordingly Strawson insists that an assertion or denial that all John's children are asleep "presupposes" a statement that there exist children of John's (p. 175). He does not remark, however, that the use of a sentence like this would be equally odd if in fact John had only one child or even only two children; and he gives no reason for thus exclusively attending to a "presupposition" of non-emptiness, rather than of non-singularity or non-duality, on the part of the term 'child of John.' Indeed, by implication Strawson denies that the oddity I have just discussed exists; for he expressly says that "with the reservation noted above" (concerning 'some') his account of the matter "gives the constants of the system just the sense which they have in a vast group of statements of ordinary speech" (p. 178).

(2) Strawson raises difficulties over the entailment of '*p* or *q*' by '*p*,' on the score that '*p*, ergo *p* or *q*' is not a "logically proper step"; "the alternative statement carries the implication of the speaker's uncertainty . . . and this implication is inconsistent with the assertion" of the first alternative (p. 91). It is needless for us to discuss whether these difficulties have any substance; it ought, in any case, to be clear that there is a very similar

oddity or difficulty over the inference-pattern 'all S is P, *ergo* some S is P,' since the assertion that *some* are very often carries with it the implication of the speaker's uncertainty as to whether *all* are. But *this* inference-pattern is a part of the traditional formal logic; and Strawson claims, on behalf of his own way of reading the traditional forms, that "it enables the whole body of the laws of the system to be accepted without inconsistency" (p. 178); moreover, in the passage where he expressly mentions the 'all'— 'some' entailment (p. 158), he gives us no hint that this entailment is at all open to exception.

(3) Strawson raises a number of objections to the symbolic rendering of 'there was at least one woman among the survivors' in quantificational form:

(A) (∃x) (x is a woman.   x was among the survivors)

He first considers what we got if we read '(∃x) (x . . . x . . .)' as 'there *is* at least one person who . . . and who . . .' (his italics). On this reading the formula is alleged "at least to suggest that the person is alive at the time the sentence is uttered. . . . Changing the . . . 'is' to 'was' will not help; it will merely prompt the question 'What became of her then? Has she changed her sex?" (pp. 150 f.). The natural rejoinder that we ought not to read '(∃x) (x . . .)' as 'there *is* (etc.), with an emphatic present-tense 'is,' is met with the argument that surely "the question of time-reference" does arise "when we speak of persons and incidents."

I do not think much of these difficulties. What a formula suggests, what question it prompts, is not relevant to a logician; for in these respects logically equivalent formulas may differ. Again, since the verbs following '(∃x)' are tensed, it is not clear why '(∃x)' need also be so in order to give the whole formula a time-reference. But however this may be, the rendering of our ordinary-language expression in a traditional I schedule, *viz.*

(B) Some woman is a person who was among the survivors,

generates parallel difficulties. 'Some woman is . . .' suggests that we are speaking of a woman now living; and worries about the propriety of the expression if there had been a change of sex are at least as relevant here as they are for (A). Strawson, however, refuses to concern himself with the problems of fitting tensed statements into the traditional four-fold schedule; this schedule gives us only "representative patterns" which need not be "strictly exemplified" (p. 153).

(4) Strawson is concerned at the (alleged) fact that only a few sentences of ordinary language, beginning with "rather strained and awkward phrases," give us formulas to which quantification theory can be straightforwardly applied (p. 147); and he elaborately argues that twisting sentences around so as to make the theory applicable does not just give us clumsy English but leads to philosophical errors as well (pp. 148 f., 185 ff.). Now to be sure Strawson does at one point mention the fact that if we

turn sentences into one or other of the four categorical forms "the results would be, as English, often clumsy and sometimes absurd" (p. 153); but he does not display this clumsiness and absurdity in any actual example; and he never considers the possibility that the traditional manipulations may lead to philosophical errors—his harshest judgment on the traditional logic of categoricals is that it is "very limited" (p. 192). He does not remark the extreme grammatical oddity of the traditional 'all S is P' for most readings of 'S';[1] and this oddity at least is not philosophically innocent. The wrong idea that a universally quantified subject-term stands for the whole class of Ss [2] *can* be put across where that term has the form 'every S' or 'all Ss': but how much the illusion is helped by using 'all S'!

(5) The undeniable extent of formal parallelism between '⊃' in symbolic logic and 'if . . . then' in ordinary language (*cf.* pp. 86–87) does not in Strawson's eyes at all justify, or even excuse, our reading '⊃' as 'if . . . then.' On the other hand, the class of statements to the effect that Socrates is such and such has a certain formal parallelism to the class of statements to the effect that every man is such and such; *e.g.* within either class we may reach the member with 'P' for predicate as a conclusion from the member with 'M' for predicate and the further premise 'every M is P.' Now Strawson *does* regard this partial formal parallelism as showing that the traditional logic was "not absurd" in classifying statements to the effect that Socrates is such and such as universal affirmatives (p. 181).

I have not here tried to appraise Strawson's general doctrine as to the relation between formal logic and ordinary-language arguments. It will be enough to say that that doctrine affords no grounds for treating the traditional syllogistic logic as raising fewer or less radical problems of application than the modern calculi of truth-functions and quantifiers. In one place Strawson seems to recognise that he may have given a false impression:

> Some of the foregoing sections may appear to wear the guise of a defence of the traditional system. But the appearance is, at least in part, misleading . . . it would be mistaken in fact, and in principle, to represent the traditional system as succeeding in an enterprise in which the modern logic fails, or *vice versa* (pp. 193 f.).

I am afraid this disclaimer will not have remedied the false impression. Many readers will vaguely think Strawson has *proved* that the traditional system with all its faults is philosophically less misleading than the new-fangled one. Those Colleges of Unreason where the pseudo-Aristotelian logic is presented as the only genuine logic, and those lecturers who would like to teach the philosophy of logic without having to learn any modern logic, may well thus have been supplied with a pretext for supine ignorance.

[1] How did this odd form originate? Was it a mistranslation of 'omne S est P,' which should of course be 'every S is P'? And who introduced it?

[2] On the nature of this error see my paper "The Doctrine of Distribution," *Mind*, January 1956.

## SUGGESTIONS FOR FURTHER READING
## ON LOGIC AND ORDINARY LANGUAGE

BETH, E. W.   "Carnap's Views on the Advantages of Constructed Systems Over Natural Languages in the Philosophy of Science," *The Philosophy of Rudolf Carnap*, P. A. Schilpp, ed. La Salle, Ill.: Open Court Publishing Co., 1963, pp. 469–502.

CARNAP, R.   "E. W. Beth on Constructed Language Systems," *ibid.* pp. 927–933.

———.   "P. F. Strawson on Linguistic Naturalism," *ibid.* pp. 933–940.

CATON, C. E.   *Philosophy and Ordinary Language.* Urbana, Ill.: University of Illinois Press, 1963.

GELLNER, E.   *Words and Things.* London: Gollanez, 1959.

LEWIS, C. I. and C. H. LANGFORD.   "Propositions of Ordinary Discourse," *Symbolic Logic.* New York: Appleton-Century-Crofts, 1932, pp. 310–334.

QUINE, W. V. O.   "Logic as a Source of Syntactical Insights," *The Ways of Paradox.* New York: Random House, Inc., 1966, pp. 42–47.

STRAWSON, P. F.   "Carnap's Views on Constructed Systems versus Natural Languages in Analytic Philosophy," *The Philosophy of Rudolf Carnap.* P. A. Schilpp, ed. La Salle, Ill.: Open Court, 1963, pp. 503–518.

TEICHMANN, J.   "Propositions," *The Philosophical Review*, Vol. 70 (1961), pp. 500–517.

WITTGENSTEIN, L.   *Philosophical Investigations.* G. E. M. Anscombe, trans. New York: The Macmillan Company, 1953.

# Part
# 7 MODAL LOGIC

## *Introduction*

Historically, modal logic arose out of C. I. Lewis's dissatisfaction with the notion of *material implication*. In the usual
(truth functional or extensional) propositional calculus, the conditional "if $p$ then $q$" is rendered by the formula "$p \supset q$," which is
logically or definitionally equivalent to "$\sim p \vee q$" or "$\sim (p \cdot \sim q)$."
Such a truth functional conditional is often described as stating that
$p$ materially implies $q$. In such logical systems it can be proved that
a false proposition implies any proposition, and that a true proposition is implied by any proposition. These are the so-called paradoxes of material implication. Lewis sought to construct a new and
different calculus of propositions ". . . based upon a meaning of
'implies' such that '$p$ implies $q$' will be synonymous with '$q$ is deducible from $p$.'" * It involved the use of modal functions of prop-
sitions, such as "$p \circ q$" ($p$ is consistent with $q$), "$\diamondsuit p$" ($p$ is possible), "$\square p$" ($p$ is necessary), and "$p \prec q$" ($q$ is deducible from $p$,
or $p$ strictly implies $q$). Lewis called this new logic a "System of
Strict Implication." The general area of such investigation has
come to be called "modal logic."

It soon developed that even without the complications introduced by quantification theory, there were a number of alternative
systems of strict implication. The five earliest and most widely discussed systems, S1 through S5, are presented in the first selection
included in this part, Appendix II of Lewis and Langford's *Sym-*

---

* C. I. Lewis and C. H. Langford, *Symbolic Logic*, Appleton-Century-Crofts, New
York and London, 1932, p. 122.

*bolic Logic.* It is highly compressed and quite technical, but very important historically. It provides useful background material for the more polemical and controversial selections that follow it.

The second selection in this part, Quine's "The Problem of Interpreting Modal Logic," serves to explain some aspects of modal logic as well as to pose a serious problem for its interpretation, at least for modal logic extended to include quantification theory. His point, briefly put, is that quantification over modal contexts disrupts our familiar notions of identity, and causes a vexing proliferation of values for variables which cannot be identified with each other even though they are identical—as are the morning star and the evening star.

The third selection is Fitch's explicit reply to Quine's essay. Fitch argues that "Quine's dilemma" can be avoided in either of two different ways, both of which he commends as "orthodox, natural, and available." Fitch maintains that interpreting "the morning star" and "the evening star" either as proper names or as definite descriptions will suffice to make quantification in modal logic consistent without requiring the introduction of "individual concepts," which Fitch regards as an objectionable kind of Platonism.

In the somewhat longer fourth selection Ruth Barcan Marcus presents a more extensive discussion of Quine's objections to modal logic. She considers a whole range of modal logics containing quantification and relates them to several of the different modal systems formulated by Lewis in the first selection. Her discussion is interesting for distinguishing different degrees of extensionality, as well as for indicating the kind of semantical system in which systems of modal logic can be interpreted.

In the fifth and final selection Quine criticizes the preceding essay and continues his attack on modal logic. He rejects the suggestion that 'identity, substitutivity, and extensionality are things that come in grades,' and offers an absolute criterion for the identity predicate and an absolute substitutivity condition. He shows that even intensions can be specifiable contingently, and concludes that limiting the universe (of discourse) to intensions does not avoid the difficulties involved in quantifying into modal contexts.

# THE STRUCTURE OF THE SYSTEM OF STRICT IMPLICATION*[1]

Clarence Irving Lewis (1883–1964). See page 3.

The System of Strict Implication, as presented in Chapter V of A *Survey of Symbolic Logic* (University of California Press, 1918), contained an error with respect to one postulate. This was pointed out by Dr. E. L. Post, and was corrected by me in the *Journal of Philosophy, Psychology, and Scientific Method* (XVII [1920], 300). The amended postulates (set A below) compare with those of Chapter VI of this book (set B below) as follows:

| | | |
|---|---|---|
| A1. $pq . \mathbin{⥽} . qp$ | | B1. $pq . \mathbin{⥽} . qp$ |
| A2. $qp . \mathbin{⥽} . p$ | | B2. $pq . \mathbin{⥽} . p$ |
| A3. $p . \mathbin{⥽} . pp$ | | B3. $p . \mathbin{⥽} . pp$ |
| A4. $p(qr) . \mathbin{⥽} . q(pr)$ | | B4. $(pq)r . \mathbin{⥽} . p(qr)$ |
| A5. $p \mathbin{⥽} \sim(\sim p)$ | | B5. $p \mathbin{⥽} \sim(\sim p)$ |

---

* From *Symbolic Logic* by Clarence I. Lewis and Cooper H. Langford. Copyright 1932, 1959 by C. I. Lewis and C. H. Langford. Published by Dover Publications, Inc., New York 14, N.Y. at $2.35, and reprinted through permission of the publisher.

[1] This appendix is written by Mr. Lewis, but the points demonstrated are, most of them, due to other persons.

Groups II and III, below, were transmitted to Mr. Lewis by Dr. M. Wajsberg, of the University of Warsaw, in 1927. Dr. Wajsberg's letter also contained the first proof ever given that the System of Strict Implication is not reducible to Material Implication, as well as the outline of a system which is equivalent to that deducible from the postulates of Strict Implication with the addition of the postulate later suggested in Becker's paper and cited below as C11. It is to be hoped that this and other important work of Dr. Wajsberg will be published shortly.

Groups I, IV, and V are due to Dr. William T. Parry, who also discovered independently Groups II and III. Groups I, II, and III are contained in his doctoral dissertation, on file in the Harvard University Library. Most of the proofs in this appendix have been given or suggested by Dr. Parry.

It follows from Dr. Wajsberg's work that there is an unlimited number of groups, or systems, of different cardinality, which satisfy the postulates of Strict Implication. Mr. Paul Henle, of Harvard University, later discovered another proof of this same fact. Mr. Henle's proof, which can be more easily indicated in brief space, proceeds by demonstrating that any group which satisfies the Boole-Schröder Algebra will also satisfy the postulates of Strict Implication if $\Diamond p$ be determined as follows:

$$\Diamond p = 1 \text{ when and only when } p \neq 0;$$
$$\Diamond p = 0 \text{ when and only when } p = 0.$$

This establishes the fact that there are as many distinct groups satisfying the postulates as there are powers of 2, since it has been shown by Huntington that there is a group satisfying the postulates of the Boole-Schröder Algebra for every power of 2 ("Sets of Independent Postulates for the Algebra of Logic," *Trans. Amer. Math. Soc.*, V [1904], 309).

A6.  $p \mathrel{\dashv} q . q \mathrel{\dashv} r : \mathrel{\dashv} . p \mathrel{\dashv} r$     B6.  $p \mathrel{\dashv} q . q \mathrel{\dashv} r : \mathrel{\dashv} . p \mathrel{\dashv} r$

A7.  $\sim \Diamond p \mathrel{\dashv} \sim p$     B7.  $p . p \mathrel{\dashv} q : \mathrel{\dashv} . q$

A8.  $p \mathrel{\dashv} q . \mathrel{\dashv} . \sim \Diamond q \mathrel{\dashv} \sim \Diamond p$     B8.  $\Diamond (p q) \mathrel{\dashv} \Diamond p$

     B9.  $(\exists p, q) : \sim (p \mathrel{\dashv} q) . \sim (p \mathrel{\dashv} \sim q)$

The primitive ideas and definitions are not identical in the two cases; but they form equivalent sets, in connection with the postulates.

Comparison of these two sets of postulates, as well as many other points concerning the structure of Strict Implication, will be facilitated by consideration of the following groups. Each of these is based upon the same matrix for the relation $p q$ and the function of negation $\sim p$. (This is a four-valued matrix which satisfies the postulates of the Boole-Schröder Algebra.) The groups differ by their different specification of the function $\Diamond p$. We give the fundamental matrix for $p q$ and $\sim p$ in the first case only. The matrix for $p \mathrel{\dashv} q$, resulting from this and the particular determination of $\Diamond p$, is given for each group:

GROUP    I

| $pq$ | | $q$ | | | $\sim p$ | $\Diamond$ | $\dashv$ | 1 | 2 | 3 | 4 |
|---|---|---|---|---|---|---|---|---|---|---|---|
| | 1 | 2 | 3 | 4 | | | | | | | |
| $p$ 1 | 1 | 2 | 3 | 4 | 4 | 1 | 1 | 2 | 4 | 4 | 4 |
| 2 | 2 | 2 | 4 | 4 | 3 | 1 | 2 | 2 | 2 | 4 | 4 |
| 3 | 3 | 4 | 3 | 4 | 2 | 1 | 3 | 2 | 4 | 2 | 4 |
| 4 | 4 | 4 | 4 | 4 | 1 | 3 | 4 | 2 | 2 | 2 | 2 |

GROUP    II

| $\Diamond$ | $\dashv$ | 1 | 2 | 3 | 4 |
|---|---|---|---|---|---|
| 1 | 1 | 1 | 4 | 3 | 4 |
| 2 | 2 | 1 | 1 | 3 | 3 |
| 1 | 3 | 1 | 4 | 1 | 4 |
| 4 | 4 | 1 | 1 | 1 | 1 |

GROUP    III

| $\Diamond$ | $\dashv$ | 1 | 2 | 3 | 4 |
|---|---|---|---|---|---|
| 1 | 1 | 1 | 4 | 4 | 4 |
| 1 | 2 | 1 | 1 | 4 | 4 |
| 1 | 3 | 1 | 4 | 1 | 4 |
| 4 | 4 | 1 | 1 | 1 | 1 |

GROUP    IV

| $\Diamond$ | $\dashv$ | 1 | 2 | 3 | 4 |
|---|---|---|---|---|---|
| 2 | 1 | 1 | 3 | 3 | 3 |
| 2 | 2 | 1 | 1 | 3 | 3 |
| 2 | 3 | 1 | 3 | 1 | 3 |
| 4 | 4 | 1 | 1 | 1 | 1 |

GROUP    V

| $\Diamond$ | $\dashv$ | 1 | 2 | 3 | 4 |
|---|---|---|---|---|---|
| 1 | 1 | 2 | 4 | 3 | 4 |
| 2 | 2 | 2 | 2 | 3 | 3 |
| 1 | 3 | 2 | 4 | 2 | 4 |
| 3 | 4 | 2 | 2 | 2 | 2 |

The 'designated values,' for all five groups, are 1 and 2; that is, the group is to be taken as satisfying any principle whose values, for all combinations of the values of its variables, are confined to 1 and 2. (In Groups II, III, and IV, 1 alone might be taken as the designated value: but in that case it must be remembered that, since

$$(\exists p, q) : \sim (p \mathrel{\dashv} q) . \sim (p \mathrel{\dashv} \sim q) : . = : . \sim [(p, q) : p \mathrel{\dashv} q . \mathrm{v} . p \mathrel{\dashv} \sim q],$$

B9 would be satisfied *unless* $p \dashv q . \text{v} . p \dashv \sim q$ *always* has the value 1. It is simpler to take 1 and 2 both as designated values; in which case B9 is satisfied if and only if $\sim (p \dashv q) . \sim (p \dashv \sim q)$ has the value 1 or the value 2 for some combination of the values of $p$ and $q$.)

All of these groups satisfy the operations of 'Adjunction,' 'Inference,' and the substitution of equivalents. If $P$ and $Q$ are functions having a designated value, then $P Q$ will have a designated value. If $P$ has a designated value, and $P \dashv Q$ has a designated value, then $Q$ will have a designated value. And if $P = Q$—that is, if $P \dashv Q . Q \dashv P$ has a designated value—then $P$ and $Q$ will have the same value, and for any function $f$ in the system, $f(P)$ and $f(Q)$ will have the same value.

The following facts may be established by reference to these groups:

(1) The system, as deduced from either set of postulates, is consistent. Group I, Group II, and Group III each satisfy all postulates of either set. For any one of these three groups, B9 is satisfied by the fact that $\sim (p \dashv q) . \sim (p \dashv \sim q)$ has a designated value when $p = 1$ and $q = 2$, and when $p = 1$ and $q = 3$.

(2) The system, as deduced from either set, is not reducible to Material Implication. For any one of the five groups, $\sim (p \sim q) . \dashv . p \dashv q$ has the value 3 or 4 when $p = 1$ and $q = 2$. None of the 'paradoxes' of Material Implication, such as $p . \supset . q \supset p$ and $\sim p . \supset . p \supset q$, will hold for any of these groups if the sign of material implication, $\supset$, is replaced by $\dashv$ throughout.

(3) The Consistency Postulate, B8, is independent of the set (B1–7 and B9) and of the set A1–7. Group V satisfies B1–7, and satisfies $\sim (p \dashv q) . \sim (p \dashv \sim q)$ for the values $p = 1$, $q = 2$. It also satisfies A1–7. But Group V fails to satisfy B8: B8 has the value 4 when $p = 2$ and $q = 3$, and when $p = 2$ and $q = 4$.

(4) Similarly, A8 is independent of the set A1–7, and of the set (B1–7 and B9). For Group V, A8 has the value 4 when $p = 1$ and $q = 3$, and when $p = 2$ and $q = 3$.

(5) Postulate B7 is independent of the set (B1–6 and B8, 9), and of the set (A1–6 and A8). Group IV satisfies B1–6, B8, and B9, and satisfies A1–6 and A8. But for this group, B7 has the value 3 when $p = 1$ and $q = 2$, and for various other combinations of the values of $p$ and $q$.

(6) Similarly, A7 is independent of the set (A1–6 and A8) and of the set (B1–6 and B8, 9). For Group IV, A7 has the value 3 when $p = 1$ and when $p = 3$.

That the Existence Postulate, B9, is independent of the set B1–8, and of the set A1–8, is proved by the following two-element group, which satisfies B1–8 and A1–8:

| $pq$ | 1 | 0 | $\sim p$ |
|---|---|---|---|
| 1 | 1 | 0 | 0 |
| 0 | 0 | 0 | 1 |

| $\diamond$ | $\dashv$ | 1 | 0 |
|---|---|---|---|
| 1 | 1 | 1 | 0 |
| 0 | 0 | 1 | 1 |

(This is, of course, the usual matrix for Material Implication, with the function $\Diamond p$ specified as equivalent to $p$.) For this group, $\sim (p \dashv q) . \sim (p \dashv \sim q)$ has the value 0 for all combinations of the values of $p$ and $q$.

Dr. Parry has been able to deduce B2 from the set (B1 and B3–9). However, the omission of B2 from the postulate set of Chapter VI would have been incompatible with the order of exposition there adopted, since the Consistency Postulate is required for the derivation of B2. Whether with this exception the members of set B are mutually independent has not been fully determined.

The question naturally arises whether the two sets A1–8 and B1–8 are equivalent. I have discovered no proof but believe that they are not. B1–8 are all deducible from A1–8: and A1–7 are all deducible from B1–8. The question is whether A8 is deducible from B1–8. If it is not, then the system as deduced from the postulate set of Chapter VI, B1–9, is somewhat 'stricter' than as deduced in the *Survey* from set A.

The logically important issue here concerns certain consequences which enter the system when A8 is introduced. Both Dr. Wajsberg and Dr. Parry have proved that the principle

$$p \dashv q . \dashv : q \dashv r . \dashv . p \dashv r$$

is deducible from A1–8. I doubt whether this proposition should be regarded as a valid principle of deduction: it would never lead to any inference $p \dashv r$ which would be questionable when $p \dashv q$ and $q \dashv r$ are given premises; but it gives the inference $q \dashv r . \dashv . p \dashv r$ whenever $p \dashv q$ is a premise. Except as an elliptical statement for "$p \dashv q . q \dashv r : \dashv . p \dashv r$ and $p \dashv q$ is true," this inference seems dubious.

Now as has been proved under (3) above, the Consistency Postulate, B8, is not deducible from the set (B1–7 and B9). Likewise the principle mentioned in the preceding paragraph is independent of the set (B1–7 and B9): Group V satisfies this set, but for that group the principle in question has the value 4 when $p = 1$, $q = 3$, and $r = 1$, as well as for various other values of $p$, $q$, and $r$. But Group V also fails to satisfy B8, as was pointed out in (3) above. If it should hereafter be discovered that the dubious principle of the preceding paragraph is deducible from the set B1–9, then at least it is not contained in the system deducible from the set (B1–7 and B9); and I should then regard that system—to be referred to hereafter as S1—as the one which coincides in its properties with the strict principles of deductive inference. As the reader will have noted, Chapter VI was so developed that the theorems belonging to this system, S1, are readily distinguishable from those which require the Consistency Postulate, B8.

The system as deduced either from set A or from set B leaves undetermined certain properties of the modal functions, $\Diamond p$, $\sim \Diamond p$, $\Diamond \sim p$, and

$\sim \Diamond \sim p$. In view of this fact, Professor Oskar Becker [2] has proposed the following for consideration as further postulates, any one or more of which might be added to either set:

C10. $\quad \sim \Diamond \sim p \dashv \sim \Diamond \sim \sim \Diamond \sim p \qquad \sim \Diamond \sim \sim \Diamond \sim p = \sim \Diamond \sim p$

C11. $\quad \Diamond p \dashv \sim \Diamond \sim \Diamond p \qquad\qquad \Diamond p = \sim \Diamond \sim \Diamond p$

C12. $\quad p \dashv \sim \Diamond \sim \Diamond p$

(Becker calls C12 the "Brouwersche Axiom.")

When A1–8, or B1–9, are assumed, the second form in which C10 is given can be derived from the first, since the converse implication, $\sim \Diamond \sim \sim \Diamond \sim p \dashv \sim \Diamond \sim p$, is an immediate consequence of the general principle, $\sim \Diamond \sim p \dashv p$ (18·42 in Chapter VI). The second form of C11 is similarly deducible from the first.

An alternative and notationally simpler form of C10 would be

$$\text{C10·1} \quad \Diamond \Diamond p \dashv \Diamond p \qquad\qquad \Diamond \Diamond p = \Diamond p$$

(As before, the second form of the principle can be derived from the first; since the converse implication, $\Diamond p \dashv \Diamond \Diamond p$, is an instance of the general principle $p \dashv \Diamond p$, which is 18·4 in Chapter VI, deducible from A1–8, or B1–9.)

Substituting $\sim p$ for $p$, in C10·1, we have

$$\Diamond \Diamond \sim p \dashv \Diamond \sim p \qquad\qquad\qquad \text{(a)}$$
$$\text{(a)} \; . = . \sim \Diamond \sim p \dashv \sim \Diamond \Diamond \sim p \; . = . \sim \Diamond \sim p \dashv \sim \Diamond \sim \sim \Diamond \sim p.$$

And substituting $\sim p$ for $p$ in C10, we have

$$\sim \Diamond \sim (\sim p) \dashv \sim \Diamond \sim \sim \Diamond \sim (\sim p) \qquad\qquad \text{(b)}$$
$$\text{(b)} \; . = . \sim \Diamond p \dashv \sim \Diamond \sim \sim \Diamond p \; . = . \sim \Diamond p \dashv \sim \Diamond \Diamond p \; . = . \Diamond \Diamond p \dashv \Diamond p.$$

(The principles used in these proofs are 12·3 and 12·44 in Chapter VI.)

For reasons which will appear, we add, to this list of further postulates to be considered, the following:

$$\text{C13.} \quad \Diamond \Diamond p$$

That is. "For every proposition $p$, the statement '$p$ is self-consistent' is a self-consistent statement."

Concerning these proposed additional postulates, the following facts may be established by reference to Groups I, II, and III, above, all of which satisfy the set A1–8 and the set B1–9:

(7) C10, C11, and C12 are all consistent with A1–8 and with B1–9 and with each other. Group III satisfies C10, C11, and C12.

(8) C10, C11, and C12 are each independent of the set A1–8 and of the set B1–9. For Group I, C10, C11, and C12 all fail to hold when $p = 3$.

---

[2] See his paper "Zur Logik der Modalitäten," *Jahrbuch für Philosophie und Phäno-menologische Forschung*, XI (1930), 497–548.

(9) Neither C11 nor C12 is deducible from the set (A1–8 and C10) or from the set (B1–9 and C10). Group II satisfies C10; but C11 fails, for this group, when $p = 2$ or $p = 4$; and C12 fails when $p = 2$.

(10) C13 is consistent with the set A1–8 and with the set B1–9. Group I satisfies C13.

(11) C13 is independent of the set A1–8 and of the set B1–9, and of (A1–8 and C10, C11, and C12) or (B1–9 and C10, C11, and C12). Group III satisfies all these sets; but for this group, C13 fails when $p = 4$.

When A1–8, or B1–9, are assumed, the relations of C10, C11, and C12 to each other are as follows:

(12) C10 is deducible from C11. By C11 and the principle $\sim (\sim p) = p$,

$$\sim \Diamond \sim p = \sim [\Diamond (\sim p)] = \sim [\sim \Diamond \sim \Diamond (\sim p)] = \Diamond [\sim \Diamond (\sim p)]$$
$$= \sim \Diamond \sim \Diamond (\sim \Diamond \sim p) = \sim \Diamond [\sim \Diamond \sim \Diamond (\sim p)]$$
$$= \sim \Diamond [\Diamond (\sim p)] = \sim \Diamond \{ \sim [\sim (\Diamond \sim p)] \} = \sim \Diamond \sim \sim \Diamond \sim p.$$

(13) C12 also is deducible from C11. By 18·4 in Chapter VI, $p \dashv \Diamond p$; and this, together with C11, implies C12, by A6 or by B6.

(14) From C10 and C12 together, C11 is deducible. Substituting $\Diamond p$ for $p$ in C12, we have

$$\Diamond p \dashv \sim \Diamond \sim \Diamond \Diamond p. \qquad (a)$$

And by C10·1, $\sim \Diamond \sim \Diamond \Diamond p = \sim \Diamond \sim \Diamond p$. Hence (a) is equivalent to C11.

From (12), (13), and (14), it follows that as additional postulates to the set A1–8, or the set B1–9, C11 is exactly equivalent to C10 and C12 together. But as was proved in (9), the addition of C10 alone, gives a system in which neither C11 nor C12 is deducible.

Special interest attaches to C10. The set A1–8, or the set B1–9, *without* C10, gives the theorem

$$\sim \Diamond \sim \sim \Diamond \sim p . \dashv : \sim \Diamond \sim p = p.$$

This is deducible from 19·84 in Chapter VI. It follows from this that if there should be some proposition $p$ such that $\sim \Diamond \sim \sim \Diamond \sim p$ is true, then the equivalences

$$p = \sim \Diamond \sim p \qquad \text{and} \qquad \sim \Diamond \sim p = \sim \Diamond \sim \sim \Diamond \sim p$$

would hold for that particular proposition. And since, by 19·84 itself, all necessary propositions are equivalent, it follows that if there is *any* proposition $p$ which is necessarily-necessary—such that $\sim \Diamond \sim \sim \Diamond \sim p$ is true— then *every* proposition which is necessary is also necessarily-necessary; and the principle stated by C10 holds universally. But as was proved in (8), this principle, $\sim \Diamond \sim p = \sim \Diamond \sim \sim \Diamond \sim p$, is not deducible from A1–8 or from B1–9. Hence the two possibilities, with respect to necessary propositions, which the system, as deduced from A1–8 or from B1–9, leaves open are:

(a) that there exist propositions which are necessarily-necessary, and that for every proposition $p$, $\sim \Diamond \sim p = \sim \Diamond \sim \sim \Diamond \sim p$; and (b) that there exist propositions which are necessary—as 20·21 in Chapter VI requires— but *no* propositions which are *necessarily*-necessary. This last is exactly what is required by C13, $\Diamond \Diamond p$. Substituting here $\sim p$ for $p$, we have, as an immediate consequence of C13, $\Diamond \Diamond \sim p$. This is equivalent to the theorem "For every proposition $p$, '$p$ is necessarily-necessary' is false": $\Diamond \Diamond \sim p = \Diamond \sim \sim \Diamond \sim p = \sim (\sim \Diamond \sim \sim \Diamond \sim p)$ [by the principle $\sim (\sim p)$ $= p$]. Thus C10 expresses alternative (a) above; and C13 expresses alternative (b). Hence as additional postulates, C10 and C13 are contrary assumptions.

(As deduced from A1–8, the system leaves open the further alternative that there should be no necessary propositions, or that the class of necessary propositions should merely coincide with the class of true propositions; but in that case the system becomes a redundant form of Material Implication.)

From the preceding discussion it becomes evident that there is a group of systems of the general type of Strict Implication and each distinguishable from Material Implication. We shall arrange these in the order of increasing comprehensiveness and decreasing 'strictness' of the implication relation:

S1, deduced from the set B1–7, contains all the theorems of Sections 1–4 in Chapter VI. It contains also all theorems of Section 5, in the form of $T$-principles, but not with omissions of the $T$. This system does not contain A8 or the principle

$$p \dashv q . \dashv : q \dashv r . \dashv . p \dashv r.$$

However, it does contain, in the form of a $T$-principle, any theorem which could be derived by using A8 as a principle of inference: because it contains

$$p \dashv q . \sim \Diamond q : \dashv . \sim \Diamond p;$$

and hence if (by substitutions) $p \dashv q$ becomes an asserted principle, we shall have

$$T . \sim \Diamond q : \dashv . \sim \Diamond p.$$

When the Existence Postulate, B9, is added, this system S1 contains those existence theorems which are indicated in Section 6 of Chapter VI as not requiring the Consistency Postulate, B8.

S2, deduced from the set B1–8, contains all the theorems of Sections 1–5 in Chapter VI, any $T$-principle being replaceable by the corresponding theorem without the $T$. When the Existence Postulate, B9, is added, it contains all the existence theorems of Section 6. Whether S2 contains A8 and the principle

$$p \dashv q . \dashv : q \dashv r . \dashv . p \dashv r$$

remains undetermined. If that should be the case, then it will be equivalent to S3.

S3, deduced from the set A1–8, as in the *Survey*, contains all the theorems of S2 and contains such consequences of A8 as

$$p \dashv q . \dashv : q \dashv r . \dashv . p \dashv r.$$

If B9 is added, the consequences include all existence theorems of S2.

For each of the preceding systems, S1, S2, and S3, any one of the additional postulates, C10, C11, C12, and C13, is consistent with but independent of the system (but C10 and C13 are mutually incompatible).

S4, deduced from the set (B1–7 and C10), contains all theorems of S3, and in addition the consequences of C10. A8 and B8 are deducible theorems. S4 is incompatible with C13. C11 and C12 are consistent with but independent of S4. If B9 be added, the consequences include all existence theorems of S2.

S5, deduced from the set (B1–7 and C11), or from the set (B1–7, C10, and C12), contains all theorems of S4 and in addition the consequences of C12. If B9 be added, all existence theorems of S2 are included. A8 and B8 are deducible theorems. S5 is incompatible with C13.

Dr. Wajsberg has developed a system mathematically equivalent to S5, and has discovered many important properties of it, notably that it is the limiting member of a certain family of systems. Mr. Henle has proved that S5 is mathematically equivalent to the Boole-Schröder Algebra (*not* the Two-valued Algebra), if that algebra be interpreted for propositions, and the function $\lozenge p$ be determined by:

$$\lozenge p = 1 \text{ when and only when } p = 0;$$

$$\lozenge p = 0 \text{ when and only when } p = 0.$$

In my opinion, the principal logical significance of the system S5 consists in the fact that it divides all propositions into two mutually exclusive classes: the intensional or modal, and the extensional or contingent. According to the principles of this system, all intensional or modal propositions are either necessarily true or necessarily false. As a consequence, for any modal proposition—call it $p_m$—

$$\lozenge (p_m) = (p_m) = {\sim} \lozenge {\sim} (p_m),$$

$$\text{and } \lozenge {\sim} (p_m) = {\sim} (p_m) = {\sim} \lozenge (p_m).$$

For extensional or contingent propositions, however, possibility, truth, and necessity remain distinct.

Prevailing good use in logical inference—the practice in mathematical deductions, for example—is not sufficiently precise and self-conscious to determine clearly which of these five systems expresses the acceptable principles of deduction. (The meaning of 'acceptable' here has been discussed in Chapter VIII.) The issues concern principally the nature of the relation of 'implies' which is to be relied upon for inference, and certain subtle questions about the meaning of logical 'necessity,' 'possibility' or 'self-consistency,' etc.—for example, whether C10 is true or false. (Professor Becker has discussed at length a number of such questions, in his paper above referred to.) Those interested in the merely mathematical properties of such systems of symbolic logic tend to prefer the more comprehensive and less 'strict' systems, such as S5 and Material Implication. The interests of logical study would probably be best served by an exactly opposite tendency.

# THE PROBLEM OF INTERPRETING MODAL LOGIC*

Willard Van Orman Quine (1908–    ). See page 165.

There are logicians, myself among them, to whom the ideas of modal logic (e.g. Lewis's) are not intuitively clear until explained in non-modal terms. But so long as modal logic stops short of quantification theory, it is possible (as I shall indicate in §2) to provide somewhat the type of explanation desired. When modal logic is extended (as by Miss Barcan [1]) to include quantification theory, on the other hand, serious obstacles to interpretation are encountered—particularly if one cares to avoid a curiously idealistic ontology which repudiates material objects. Such are the matters which it is the purpose of the present paper to set forth.

1. *Analytic statements from the standpoint of non-modal logic.* All true statements which (like '$(x)(x = x)$') contain only logical signs are naturally to be classified as logically true. But there are also other logically true statements (e.g., 'Socrates is mortal $\supset$ Socrates is mortal') which contain extra-logical signs. Now every logical truth of the latter kind is (if for the present we disregard modal logic) either *provable within* the familiar logic of truth-functions and quantification alone, or else *deducible by* the logic of truth-functions and quantification *from* logical truths of the kind which contain only logical signs. So *every* logical truth is either:

(a)  a true statement containing only logical signs, or
(b)  provable in the logic of truth-functions and quantification, or

* Reprinted by kind permission of the author and publisher, from *The Journal of Symbolic Logic*, Vol. 12, 1947, pp. 42–48.
[1] Ruth C. Barcan, *A functional calculus of first order based on strict implication*, this Journal, vol. 11 (1946), pp. 1–16.

(c)    *deducible by the logic of truth-functions and quantification from true statements containing only logical signs.*

But (c) includes (b), since whatever is provable is also, vacuously, deducible from anything else. Also (c) includes (a), since any statement is deducible from itself. Thus (c) by itself might be adopted as an appropriate *definition of logical truth* (outside modal logic). The "deducibility" spoken of in (c) can be expanded into purely syntactical terms by an enumeration of the familiar rules, which are known to be complete; and the reference to "logical signs" can likewise be expanded by enumeration of the familiar primitives. The word 'true' in (c) cannot indeed be expanded; no enumeration of axioms or axiom-schemata would serve the purpose here, because of Gödel's proof that there can be no complete consistent system of higher logic. We could desire otherwise, especially in view of the logical paradoxes which are known to be connected with the general concept of truth.[2] Nevertheless (c) is not without explicative value, as marking out the special notion of logical truth within the general notion (such as it is) of truth.

The class of *analytic* statements is broader than that of logical truths, for it contains in addition such statements as 'No bachelor is married.' This example might be assimilated to the logical truths by considering it a definitional abbreviation of 'No man not married is married,' which is indeed a logical truth; but I should prefer not to rest analyticity thus on an unrealistic fiction of there being standard definitions of extra-logical expressions in terms of a standard set of extra-logical primitives. What is rather in point, I think, is a relation of *synonymy*, or sameness of meaning, which holds between expressions of real language though there be no standard hierarchy of definitions. In terms of synonymy and logical truth we could define analyticity: a statement is *analytic* if by putting synonyms for synonyms (e.g., 'man not married' for 'bachelor') it can be turned into a logical truth.

The particular synonymy relation wanted is one of several which have about equal right to the name "synonymy" and are all describable as "sameness of meaning"—in varying senses of "meaning." Synonymy of the kind which renders expressions interchangeable without violence to indirect quotation, for example, would be a narrower relation than the one here concerned; and the sense of synonymy proposed by Lewis [3] is yet a third relation, I believe, intermediate between the two.

The particular synonymy relation which I have in mind can easily be described in terms of analyticity, at least when the expressions related happen to be statements, names, or predicates. Statements are synonymous if the biconditional ('if and only if') which joins them is analytic; names are

[2] See Alfred Tarski, *The semantic conception of truth and the foundation of semantics, Philosophy and phenomenological research*, vol. 4 (1944), pp. 341–376.
[3] C. I. Lewis, *The modes of meaning*, ibid., vol. 4 (1943), p. 245.

synonymous if the statement of identity which joins them is analytic; and predicates are synonymous if, when they are applied to like variables and then combined into a universally quantified biconditional, the result is analytic.

But of course we must seek some other definition of synonymy so as to avoid circularity, if synonymy is to be available for use in defining analyticity. Actually the synonymy relation sought is, insofar as applied to propositions, names, and predicates, precisely what Lewis (*loc. cit.*) calls *sameness of intension*; but expansion in turn of his definition of "intension" leaves us with phrases which I do not feel to be appreciably clearer than "synonymy" and "analyticity" themselves.

Synonymy, like other linguistic concepts, involves parameters of times and persons, suppressible in idealized treatment: the expression $x$ is synonymous with the expression $y$ for person $z$ at time $t$. A satisfactory definition of this tetradic relation would no doubt be couched, like those of other general concepts of general linguistics, in behavioristic terms. I should like, as a service both to empirical semantics and to philosophy, to offer a satisfactory definition; but I have none. So long, however, as we persist in speaking of expressions as alike or unlike in meaning (and regardless of whether we countenance meanings themselves in any detached sense), we must suppose that there is an eventually formulable criterion of synonymy in some reasonable sense of the term—and probably, in particular, in the sense appropriate to present purposes. Given it, and given the general notion of truth (in terms of which logical truth has been seen to be definable), we could define analyticity as previously indicated.

The notion of analyticity thus appears, at the present writing, to lack a satisfactory foundation. Even so, the notion is clearer to many of us, and obscurer surely to none, than the notions of modal logic; so we are still well advised to explain the latter notions in terms of it. This can be done, as sketched in the next section, so long as modal logic stops short of quantification theory.[4]

2. *Interpretation of pre-quantificational modal logic.* We need consider only the mode of logical *necessity*, symbolized by '□'; for the other modal ideas (possibility, impossibility, and the strict conditional and biconditional) are expressible in terms of necessity in obvious fashion. Now '□' is not quite interchangeable with 'is analytic,' for this reason: the former

[4] Dr. Nelson Goodman has suggested (in conversation) the dismal possibility that what we think of as synonymy may be wholly a matter of degree, ranging from out-and-out orthographical sameness of expressions on the one hand to mere factual sameness of designatum (as in the case of 'nine' and 'the number of the planets') on the other. In this case analyticity in turn would become a matter of degree—a measure merely of our relative reluctance to give up one statement rather than another from among a set of statements whose conjunction has proved false. But if it does develop that the boundary between analytic and synthetic statements has thus to be rubbed out, no doubt it will be generally agreed that the logical modalities have to be abandoned as well. The explanation of modal logic in terms of analyticity remains of interest so long as there is interest in modal logic itself.

attaches to a *statement* (as '∼' does) to form a statement *containing* the original statement, whereas 'is analytic' (like 'is true,' 'is false') attaches to the *name* of a statement to form a statement *about* the named statement. Grammatically '□' is an adverb; 'is analytic' is a verb. The formal difference becomes immediately apparent in the case of iteration: '□' can significantly be applied repeatedly (because the result of any application, being a statement, is the kind of expression to which '□' can still significantly be prefixed) whereas 'is analytic' can be applied only once (because the result of the application is a statement, whereas 'is analytic' can be appended only to a name).[5]

However, '□' can be explained in terms of analyticity as follows:

(i)   *The result of prefixing* '□' *to any statement is true if and only if the statement is analytic.*

Let us speak of a statement as of *first intention* if it is non-modal; and let us speak of a statement as of $(n+1)$st intention if '□' occurs in it in application to statements of $n$th intention and no higher. The portion of modal logic which admits statements of $n$th intention at most (and includes also all non-modal logic) will be called the logic of $n$th intention; non-modal logic itself is the logic of first intention. Then (i) above may be taken as our explanation of all statements of second intention; and the word 'analytic' in it (explained in the preceding section) may be read 'analytic in first intention.' Relative to the logic of second intention, now, which has some new truths of its own in addition to those of the logic of first intention, we may adopt new definitions of logical truth and analyticity paralleling those of the preceding section (but admitting uniterated use of '□' in addition to truth-functions in (c)). Thereupon we may repeat (i) above as an explanation now of all statements of third intention. Supposing this process continued *ad infinitum*, we have an explanation of '□' in application to any statements.

I suppose that some such conception underlies the intuition whereby axioms are evaluated and adopted for modal logic. The explanation of modal logic thus afforded is adequate so long as modalities are not used inside the scopes of quantifiers; i.e., so long as '□' is applied only to statements and not to matrices.[6] Of course in actual presentations even of this part of modal logic the sign '□' commonly appears before non-statements such as '$p$' or '$p \supset p$,' but there is no harm in this; such expressions are schemata, used diagrammatically and imagined replaced in any given case by actual statements of the depicted forms.

---

[5] Cf. my *Mathematical logic*, pp. 27–33.

[6] I used the word 'matrix' (as in *Mathematical logic*) for one of the meanings of the ambiguous phrase 'propositional function.' A matrix is an expression which is like a statement except for containing, at grammatically permissible places, some free occurrences of variables of the kind that are admissible in quantifiers. Briefly, a matrix is a non-statement which can be turned into a statement by applying quantifiers.

3. *Quantification in modal logic.*   It will be convenient now to think of our basic modality not as '□' but as '◊' (possibility); the two are inter-definable, amounting respectively to '~ ◊ ~' and '~□~.' And let us think of our quantifiers as existential, since the universal quantifier '$(x)$' can be explained as '~$(\exists x)$~.'

When '◊' is applied to a matrix within a quantification, the whole context admits, in certain cases, of reduction to the type of case dealt with in the preceding section. For example, the combined prefix '$(\exists x)$ ◊' is equated by Miss Barcan [7] to '◊ $(\exists x)$,' wherein '◊' applies no longer to the matrix but to the statement formed by quantifying it (supposing there are no further free variables); and accordingly the explanation of the pre-ceding section can thereupon be brought to bear. If every matrix containing '◊' were transformable into a matrix containing '◊' only at the beginning, then repeated conversion of $\ulcorner(\exists \alpha)$ ◊$\urcorner$ to $\ulcorner$◊ $(\exists \alpha)\urcorner$ would be adequate to explaining the general case; but unfortunately matrices are not generally thus transformable.

Equating '$(\exists x)$ ◊' with '◊ $(\exists x)$' gives us no clue to the interpretation of such statements, for example, as:

$$(\exists x) (x \text{ is red} \, . \, ◊ \, (x \text{ is round})).$$

No doubt a modal logician would regard this example as true, but only by virtue of some supplementary intuitive criterion—perhaps this:

(ii)   *An existential quantification holds if there is a constant whose substi-tution for the variable of quantification would render the matrix true.*

This is at best a partial criterion (both in modal and non-modal logic), because of unnameable objects; an unnameable object might satisfy the matrix though there be no constant expression whose substitution for the variable would yield a truth. But let us adopt (ii) as a partial criterion (suffi-cient condition) and see how it fares.

What I shall show is that it has queer ontological consequences. It leads us to hold that there are no concrete objects (men, planets, etc.), but rather that there are only, corresponding to each supposed concrete object, a multitude of distinguishable entities (perhaps "individual concepts," in Church's phrase). It leads us to hold, e.g., that there is no such ball of mat-ter as the so-called planet Venus, but rather at least three distinct entities: Venus, Evening Star, and Morning Star.

To see this, let us use 'C' (for 'congruence') to express the relation which Venus, the Evening Star, and the Morning Star, e.g., bear to themselves and, according to empirical evidence, to one another. (It is the relation of *identity* according to materialistic astronomy, but let us not prejudge this.)

---

[7] *Op. cit.*, theorem 38.

Then

Morning Star **C** Evening Star. $\square$ (Morning Star **C** Morning Star).

Therefore, according to (ii),

(1)    ($\exists x$) ($x$ **C** Evening Star. $\square$ ($x$ **C** Morning Star)).

But also

Evening Star **C** Evening Star. $\sim\square$ (Evening Star **C** Morning Star),

so that, by (ii),

(2)    ($\exists x$) ($x$ **C** Evening Star. $\sim\square$ ($x$ **C** Morning Star)).

Since the matrix quantified in (1) and the matrix quantified in (2) are mutual contraries, the $x$ whose existence is affirmed in (1) and the $x$ whose existence is affirmed in (2) are two objects; so there must be at least two objects $x$ such that $x$ **C** Evening Star. If we were to introduce the term 'Venus' we could infer a third such object in similar fashion.

Thus it is that the contemplated version of quantified modal logic is committed to an ontology which repudiates material objects (such as the Evening Star properly so-called) and leaves only multiplicities of distinct objects (perhaps the Evening-Star-concept, the Morning-Star-concept, etc.) in their place. For, the ontology of a logic is nothing other than the range of admissible values of the variables of quantification.[8]

A quite parallel conclusion could be drawn in higher logical types, to show that the contemplated version of quantified modal logic is committed to an ontology which repudiates classes and admits only attributes. But this consequence is likely to be regarded as less objectionable, from the point of view at least of modal logicians, than the consequence concerning individuals.

The modal logician who finds the repudiation of material objects (or, indeed, of classes) uncongenial may have recourse to either of the following alternatives.

(a) He may regard his quantified modal logic as only a fragment of the total logic to which he is prepared to subscribe, so that the undesirably limited ontology of the former comes to be only a fragment of a more inclusive ontology which embraces also material objects (and perhaps even classes). Those variables of the total logic which do admit material objects (or classes) as values would then be withheld from quantified modal contexts, or limited to harmless manners of occurrence in them,[9] by special

---

[8] See my *Designation and existence, Journal of philosophy*, vol. 36 (1939), pp. 701–709.

[9] Such is Church's procedure in A *formulation of the logic of sense and denotation* (abstract) this JOURNAL, vol. 11 (1946), p. 31. I am indebted to Professor Church for several helpful letters in this connection. I am also indebted, along more general lines, to Professor Rudolf Carnap; correspondence with him on modal logic over recent years has been very instrumental in clarifying my general position.

grammatical rules. The total logic would not be one in which we could meaningfully apply a modal operator to any matrix at will and then meaningfully quantify the result at will with respect to any free variable.

(b) He may insist on the universality of his quantified modal logic, but disavow the criterion (ii) which underlies my argument. But then we have yet to see what might plausibly be put forward in its stead.

# THE PROBLEM OF THE MORNING STAR
# AND THE EVENING STAR*

Frederic B. Fitch (1908–      ). See page 154.

An argument opposing the unrestricted use of quantification in modal logic has been put forward by Quine.[1] Central to this argument are the two phrases,

(1)   The Morning Star,
(2)   The Evening Star.

One form of the argument is obtained by considering the following two statements:

(3)   It is necessary that the Morning Star is identical with the Morning Star.
(4)   It is not necessary that the Evening Star is identical with the Morning Star.

If it is granted that (3) and (4) are true, as indeed they seem to be if by "necessary" is meant "logically necessary," then the claim can be made that the Morning Star has a property or attribute not possessed by the Evening Star, namely the property of being necessarily identical with the Morning Star. This result leads to the conclusion that the Morning Star

* Reprinted by kind permission of the author and publisher, from Frederic B. Fitch, "The Problem of the Morning Star and the Evening Star," *Philosophy of Science*, Volume 16, 1949, pp. 131–141. Copyright © 1949, The Williams & Wilkins Company, Baltimore, Maryland 21202, U.S.A.
[1] W. V. Quine, The problem of interpreting modal logic, Journal of symbolic logic, vol. 12 (1947), pp. 43–48. See also ibid., pp. 95–96, where Quine reviews two papers by Ruth C. Barcan. These are the second and third of the three papers by Miss Barcan referred to in footnote 6.

is a different individual from the Evening Star, since otherwise it would have exactly the same properties. But of course there is good empirical evidence that the Evening Star and the Morning Star are one and the same individual, known as the planet Venus. Hence the paradox.

To avoid this difficulty, Quine follows Carnap [2] in proposing that the concept of "identity" be omitted in modal logic in favor of a concept of "congruence," and that quantification in modal logic be restricted in such a way that variables range over so-called "individual concepts" instead of ranging over actual individuals.[3] We would then regard (1) and (2) as names of individual concepts rather than as names of actual individuals, and we would revise (3) and (4) to read as follows:

(3') It is necessary that the Morning Star is congruent with the Morning Star.

(4') It is not necessary that the Evening Star is congruent with the Morning Star.

The relation of congruence holds among individual concepts. It serves in a sort of roundabout way to indicate pairs of individual concepts that correspond to the same individual. Thus to say that the concept Morning Star is congruent with the concept Evening Star is an oblique way of saying that the actual Morning Star is identical with the actual Evening Star. The conclusion that follows from (3') and (4') is then merely the innocuous result that the concept Morning Star is different from the concept Evening Star. These two concepts can be "congruent" though different in the sense that one has a property not possessed by the other. We are left, however, with a modal logic which cannot in any very satisfactory way handle the notion of identity among actual individuals.

But there is really no need to resort to Carnap's "individual concepts" in

---

[2] R. Carnap, Meaning and necessity.

[3] Though Quine perhaps ultimately rejects this notion of "individual concepts," he nevertheless seems to feel that modal logic is forced to employ it to overcome difficulties connected with quantification. Miss Barcan, in her third paper (see footnote 6), defines two kinds of identity. The first or "weak" kind, called $I_m$, is Leibnitzian identity using material implication. The second or "strong" kind, called I, is Leibnitzian identity using strict implication. In his review of Miss Barcan's third paper, Quine seems to regard the "weak" identity as analogous to his own "congruence." He says: "It should be noted that only the strong identity is . . . interpretable as identity in the ordinary sense of the word. The system is accordingly best understood by reconstruing the so-called individuals as 'individual concepts.' " Quine apparently overlooks the important fact that the two kinds of identity are materially equivalent in Miss Barcan's system $S2^2$, and even strictly equivalent in her system $S4^2$, as is established in her theorems 2.31 and 2.33*. (The quadruple bar in 2.31 should be a triple bar. A quadruple bar should be inserted between the back-to-back parentheses in the theorem 2.32*.) In the same review Quine also says, "As is to be expected, only the strong kind of identity is subject to a law of substitutivity valid for all modal contexts." But this is not true for $S4^2$, and the fact that it is apparently true for $S2^2$ can be taken as an indication of an inadequacy in $S2^2$. This defect in $S2^2$ can be overcome by adding a rule of procedure to $S2^2$ according to which □ A is an axiom of $S2^2$ whenever A is. It would then follow that the two kinds of identity would be in all respects equivalent even in $S2^2$.

order to make quantified modal logic consistent with the facts of astronomy. The modal logician is free to deal directly with actual individuals and to employ the relation of identity with respect to them. Quine's dilemma may be avoided either of two different ways, both of which eschew such contrivances as "individual concepts" and "congruence." The first of these ways is to regard (1) and (2) as proper names of individuals. The second is to regard (1) and (2) as descriptive phrases in accordance with definitions of Section *14 of Whitehead and Russell's *Principia Mathematica*. Both of these ways are orthodox, natural, and available.

With respect to the first of these ways, Smullyan [4] has pointed out that if the phrases (1) and (2) are regarded as proper names of the same individual, then Quine's argument fails because (4) would clearly be false. On the other hand, to assume that (1) and (2) are proper names of different individuals would be to assume at the outset the very result that Quine's argument is designed to establish. Thus the whole argument fails and no paradox arises in the case where (1) and (2) are treated as proper names.

Turning next to the second method for avoiding the dilemma, we regard (1) and (2) as abbreviations for descriptive phrases. Let us use essentially the notation of *14 of *Principia Mathematica*, and also employ the modal operator '$\square$' for the concept "necessity." Let '$f$' designate the attribute "Morning-Starness" and '$g$' the attribute "Evening-Starness." Then the phrase "the Morning Star" can be regarded as an abbreviation for the descriptive phrase '$(\imath x)fx$' which means "the thing which has the attribute Morning-Starness," while the phrase "the Evening Star" can similarly be regarded as an abbreviation for '$(\imath x)gx$.'

Smullyan [5] would then apparently formalize (3) thus:

(5)  $$\square([(\imath x)fx]((\imath x)fx = (\imath x)fx)).$$

But this is by *14.01 of *Principia Mathematica* an abbreviation for

(6)  $$\square(\exists b)((fx \equiv_x (x = b)) \cdot (b = b)).$$

---

[4] See the Journal of symbolic logic, vol. 12 (1947), pp. 139–141, where A. F. Smullyan reviews Quine's paper, The problem of interpreting modal logic, referred to above. See also by Smullyan, Modality and description, ibid., vol. 13 (1948), pp. 31–37. Both of these papers by Smullyan are largely in agreement with the position of the present writer. It is perhaps worth remarking that on p. 36 of Modality and description it is possible to retain S3 in preference to S1 provided that the necessity operator in S2 is applied to the formal equivalence preceding the implication symbol rather than to the whole expression. This would amount to assuming that if it is necessary that $\alpha$ and $\beta$ have the same members, then $\alpha$ and $\beta$ are the same class. This assumption is the same as the form of the axiom of extensionality mentioned near the end of the present paper.

[5] In his review of Quine's paper. Actually Smullyan retains Quine's notion of congruence in the portion of the review relevant to (5), (6) and (7). He says, "On the other hand, if, more naturally we view 'Evening Star' and 'Morning Star' as abbreviations of descriptive phrases [rather than as proper names of individuals], we find that A [that is, 'Morning Star is congruent with Evening Star $\cdot \square$(Morning Star is congruent with Morning Star)'] expresses an evidently impossible proposition. For if it is not necessary that the morning star exists then it is not necessary that the morning star is self-congruent. And if a proposition is not necessary, then necessarily it is not necessary."

Now Smullyan has rightly pointed out, or at least insinuated, that (6) cannot be regarded as true since it entails the false result,

(7) $$\Box(\exists b)fb.$$

Hence (3) must be regarded as false from this standpoint, and Quine's argument therefore fails.

We might, however choose a different scope for the descriptive phrase of (3), and interpret (3) in a way apparently not considered by Smullyan:

(8) $$[(\imath x)fx](\Box((\imath x)fx = (\imath x)fx)).$$

By *14.01 this is an abbreviation for

(9) $$(\exists b)((fx \equiv_x (x = b)) \cdot \Box(b = b)).$$

Now (9) is clearly true, because of Miss Barcan's theorems [6] 2.6 and 2.32*, giving $\Box(b = b)$, and because of the empirical fact that there is exactly one Morning Star. This means that, under this interpretation, (3) itself is true, so that Quine's dilemma cannot now be avoided by regarding (3) as false. There will be reason, however, to regard (4) as false when interpreted by a similar method. The corresponding interpretation of (4) must be

(10) $$[(\imath x)fx, (\imath x)gx](\sim\Box((\imath x)gx = (\imath x)fx)).$$

By *14.03 and *14.01 of *Principia Mathematica* this is an abbreviation for

(11) $$(\exists b)((fx \equiv_x (x = b)) \cdot (\exists c)((gx \equiv_x (x = c)) \cdot \sim \Box(c = b))).$$

By Miss Barcan's theorem 2.32* it is seen that (11) is equivalent to the following:

(12) $$(\exists b)((fx \equiv_x (x = b)) \cdot (\exists c)((gx \equiv_x (x =_x c)) \cdot \sim (c = b))).$$

But (12) says that the Morning Star is different from the Evening Star, so that (4) itself, under this interpretation, is equivalent to Quine's anomalous result and is unacceptable for the same reason. Therefore Quine's argument, under this interpretation, can be established only by assuming a proposition equivalent to the final unacceptable result.

Thus by using one scope for the descriptive phrases in (3) and (4) we find that (3) leads to false result (7) and so must be regarded as false for that interpretation; while by using another scope for these descriptive

[6] See the correction to 2.32 * given in footnote 3 above. Miss Barcan's three papers on quantified modal logic are as follows: A functional calculus of first order based on strict implication, Journal of symbolic logic, vol. 11 (1946), pp. 1–16; The deduction theorem in a functional calculus of first order based on strict implication, ibid., pp. 115–118; The identity of individuals in a strict functional calculus of second order, ibid., vol. 12 (1947), pp. 12–15. The writer wishes to acknowledge his debt to Miss Barcan for some helpful discussions concerning the ideas of this paper. In particular she pointed out the importance of the equivalence of the two kinds of identity defined in her third paper.

phrases we find that (4) is equivalent to the false result (12) and so must be regarded as false under the second interpretation. In the first case the scope was taken to be as small as possible, and in the second case as large as possible. The reason that (3) seems to be true is perhaps because it is true when the scope is taken as small as possible, and the reason that (4) seems to be true is perhaps because (4) is true when the scope is taken as large as possible. The source of the apparent paradox seems to lie in this ambiguity of the scope of the descriptive phrases.

In ordinary non-modal, truth-functional logic the choice of the scopes of the descriptive phrases '$(\imath x)fx$' and '$(\imath x)gx$' would be indifferent in result, provided only that each of these phrases is assumed to describe some entity uniquely (in other words, provided $E!(\imath x)fx$ and $E!(\imath x)gx$). If it is demanded that descriptive phrases exhibit in modal logic this same indifference to scope which they exhibit in truth-functional logic (under the provision stated),[7] then of course it can be claimed that Quine's paradox does arise in quantified modal logic, and resort has to be made to such devices as "congruence" and "individual concepts." The writer sees no ground for making such a demand, however, and would feel very dissatisfied with the encumbrances and limitations that would have to be imposed on modal logic as a consequence of it. In modal logic the condition for the interchangeability of scopes of '$(\imath x)fx$' is $\Box E!(\imath x)fx$ and $fx \, \dashv_x \, \Box fx$ rather than merely $E!(\imath x)fx$.

The usage of ordinary language with respect to descriptive phrases is so vague that not only does there fail to be any set convention as to whether the scope is to be large or small, but there even usually fails to be any systematic account taken of the notion of scope at all. It is usually not possible to take at random various sentences of ordinary language involving descriptive phrases and interpret them all correctly by some uniform use of Russell's theory of descriptions. The correct interpretations of (3) and (4) seem to the writer to be given respectively by (13) and (14) below. This conclusion was reached by a study of what (3) and (4) seem in themselves to mean, rather than by a mechanical application of the theory of descriptions.

(13)    $$(E!(\imath x)fx) \cdot \Box(fx \equiv_x fx).$$
(14)    $$(E!(\imath x)fx) \cdot (E!(\imath x)gx) \cdot \sim \Box(gx \equiv_x fx).$$

It is clear that (13) and (14) are both true, and this would account for the fact that (3) and (4) both seem to be true.

From (13) and (14) it follows that $\Box(fx \equiv_x fx)$ and $\sim\Box(gx \equiv_x fx)$ are both true, so we conclude that

(15)    $$f \neq g.$$

---

[7] Quine has suggested in correspondence and conversation with the writer that such a demand might be desirable.

There is empirical evidence that leads us to assume

(16)                                  $fx \equiv_x gx.$

But there is no conflict between (15) and (16) in modal logic, because the axiom of extensionality need not be used at all, or only in such a way that $(f = g)$ follows from $\square(fx \equiv_x gx)$ rather than from $(fx \equiv_x gx)$.

Thus (13) and (14) give rise merely to (15) instead of to (12). The attributes $f$ and $g$ here play rôles analogous to those assigned by Carnap and Quine to their "individual concepts." The attributes $f$ and $g$ are equivalent to each other in the sense of applying to exactly the same things, but they are not identical with each other. Similarly Quine's "concept" of Morning Star is "congruent" with the "concept" of the Evening Star, but not identical with it. These "individual concepts" seem to the writer to be almost reifications of attributes, and just as objectionable or more so if one is trying, with Quine, to avoid any ontology that savors of Platonism. The writer objects to a Platonism of "individual concepts" but not to a Platonism of attributes.


# MODALITIES AND INTENSIONAL LANGUAGES*

RUTH BARCAN MARCUS is Professor of Philosophy at The University of Illinois at Chicago Circle. She has written extensively on logic and philosophy of science.

There is a normative sense in which it has been claimed that modal logic is without foundation. Professor Quine, in *Word and Object*, suggests that it was conceived in sin: the sin of confusing use and mention. The original transgressors were Russell and Whitehead. Lewis elaborated the error and constructed a logic in which an operator corresponding to "necessarily" operates on sentences whereas "is necessary" ought to be viewed as a predicate of sentences. As Professor Quine reconstructs the history of the enterprise,[1] the operational use of modalities promised only one advantage: the possibility of quantifying into modal contexts.

---

* A revised version of a paper presented at the meeting of the Boston Colloquium for the Philosophy of Science, February 7, 1962. Reprinted by kind permission of the author and publisher from *Synthese*, Vol. 27, 1962, pp. 303–322.
[1] W. V. Quine, *Word and Object*, 1960, pp. 195–196.

This several of us [2] were enticed into doing. But the evils of the sentential calculus were found out in the functional calculus, and with it—to quote again from *Word and Object*—"the varied sorrows of modality."

I do not claim that modal logic is wholly without sorrows, but only that they are not those which Professor Quine describes. I do claim that it is worthy of defense, for it is useful in connection with many interesting and important questions such as the analysis of causation, entailment, obligation and belief statements. My purpose in this paper is to allay some of the doubts concerning the systematic use of modalities.

## INTENSIONAL LANGUAGES

I will begin with the notion of an intensional language. I will make a further distinction between languages which are explicitly and implicitly intensional. Our notion of intensionality does not divide languages into mutually exclusive classes but rather orders them loosely as strongly or weakly intensional. A language is *explicitly* intensional to the degree to which it does *not* equate the identity relation with some weaker form of equivalence. We will assume that we are here concerned with languages which have expressions for referring to objects (things), and expressions for describing a plurality of things. We will not go into the question as to how we come to regard some elements of experience as things, but one criterion for sorting out the elements of experience which we regard as things is that they may enter into the identity relation. In a formalized language, those symbols which name things will be those for which it is meaningful to assert that I holds between them, where "I" names the identity relation.

Ordinarily, and in the familiar constructions of formal systems, the identity relation must be held appropriate for individuals. If "x" and "y" are individual names then

(1)                                     xIy

is a sentence, and if they are individual variables, then (1) is a sentential function. Whether a language confers thinghood on attributes, classes, propositions, is not so much a matter of whether variables appropriate to them can be quantified upon (and we will return to this later), but rather whether (1) is meaningful where "x" and "y" may take as substitution instances names of attributes, classes, propositions. We note in passing

[2] (a) F. B. Fitch, *Symbolic Logic*, New York, 1952.
(b) R. Carnap, "Modalities and quantification," *Journal of Symbolic Logic*, Vol. XI (1946), pp. 33–64.
(c) R. C. Barcan (Marcus), "A functional calculus of first order based on strict implication," *Journal of Symbolic Logic*, Vol. XI (1946), pp. 1–16.
(d) R. C. Barcan (Marcus), "The identity of individuals in a strict functional calculus of first order," *Journal of Symbolic Logic*, Vol. XII (1947), pp. 12–15.

that the meaningfulness of (1) with respect to attributes and classes is more frequently allowed in formal systems than the meaningfulness of (1) in connection with propositions.

Returning now to the notion of explicit intensionality, if identity is appropriate to propositions, attributes, classes, as well as individuals, then any weakening of the identity relation with respect to any of these entities will be reflected in an extensionalizing of the language. By a weakening of the identity relation is meant equating it with some weaker equivalence relation.

On the level of individuals, one or perhaps two equivalence relations are customarily present: identity and indiscernibility. This does not preclude the introduction of others such as similarity or congruence, but the strongest of these is identity. Where identity is defined rather than taken as primitive, it is customary to define it in terms of indiscernibility. Indiscernibility may in turn be defined as

(2)             $x \text{ Ind } y = \text{df } (\phi) \; (\phi x \text{ eq } \phi y)$

In a system of material implication (Sm) eq is taken as material equivalence ($\equiv$). In modal systems eq may be taken as strict equivalence ($\equiv$). In more strongly intensional systems eq may be taken as the strongest equivalence relation appropriate to such expressions as "$\phi x$." In separating (1) and (2) I should like to suggest the possibility that to equate (1) and (2) may already be an explicit weakening of the identity relation, and consequently an extensionalizing principle.[3]

Proceeding now to functional calculi with theory of types, an extensionality principle is of the kind

(3)             $x \text{ eq } y \rightarrow xIy.$

The arrow may represent one of the implication relations named within the system or some metalinguistic conditional and eq one of the equivalence relations appropriate to x and y, but not identity. For example, within the system of material implication, "x" and "y" may be taken as symbols for classes, eq as class equality (in the sense of having the same members); or "x" and "y" may be taken as symbols for propositions and "eq" as the triple bar for material equivalence. In extended modal systems "eq" may be taken as the quadruple bar for strict equivalence where "x" and "y" are symbols for propositions. If the extended system is a modal system and has symbols for classes, eq may be interpreted as "having the same members," which with modalities can be expressed, within such a language. If we wish to distinguish classes from attributes in such a system

---

[3] F. P. Ramsey makes this point in *The Foundations of Mathematics*, London, 1931, pp. 30–32. Doubts about defining identity in terms of indiscernibility are plausible, since although it is obviously absurd to say of two things that they are the same thing, it seems less absurd to say of two things that they are indiscernible from one another. However, in my extensions of modal logic, identity is defined as indiscernibility.

"eq" may be taken as "necessarily applies to the same thing," which is similarly directly expressible within the system. In a language which permits epistemic contexts such as belief contexts, an even stronger equivalence relation than either material or strict equivalence would have to be present. Taking that stronger relation as eq, (3) would still be an extensionalizing principle (albeit weaker) in such a strongly intensional language. A system may therefore include a plurality of principles of extensionality, which vary with respect to strength as well as the object to which they apply.

I should now like to turn to the notion of *implicit* extensionality, which is bound up with the kinds of substitution theorems available in a language. Confining ourselves for the sake of simplicity of exposition to a sentential calculus, one form of the substitution theorem is

$$(4) \qquad\qquad x \; eq_1 \; y \rightarrow z \; eq_2 \; w$$

where x, y, z, w are well-formed, w is the result of replacing one or more occurrences of x by y in z, and "$\rightarrow$" symbolizes implication or a metalinguistic conditional. In the system of material implication (Sm), (4) is provable where $eq_1$ and $eq_2$ are both taken as material equivalence for appropriate values of x, y, z, w. That is

$$(5) \qquad\qquad (x \equiv y) \supset (z \equiv w).$$

Now (5) is clearly false if we are going to allow contexts involving belief, logical necessity, physical necessity and so on. We are familiar with the examples. If "x" is taken as "John is a featherless biped," and "y" as "John is a rational animal," then an unrestricted (5) fails. Our choice is to reject (5) as it stands, or to reject all contexts in which it fails. If the latter choice is made, the language is *implicitly* extensional since it cannot countenance *contexts* where (5) fails. Professor Quine's solution is the latter. All such contexts are consigned to a shelf labelled "referential opacity" or more precisely "contexts which confer referential opacity," and are disposed of. But the contents of that shelf are of interest and we would like to examine them in a systematic and formal manner. For this we need a language which is appropriately intensional.

In the modal calculi, since there are more than one kind of equivalence (4) represents several possible substitution theorems, some of which are provable. We will return to this below.

Similarly, if we are going to permit epistemic contexts, the modal analogue of (4), if unrestricted, fails in *those* contexts and a more appropriate one will have to supplement it.

# IDENTITY AND SUBSTITUTION IN QUANTIFIED MODAL LOGIC

In the light of previous remarks I would like to turn specifically to the criticism raised against extended modal systems in connection with identity and substitution. In particular, I will refer to the [4] extension of Lewis' [5] S4 which consists of introducing quantification in the usual manner and the addition of the axiom [6]

$$(6) \qquad \Diamond\,(\exists\,x)\,(\phi x) \dashv (\exists.x)\,\Diamond\,(\phi x)$$

I will call this system QS4. In QS4 (1) is defined in terms of (2). (2), and consequently (1), admit of alternatives for "eq" may be taken as material or strict equivalence: thus defining "$I_m$" and "$I$" respectively. But the following are theorems of QS4:

$$(7) \qquad (xImy) \equiv (xIy)$$

$$(8) \qquad (xIy) \equiv \Box\,(xIy)$$

where "$\Box$" is the modal symbol for logical necessity. Given (7), "$I_m$" and "$I$" are strictly equivalent. Within such a modal language, they are therefore indistinguishable by virtue of a substitution theorem for strict equivalence. Contingent identities are disallowed by (8). Since

$$(9) \qquad (xIy)\,.\,\Diamond \sim (xIy).$$

Professor Quine [7] finds these results offensive, for he sees (8) as "purifying the universe." Concrete entities are said to be banished and replaced by pallid concepts. The argument is familiar:

$$(10) \qquad \text{The evening star eq the morning star}$$

is said to express a "true identity," yet "evening star" and "morning star" are not validly intersubstitutable in

$$(11) \qquad \text{It is necessary that the evening star is the evening star.}$$

But consider the claim that

$$(12) \qquad aIb$$

is a true identity. Now if (12) is such a true identity, then a and b are the same thing. It doesn't say that a and b are two things which happen,

[4] *Op. cit.* notes 2c, 2d.
[5] C. I. Lewis and C. H. Langford, *Symbolic Logic*, New York, 1932.
[6] See A. N. Prior, *Time and Modality*, Oxford, 1932, for an extended discussion of this axiom.
[7] W. V. Quine, *From a Logical Point of View*, Cambridge, 1953, pp. 152–154.

through some accident, to be one. True, we are using two different names for that same thing, but we must be careful about use and mention. If, then, (12) is true, it must have the same import as

(13)                          aIa.

But if (13) is necessarily true (12) is necessarily true as well. This is precisely the import of theorem (8). We would therefore expect, indeed it would be a consequence of the truth of (12), that "a" is replaceable by "b" in any context except those which are about the names "a" and "b." Now suppose we come upon a statement like (10) or as in the other familiar example

(14)                Scott is the author of *Waverley*.

How are we to understand "eq" as it occurs in (10) or "is" as it occurs in (14)? It is possible to interpret the "eq" of (10) as an equivalence between propositions in accordance with the Russellian theory of descriptions or alternatively as class equivalence. It is possible to interpret the "is" of (14) as the "is" of attribution. To decide that "eq" in (10) and "is" in (14) stand for the identity relation is to decide that "the evening star" and "the morning star" are proper names for the same thing, and that "Scott" and "the author of *Waverley*" are proper names for the same things where the essential use of proper names is taken to be purely referential. As such they must be intersubstitutable in every context. In fact it often happens, in a growing changing language, that a descriptive phrase comes to be used as a proper name—an identifying tag—and the descriptive meaning is lost or ignored. Sometimes we use certain devices such as capitalization and dropping the definite article, to indicate the change in use. "The evening star" becomes "Evening Star," "the morning star" becomes "Morning Star," and they may come to be used as names for the same thing. Singular descriptions such as "the little corporal," "the Prince of Denmark," "the sage of Concord," or "the great dissenter," are as we know often used as alternative proper names of Napoleon, Hamlet, Thoreau and Oliver Wendell Holmes. One might even devise a criterion as to when a descriptive phrase is being used as a proper name. Suppose through some astronomical cataclysm, Venus was no longer the first star of the evening. If we continued to call it alternatively "Evening Star" or "the evening star" then this would be a measure of the conversion of the descriptive phrase into a proper name. If, however, we would, following such a cataclysm, then regard (10) as false, it would indicate that "the evening star" was not used as an alternative proper name of Venus. We might mention in passing that although the conversion of descriptions into proper names appears to be asymmetric; we do find proper names used in singular descriptions of something other than the thing named, as in the statement "Mao Tse-tung is the Stalin of China," where one intends to assert a similarity between the entities named.

That any language must countenance some entities as things would appear to be a precondition for language. But this is not to say that experience is given to us as a collection of things, for it would appear that there are cultural variations and accompanying linguistic variations as to what might be so singled out. It would also appear to be a precondition of language that the singling out of an entity as a thing is accompanied by many—and perhaps an indefinite number—of unique descriptions, for otherwise how would it be singled out? But to assign a thing a proper name is different from giving a unique description. The characterization of Venus as both the evening star and the morning star may be a contingent matter; it might have been otherwise. But the truth of

(16)                    Venus I Venus

and if "a" is another proper name for Venus

(17)                    Venus I a

cannot be contingent matters, for what could it possibly mean to say of a thing that it might not have been identical with itself? The import of (8) is simply that where an *identity* is true, it is necessarily true. Apparent counterexamples are generated by a confusion of identity with weaker equivalence relations.

Returning now to (10) and (14), if they express a true identity, then "Scott" ought to be anywhere intersubstitutable for "the author of *Waverly*" and similarly for "the morning star" and "the evening star." If they are not so universally intersubstitutable—that is, if our decision is that they are not simply proper names for the same thing; that they express an equivalence which is possibly false, e.g., someone else might have written *Waverley*, the star first seen in the evening might have been different from the star first seen in the morning—then they are not identities. One mode of analysis is Russell's which provides a translation of (10) and (14) such that the truth of (10) and (14) does not commit us to the logical truth of (10) and (14), and certainly not to taking the "eq" of (10) as identity, except on the *explicit* assumption of an extensionalizing axiom. Other and related analyses are in terms of membership in a non-empty unit class, or applicability of a unit attribute. But whatever the choice of explication; it will have to be one which permits intersubstitutability, or some analogue of intersubstitutability for the members of the pairs: "Scott" and "the author of *Waverley*," and "the evening star" and "the morning star," which is *short* of being universal. In a language which is implicitly strongly extensional that is, where all contexts in which such substitutions fail are simply eschewed, then of course there is no harm in equating identity with weaker forms of equivalence. But why restrict ourselves in this way when, in a more intensional language, we can still make all the substitutions permissible to this weaker form of equivalence, yet admit contexts in which such a substitutivity is not permitted. To show this, I would like to turn to the instances of (4) which are provable[8] in QS4. An unrestricted

(18) $$x \equiv y \rightarrow z \equiv w$$

is not provable whether "$\rightarrow$" is taken as material implication, strict implication or a metalinguistic conditional. It would involve us in a contradiction, if our interpreted system allowed statements such as

(19) $$(x \equiv y) \cdot \sim \square (x \equiv y)$$

as it must, if it is not to be reducible to the system of material implication. Indeed, the underlying assumption about equivalence which is implicit in the whole "evening star-morning star" controversy is that there are equivalences (misleadingly called "true identities") which are contingently true. Let x and y of (18) be taken as some p and q which satisfies (19). Let z be $\square(p \equiv p)$ and w be $\square(p \equiv q)$. Then (18) is

(20) $$(p \equiv q) \rightarrow (\square(p \equiv p) \equiv \square (p \equiv q))$$

From (19), simplification, modus ponens and $\square (p \equiv p)$, we can deduce $\square(p \equiv q)$. The latter, simplification of (19), and conjunction leads to the contradiction

(21) $$\square (p \equiv q) \cdot \sim \square (p \equiv q).$$

But a restricted form of (18) is provable. It is provable if z does not contain any modal operators. And this is exactly every context allowed in the system of material implications without at the same time banishing modal contexts. Indeed a slightly stronger (18) is provable. It is provable if x does not fall within the scope of a modal operator in z.

Where in (4), $eq_1$ and $eq_2$ are both taken as strict equivalence, the substitution theorem

(22) $$(x \equiv y) \rightarrow (z \equiv w)$$

*is* provable without restriction, and also where $eq_1$ is taken as strict equivalence and $eq_2$ is taken as material equivalence as in

(23) $$(x \equiv y) \rightarrow (z \equiv w).$$

But (22) is also an extensionalizing principle, since though it holds in modal context it fails in epistemic context such as those involving "knows that" or "believes that." For consider the statement.

(24)  When Professor Quine reviewed the paper on identity in QS4, he knew that $\vdash aI_m b \equiv aI_m b$.

and

---

[8] *Op. cit.*, note 2c. Theorem XIX* corresponds to (23). The restricted (19), given the conditions of the restriction, although not actually proved, is clearly provable in the same manner as XIX*.

(25)    When Professor Quine reviewed the paper on identity in
        QS4 he knew that $\vdash aIb \equiv aI_m b$.

Given the truth of (7) and (24), it would follow from (22) that (25) is
true; yet (25) is in fact false. But rather than repeat the old mistakes by
abandoning epistemic contexts to the shelf labelled "referential opacity"
after having rescued modal contexts, we need only conclude that (22)
confines the limits of applicability of such modal systems. If it should turn
out that statements involving "knows that" and "believes that" permit of
formal analysis, then such an analysis would have to be embedded in a
language with a still stronger equivalence relation than strict equivalence
but short of identity. Carnap's intensional isomorphism, Lewis' analytical
comparability, and perhaps Anderson and Belnap's mutual entailment are
attempts in that direction. But even these stronger equivalence relations
must be short of identity for there are surely contexts in which substitutions allowed by such stronger equivalences, would convert a truth into a
falsehood. It seems plausible to argue [9] that the identity relation need not
be introduced for anything other than the entities we clearly countenance
as things, such as individuals. Increasingly strong substitution theorems
give the force of universal substitutivity without explicit axioms of extensionality. We can talk of equivalence between propositions, classes, attributes, without thereby conferring on them thinghood by equating such
equivalences with the identity relation.

Response to criticism of quantified modal logic would be incomplete
without touching on another familiar example:

(26)                9 eq the number of planets

is said to be a true identity for which substitution fails in

(27)                            $\square(9 > 7)$

for it leads to the falsehood

(28)                $\square$(the number of planets $> 7$).

Since the argument holds (26) to be contingent ($\sim \square$(9 eq the number of
planets)), "eq" of (26) is the appropriate analogue of material equivalence
and consequently the step from (27) to (28) is not valid for the reason that
the substitution would have to be made in the scope of the square. For it
was shown above that (18) is not an unrestricted theorem in QS4. On the
other hand, since in QS4

(29)                        $(5+4) =_s 9$

where "$=_s$" is the appropriate analogue for classes of *strict* equivalence,

[9] See R. Barcan Marcus, "Extensionality," *Mind*, Vol. LXIX, n.s., pp. 55–62 which
overlaps to some extent the present paper.

"5 + 4" may replace "9" in (27) in accordance with (22). If, however, the square were dropped from (27) as it validly can since

(30)                                $\Box p \prec p$

is provable, then by the restricted (18), the same substitution permissible in systems of material implication is permissible here.

## THE INTERPRETATION OF QUANTIFICATION

The previous sections have been directed toward those criticisms of modal systems which focus on problems of identity and substitution. The second prominent area of criticism of quantified modal logic involves interpretation of the operations of quantification when combined with modalities. It appears to me that at least some of the problems stem from an absence of an adequate, unequivocal, colloquial translation of the operations of quantification. It is often not quantification but our choice of reading and implicit interpretive consequences of such a reading which leads to difficulties. Such difficulties are not confined to modal systems. The most common reading of existential quantification is

(31)    There is (exists) at least one (some) thing (person) which
        (who) . . .

Strawson,[10] for example, does not even admit of significant alternatives, for he says of (31) ". . . we might think it strange that the whole of modern formal logic after it leaves the propositional logic and before it crosses the boundary into the analysis of mathematical concepts, should be confined to the elaboration of sets of rules giving the logical interrelations of formulae which, however complex, begin with these few rather strained and awkward phrases." What we would like to have and do not have, is a direct, unequivocal colloquial reading of

(32)                                $(\exists x) \phi x$

which gives us the *force* of either of the following:

(33)            Some substitution instance of "$\phi x$" is true

or

                There is at least one value of x for which $\phi x$ is true.

I am not suggesting that (33) provides translations of (32), but only that what is wanted is a translation with the force of (32).

As seen from (33), quantification has primarily to do with truth and falsity, and open sentences. Reading in accordance with (31) may entangle us unnecessarily in ontological perplexities. For if quantification has to do

[10] P. F. Strawson, *Introduction to Logical Theory*, London, 1952, p. 216.

with things and if variables for attributes or classes can be quantified upon, then in accordance with (31) they are things. The solution is not to banish quantification on variables other than individual variables, but only not to be taken in by (31). We do in fact have some colloquial counterparts of (33). The non-temporal "sometimes" or "in some cases" or "in at least one case," which have greater ontological neutrality than (31). Such a relatively neutral interpretation of quantification is advantageous in a wide spectrum of contexts. We will focus on the way it may be employed to resolve doubts about the possibility of combining quantification with modalities.

Consider first a quantified version of the "morning star-evening star" paradox. In QS4 the following definitions are introduced: [11]

(34) $$(\phi =_m \psi) =_{df} (x)(\phi x \equiv \psi x)$$

(35) $$(\phi =_s \psi) =_{df} \Box(\phi =_m \psi)$$

Individual descriptions may be taken as higher order terms between which weaker equivalence relations than identity may be defined. Two such relations (material and strict equality), are defined by (34) and (35). Since (10) is a contingency, it is the case that

(36)        (The evening star $=_m$ the morning star)

and

(37)        $\Diamond \sim$ (the evening star $=_m$ the morning star);

but according to (11)

(38)        $\Box$ (the evening star $=_m$ the evening star).

By existential generalization on (38), it follows that

(39)        $(\exists \phi) \Box (\phi =_m$ the evening star).

In the words of (31), (39) becomes

(40)    There is a thing such that it is necessary that it is equal to the evening star.

The stubborn unlaid ghost rises again. Which thing, the evening star which by (36) is equal to the morning star? But such a substitution would lead to the falsehood.

(41)        $\Box$ (the evening star $=_m$ the morning star).

[11] *Op. cit.*, note 2c. Abstracts are introduced and attributes (classes) may be equated with abstracts. Among the obvious features of such a calculus of attributes (classes), is the presence of equivalent, non-identical, empty attributes (classes). If the null attribute (class) is defined in terms of identity, then it will be intersubstitutible with any abstract on a contradictory function.

The argument may be repeated for (26) through (28). In QS4 the solution is clear. For since (37) holds, and since in (39) "$\phi$" occurs within the scope of a square, then we cannot go from (39) to (41) by virtue of the substitution theorem. On the other hand the step from (38) to (39) (existential instantiation) is entirely valid. For surely (avoiding the ontological language of (31) and (40)) there is a case where

$$\square(\phi = \text{the evening star})$$

is true. In particular, the case where "$\phi$" is replaced by "the evening star."

There is also the specific problem of interpreting quantification in $\diamondsuit(\exists x)\phi x \dashv (\exists x)\diamondsuit \phi x$ (6), which is a postulate of QS4. Read in accordance with (31) as

(42)    If it is logically possible that there is something which $\phi$'s, then there is something such that it is logically possible that it $\phi$'s.

It is admittedly odd. The antecedent seems to be about what is logically possible and the consequent about what there is. How can one go from possibility to existence? Read in accordance with (33) we have the clumsy but not so paradoxical

(43)    If it is logically possible that $\phi x$ for some value of x, then there is some value of x such that it is logically possible that $\phi x$.

Although the emphasis has now been shifted from things and the ontological consequences of (42) are absent, it is still indirect and awkward. It would appear that questions such as the acceptability or non-acceptability of (6) are best solved in terms of some semantical construction. This will be returned to in conclusion, but first some minor matters.

## MODALITIES MISUNDERSTOOD

In what preceded, the focus has been on problems connected with identity, substitution and quantification in interpreted modal systems. A defense of modal logic would be incomplete without touching on criticisms of modalities which stem from simple misunderstanding of what is or isn't provable in modal systems. Two examples will be cited, not because they are exhaustive but because they point up the need for more systematic study.

One example is from Rosenbloom [12] who seized on the fact that a strong deduction theorem is not available in QS4 as a reason for discarding strict implication as in any way relevant to the deducibility relation. He failed to

[12] P. Rosenbloom, *The Elements of Mathematical Logic*, New York, 1950, p. 60.

note [13] that a weaker and perhaps more appropriate deduction theorem is available. Indeed, Anderson and Belnap,[14] in their attempt to formalize entailment without modalities, reject the strong form of the deduction theorem as "counter-intuitive for entailment."

Another example occurs in *Word and Object* [15] which can be summarized as follows:

(44) Modalities yield talk of a difference between necessary and contingent attributes.

(45) Mathematicians may be said to be necessarily rational and not necessarily two-legged.

(46) Cyclists are necessarily two-legged and not necessarily rational.

(47) $\alpha$ is a mathematician and a cyclist

(48) Is this concrete individual necessarily rational or contingently two-legged or vice versa?

(49) "Talking referentially of the object with no special bias toward a background grouping of mathematicians as against cyclists . . . there is no semblance of sense in rating some of his attributes as necessary and others as contingent."

Professor Quine says that (44) through (47) are supposed to "evoke the appropriate sense of bewilderment" and they surely do. For I know of no interpreted modal system which treats of necessary attributes in the manner suggested. We may translate (45) by conjoining any one of the equivalent statements in (50) with any one of the equivalent statements in (51).

(50) $(x)(Mx \dashv Rx) \equiv (x) \Box (Mx \supset Rx) \equiv (x) \sim \Diamond (Mx \cdot \sim Rx)$

(51) $(x) \sim \Box (Mx \supset Tx) \equiv (x) \Diamond \sim (Mx \supset Tx) \equiv (x) \Diamond (Mx \cdot \sim Tx)$.

Also we may translate (46) by conjoining any one of the equivalent statements in (52) with any one of the equivalent statements in (53).

(52) $(x)(Cx \dashv Tx) \equiv (x) \Box (Cx \supset Tx) \equiv (x) \sim \Diamond (Cx \cdot \sim Tx)$

(53) $(x) \sim \Box (Cx \supset Rx) \equiv (x) \Diamond \sim (Cx \supset Rx) \equiv (x) \Diamond (Cx \cdot \sim Rx)$.

Let (48) be

(54)                    $Ma \cdot Ca$

---

[13] R. Barcan Marcus, "Strict implication, deducibility, and the deduction theorem," *Journal of Symbolic Logic*, Vol. XVIII (1953), pp. 234–236.

[14] A. R. Anderson and N. D. Belnap, *The Pure Calculus of Entailment* (preprint).

[15] *Op. cit.*, note 1, pp. 199–200.

Among the non-bewildering conclusions we can draw from (50) through (54) are

$\Box(Ma \supset Ra)$, $\sim \Diamond (Ma \cdot \sim Ra)$, $\Diamond (Ma \cdot \sim Ta)$, $\sim \Box (Ma \supset Ta)$,
$\Box(Ca \supset Ta)$, $\sim \Diamond (Ca \cdot \sim Ta)$, $\Diamond (Ca \cdot \sim Ra)$, $\sim \Box (Ca \cdot \sim Ra)$,
Ta, Ra, Ta·Ra

But nothing to answer question (48), or to make any sense of (49). It would appear that Professor Quine is assuming that

(55)                     $(p \dashv q) \dashv (p \dashv \Box q)$

is a theorem of modal logic, but it is not, except where $p \equiv \Box r$ for some r. Keeping in mind that we are dealing with logical modalities (or at best, analytic modalities), none of the attributes (M,R,T,C) in (50) through (54) taken separately, or conjoined, are necessary. It is not *that* sort of attribute which modal logic, even derivatively, countenances as being necessary. A word is appropriate here about the derivative sense in which we can speak of logically necessary and possible attributes.

In QS4, for example, abstracts are introduced such that to every function there corresponds an abstract

(56)     $x \hat{\epsilon y} A =_{df} B$, where B is the result of substituting every free occurrence of y in A by x.

If r is some abstract then we can define

(57)                 $x \epsilon \boxdot r =_{df} \Box (x \epsilon r)$, $\vdash \boxdot r =_{df} (x) (x \epsilon \boxdot r)$

and

(58)                 $x \epsilon \Diamond r =_{df} \Diamond (x \epsilon r)$, $\vdash \Diamond r =_{df} (x) (x \epsilon \Diamond r)$

It is clear that among the abstracts to which $\vdash \boxdot$ may validly be affixed, will be those corresponding to tautological functions, e.g., $\hat{y} (y I y)$, $\hat{y} (\phi x \vee \sim \phi x)$, etc. It would be appropriate to call these necessary attributes, and the symbol "$\boxdot$" provides a derivative way of applying modalities to attributes. There is a similar derivative sense for "possible attribute" (58), contingent attribute but these have little to do with the traditional problem of essentialism.


## SEMANTIC CONSTRUCTIONS

I would like in conclusion to suggest that the polemics of modal logic are perhaps best carried out in terms of some explicit semantical construction. As we have seen in connection with (6) it is awkward at best and at worst has the character of a quibble, not to do so.

Let us reappraise (6) in terms of such a construction.[16] Consider for example a language (L), with truth functional connectives, a modal operator ( ◊ ), a finite number of individual constants, an infinite number of individual variables, one two-place predicate (R), quantification and the usual criteria for being well-formed. A domain (D) of individuals is then considered which are named by the constants of L. A model of L is defined as a class of ordered couples (possibly empty) of D. The members of a model are exactly those pairs between which R holds. To say therefore that the atomic sentence R $(a_1a_2)$ of L holds or is true in M, is to say that the ordered couple $(b_1b_2)$ is a member of M, where $a_1$ and $a_2$ are the names in L of $b_1$ and $b_2$. If a sentence A of L is of the form $\sim$B, A is true in M if and only if B is not true in M. If A is of the form $B_1 \cdot B_2$ then A is true in M if and only if both $B_1$ and $B_2$ are true in M. If A is of the form (∃ x)B, then A is true in M if and only if at least one substitution instance of B is true (holds) in M. If A is ◊ B then A is true in M if and only if B is true in some model $M_1$.

We see that a true sentence of L is defined relative to a model and a domain of individuals. A logically true sentence is one which would be true in every model. We are now in a position to give a rough proof of (6). Suppose (6) is false in some M. Then

(59)          $\sim ◊ ( ◊ (∃ x) \phi x \cdot \sim (∃ x) ◊ \phi x)$

is false in M. Therefore

(60)          $◊ ( ◊ (∃ x) \phi x \cdot \sim (∃ x) ◊ \phi x)$

is true in M. So

(61)          $◊ (∃ x) \phi x \cdot \sim (∃ x) ◊ \phi x$

is true in some $M_1$. Therefore

(62)          $◊ (∃ x) \phi x$

and

(63)          $\sim (∃ x) ◊ \phi x$

are true in $M_1$. Consequently, from (62)

(64)          $(∃ x) \phi x$

is true in some model $M_2$. Therefore there is a member of D (b) such that

[16] The construction here outlined corresponds to that of R. Carnap, *Meaning and Necessity*, Chicago, 1947. The statement of the construction is in accordance with the method of J. C. C. McKinsey. See also, J. C. C. McKinsey, "On the syntactical construction of systems of modal logic," *Journal of Symbolic Logic*, Vol. X (1946), pp. 88–94; "A new definition of truth," *Synthese*, Vol. VII (1948/49), pp. 428–433.

(65)                              $\phi b$

is true in $M_2$. But from (63)

$$(\exists x) \; \Diamond \; \phi x$$

is not true in $M_1$. Consequently there is no member of D such that

(66)                              $\Diamond \; \phi b$

is true in $M_1$. So there is no model $M_2$ such that $\phi b$ is true in $M_2$. But this result contradicts (65). Consequently, in such a construction, (6) must be true in every model.

If this is the sort of construction one has in mind then we are persuaded of the plausibility of (6). Indeed, going back to (43), it can be seen that this was the sort of construction which was being assumed. If (6) is to be regarded as offensive, it must be in terms of some semantic construction which ought to be made explicit.[17]

We see, that though the rough outline above corresponds to the Leibnizian distinction between true in a possible world and true in all possible worlds, it is also to be noted that there are no specifically intensional objects. No new entity is spawned in a possible world that isn't already in the domain in terms of which the class of models is defined. In such a model, modal operators have to do with truth relative to the model, not with things. On this interpretation,[18] Professor Quine's "flight from intension" may have been exhilarating, but unnecessary.[19]


# REPLY TO PROFESSOR MARCUS*

WILLARD VAN ORMAN QUINE (1908–    ). See page 165.


Professor Marcus struck the right note when she represented me as suggesting that modern modal logic was conceived in sin: the sin of confusing use and mention. She rightly did not represent me as holding

---

[17] A criticism of the construction here outlined is the assumption of the countability of members of D. McKinsey points this out in the one chapter I have seen of a projected (unpublished) study of modal logic.

[18] If one wishes to talk about possible things then of course such a construction is inadequate.

[19] This paper was written while the author was under N.S.F. Grant 24335.

* Presented as Commentary at the meeting of the Boston Colloquium for the Philosophy of Science, February 8, 1962. Reprinted with kind permission of the author and publisher from *Synthese*, Vol. 27, 1962, pp. 323–330.

that modal logic *requires* confusion of use and mention. My point was a historical one, having to do with Russell's confusion of 'if-then' with 'implies.'

Lewis founded modern modal logic, but Russell provoked him to it. For whereas there is much to be said for the material conditional as a version of 'if-then,' there is nothing to be said for it as a version of 'implies'; and Russell called it implication, thus apparently leaving no place open for genuine deductive connections between sentences. Lewis moved to save the connections. But his way was not, as one could have wished, to sort out Russell's confusion of 'implies' with 'if-then.' Instead, preserving that confusion, he propounded a strict conditional and called *it* implication.

It is logically possible to like modal logic without confusing use and mention. You could like it because, apparently at least, you can quantify into a modal context by a quantifier outside the modal context, whereas you obviously cannot coherently quantify into a mentioned sentence from outside the mention of it. Still, man is a sensemaking animal, and as such he derives little comfort from quantifying into modal contexts that he does not think he understands. On this score, confusion of use and mention seems to have more than genetic significance for modal logic. It seems to be also a sustaining force, engendering an illusion of understanding.

I am speaking empirically. There was a period twenty-five years ago when I kept being drawn into arguments with C. I. Lewis and E. V. Huntington over interpretation of modal logic; and in those arguments I found it necessary to harp continually on the theme of use versus mention. And now points that Professor Marcus has urged this evening, in favor of modal logic, force me back to that same theme again.

Thus consider her 'informal argument:

(12) If p is a tautology, and p eq q, then q is a tautology.'

Her adoption of the letters 'p' and 'q,' rather than say '$S_1$' and '$S_2$,' suggests that she intends them to occupy sentence positions. Also her 'eq' is perhaps intended as a sentence *connective*, despite her saying that it names some equivalence relation; for she says that it could be taken as '$\equiv$.' On the other hand her clauses 'p is a tautology' and 'q is a tautology' do not show 'p' and 'q' in sentence position. These clauses show 'p' and 'q' in name positions, as if they were replaceable not by sentences but by names of sentences.

Or try the opposite interpretation. Suppose that Professor Marcus, contrary to custom, is using 'p' and 'q' as variables whose values are sentences, and whose proper substitutes are therefore names of sentences. Then 'eq' is indeed to be seen as naming some equivalence *relation*, just as she says; and the mention of '$\equiv$' must be overlooked as an inadvertency. On this interpretation, (12) is unexceptionable. But on this interpretation (12) is no part of modal logic; it is ordinary non-modal metalogic. For on this interpretation 'eq' is not a non-truth-functional sentence connective at all, but an ordinary non-truth-functional two-place sentence predicate, like 'implies.' I have no objection to these. In my logical writings early and late I have used them constantly.

Twenty-five years ago, in arguing much the same matter with Lewis and Huntington at vastly greater length, I was forced to recognize my inability to make people aware of confusing use and mention. Nor have the passing years brought me the ability; they have only vindicated my despair of it. By now perhaps I should have concluded that I must be the confused one, were it not for people who do turn out to see the distinction my way. I have said that modal logic does not require confusion of use and mention. But there is no denying that confusion of use and mention engenders an irresistible case for modal logic, as witness (12).

I should not leave (12) without touching upon a third interpretation. Perhaps 'p' and 'q' are to be seen as propositional variables, whose values are propositions (or meanings of sentences) and whose appropriate substitutions are therefore names of propositions, hence names of meanings of sentences. Then again (12) is in order, if we countenance these subtle entities. But, on this interpretation, 'eq' comes to name a relation between propositions; again it is no connective of sentences. To suppose it were would be to confuse meaning with reference, and thus to view sentences as names of their meanings.

Let me move now to Professor Marcus's discussion of her (13) and (14), viz. 'aIb' and 'aIa.' Suppose that aIb. Then, she argues, anything true of a is true of b. I agree. But, she says, 'aIa' is a tautology. Again I agree, not quarreling over the term. So, she concludes, 'aIb' must be a tautology too. Why? The reasoning is as follows. We are trying to prove this about b: not just that aIb, but that tautologously aIb. Now this thing that we are trying to prove about b, viz., that tautologously aIb, is true of a; so, since b is a, it is true of b.

Again our troubles condense about the distinction between use and mention. If we take 'tautologously' as a modal operator attachable directly to sentences, then the argument is all right, but pointless so long as the merits of modal logic are under debate. If on the other hand we accept only 'tautologous', as a predicate attributable to sentences and therefore attachable to quotations of sentences, then the argument breaks down. For, the property that was to be proved about b – viz., that tautologously aIb – has to be seen now as a quotation-breaking pseudo-property on which the substitutivity of identity has no bearing. What I mean by a quotation-breaking pseudo-property will be evident if we switch for a moment to the truth ' "Cicero" has three syllables.' Obviously we cannot infer that ' "Tully" has three syllables,' even though Tully is Cicero. And from "aIa' is tautologous' there is no more reason to infer that "aIb' is tautologous,' even granted that b is a.

Professor Marcus's reflections on identity led her to conclude that identity, substitutivity, and extensionality are things that come in grades.

I have just now objected to some of the reasoning. I also do not accept the conclusion. My position is that we can settle objectively and absolutely what predicate of a theory to count as the identity predicate, if any, once we have settled what notations to count as quantifiers, variables, and the truth functions. Until we have found how to handle quantification in a given theory, of course we have no way even of telling what expressions of the theory to count as predicates and what signs to count as their subject variables; and, not being able to spot predicates, we cannot spot the identity predicate. But show me the quantifiers and the variables and the truth functions, and I can show you when to read an open sentence '$\phi xy$' as '$x = y$.' The requirements are strong reflexivity and substitutivity, thus:

$$(x)\phi xx, \quad (x)(y)(\phi xy \cdot \ldots x \ldots \cdot \supset \cdot \ldots y \ldots).$$

If these requirements are met, then, as is well known, '$\phi xy$' meets all the formal requirements of '$x = y$'; and otherwise not.

The requirements fix identity uniquely. That is, if '$\phi$' and '$\psi$' both meet the requirements of strong reflexivity and substitutivity, then they are coextensive. Let me quickly prove this. By substitutivity of '$\phi$',

$$(x)(y)(\phi xy \cdot \psi xx \cdot \supset \psi xy).$$

But, by reflexivity of $\psi$, we can drop the '$\psi xx$'. So '$\psi$' holds wherever '$\phi$' does. By the same argument with '$\phi$' and '$\psi$' interchanged, '$\phi$' holds wherever '$\psi$' does.

There are a couple of tangents that I would just mention and not use. One is that there is no assurance, given a theory with recognized notations for quantification and the truth functions, that there is an identity predicate in it. It can happen that no open sentence in '$x$' and '$y$' however complex, is strongly reflexive and substitutive. But this is unusual.

The other is that if an open sentence in '$x$' and '$y$' does meet these two requirements, we may still find it to be broader than true identity when we interpret it in the light of prior interpretations of the primitive predicates of the theory. But this sort of discrepancy is always traceable to some gratuitous distinctions in those prior interpretations of the primitive predicates. The effect of our general rule for singling out an identity predicate is a mild kind of identification of indiscernibles.[1]

Tangents aside, my point is that we have an objective and unequivocal criterion whereby to spot the identity predicate of a given theory, if such there be. The criterion is independent of what the author of the theory may do with '=' or 'I' or the word 'identity.' What it does depend on is recognition of the notations of quantification and the truth functions. The absoluteness of this criterion is important, as giving a fixed point of reference in the comparison of theories. Questions of universe, and individuation, take on a modicum of inter-systematic significance that they would otherwise lack.

[1] See my *Word and Object* (New York, 1960), p. 230.

In particular the criterion makes no doubt of Professor Marcus's law for modal logic:

$$(x)(y)(x = y \cdot \supset \cdot \text{necessarily } x = y).$$

It follows from 'necessarily x = x' by substitutivity.

Notice that my substitutivity condition was absolute. There was no question what special positions to exempt from substitutivity, and no question what special names or descriptions to exempt in special positions. Hence there was no scope for gradations of identity or substitutivity. What enabled me to cut so clean was that I talked in terms not of names or descriptions but of 'x' and 'y': variables of quantification. The great philosophical value of the eliminability of singular terms other than variables is that we can sometimes thus spare ourselves false leads and lost motion.

In her own continuing discussion, Professor Marcus developed a contrast between proper names and descriptions. Her purpose was, I gather, to shed further light on supposed grades or alternatives in the matter of identity and substitutivity. I have urged just now that we can cut through all this by focusing on the bindable variable. And I am glad, for I think I see trouble anyway in the contrast between proper names and descriptions as Professor Marcus draws it. Her paradigm of the assigning of proper names is tagging. We may tag the planet Venus, some fine evening, with the proper name 'Hesperus.' We may tag the same planet again, some day before sunrise, with the proper name 'Phosphorus.' When at last we discover that we have tagged the same planet twice, our discovery is empirical. And not because the proper names were descriptions.

In any event, this is by the way. The contrast between description and name needs not concern us if we take rather the variables of quantification as our ultimate singular terms. Already for the second time we note the philosophical value of the eliminability of singular terms other than variables: again it spares us false leads and lost motion.

Let us look then to Professor Marcus's next move. Alarmingly, her next move was to challenge quantification itself, or my object-oriented interpretation of it. Here she talks of values of variables in a sense that I must sharply separate from my own. For me the values e.g. of number variables in algebra are not the numerals that you can substitute, but the numbers that you talk about. For Professor Marcus, the values are the expressions you can substitute. I think my usage has the better history, but hers has a history too. Ryle objected somewhere to my dictum that to be is to be the value of a variable, arguing that the values of variables are expressions and hence that my dictum repudiates all things except expressions. Clearly, then, we have to distinguish between values of variables in the *real* sense and values of variables in the *Ryle* sense. To confuse these is, again, to confuse use and mention. Professor Marcus is not, so far as I observe, confusing them. She simply speaks of values of variables in the Ryle sense. But to forestall confusion I should like to say 'substitutes for variables' rather than 'values of variables' in this sense, thus reserving 'values of variables' for values of variables in the real sense.

Thus paraphrased, Professor Marcus's proposed reinterpretation of existential quantification is this: the quantification is to be true if and only if the open sentence after the quantifier is true for some substitute for the variable of quantification. Now this is, I grant, an intelligible reinterpretation, and one that does not require objects, in any sense, as values, in the real sense, of the variables of quantification. Note only that it deviates from the ordinary interpretation of quantification in ways that can matter. For one thing, there is a question of unspecifiable objects. Thus take the real numbers. On the classical theory, at any rate, they are indenumerable, whereas the expressions, simple and complex, available to us in any given language are denumerable. There are therefore, among the real numbers, infinitely many none of which can be separately specified by any expression, simple or complex. Consequently an existential quantification can come out true when construed in the ordinary sense, thanks to the existence of appropriate real numbers, and yet be false when construed in Professor Marcus's sense, if by chance those appropriate real numbers all happen to be severally unspecifiable. But the fact remains that quantification can indeed be thus reinterpreted, if not altogether *salva veritate*, so as to dissociate it from objective reference and real values of variables. Why should this be seen as desirable? As an answer, perhaps, to the charge that quantified modal logic can tolerate only intensions and not classes or individuals as values of its variables? But it is a puzzling answer. For, it abstracts from reference altogether. Quantification ordinarily so-called is purely and simply the logical idiom of objective reference. When we reconstrue it in terms of substituted expressions rather than real values, we waive reference. We preserve distinctions between true and false, as in truth-function logic itself, but we cease to depict the referential dimension. Now anyone who is willing to abstract thus from questions of universe of discourse cannot have cared much whether there were classes and individuals or only intensions in the universe of discourse. But then why the contortions? In short, if reference matters, we cannot afford to waive it as a category; and if it does not, we do not need to.

As a matter of fact, the worrisome charge that quantified modal logic can tolerate only intensions and not classes or individuals was a mistake to begin with. It goes back to 1943; my 'Notes on existence and necessity' [2] and Church's review of it. [3] To illustrate my misgivings over quantifying into modal contexts I used, in that article, the example of 9 and the number of the planets. They are the same thing, yet 9 necessarily exceeds 7 whereas the number of the planets only contingently exceeds 7. So, I argued, necessarily exceeding 7 is no trait of the neutral thing itself, the

---

[2] *Journal of Philosophy*, Vol. XL, pp. 113–127.
[3] *Journal of Symbolic Logic*, Vol. VIII, pp. 45–47.

number, which is the number of the planets as well as 9. And so it is nonsense to say neutrally that there is *something*, x, that necessarily exceeds 7. Church countered that my argument worked only for things like numbers, bodies, classes, that we could specify in contingently coincident ways: thus 9 is what succeeds 8, and is what numbers the planets, and these two specifications only contingently coincide. If we limit our objects to intensions, Church urged, this will not happen.

Now on this latter point Church was wrong. I have been slow to see it, but the proof is simple. Anything x, even an intension, is specifiable in contingently coincident ways if specifiable at all. For, suppose x is determined uniquely by the condition '$\phi$x.' Then it is also determined uniquely by the conjunctive condition 'p $\cdot$ $\phi$x' where 'p' is any truth, however irrelevant. Take 'p' as an arbitrary truth not implied by '$\phi$x,' and these two specifications of x are seen to be contingently coincident: '$\phi$x' and 'p $\cdot$ $\phi$x.'

Contrary to what Church thought, therefore, my 1943 strictures were cogent against quantification over any sorts of objects if cogent at all; nothing is gained by limiting the universe to intensions. The only course open to the champion of quantified modal logic is to meet my strictures head on: to argue in the case of 9 and the number of the planets that this number is, of itself and independently of mode of specification, something that necessarily, not contingently, exceeds 7. This means adopting a frankly inequalitarian attitude toward the various ways of specifying the number. One of the determining traits, the succeeding of 8, is counted as a necessary trait of the number. So are any traits that follow from that one, notably the exceeding of 7. Other uniquely determining traits of the number, notably its numbering the planets, are discounted as contingent traits of the number and held not to belie the fact that the number does still necessarily exceed 7.

This is how essentialism comes in: the invidious distinction between some traits of an object as essential to *it* (by whatever name) and other traits of it as accidental. I do not say that such essentialism, however uncongenial to me, should be uncongenial to the champion of quantified modal logic. On the contrary, it should be every bit as congenial as quantified modal logic itself.[4]

[4] For more in the vein of these last few paragraphs see my *From a Logical Point of View*, Revised Edition (Cambridge, Mass., 1961), pp. 148–157.

## SUGGESTIONS FOR FURTHER READING ON MODAL LOGIC

ANDERSON, A. R. et al. *Modal and Many-Valued Logics. Acta Philosophica Fennica*, Fasc. XVI. Helsinki, 1963.

BARCAN (MARCUS), R. C. "A Functional Calculus of First Order Based on Strict Implication," *The Journal of Symbolic Logic*, Vol. 11 (1946), pp. 1–16.

BERGMANN, G.    "The Philosophical Significance of Modal Logic," *Mind*, Vol. 69 (1960), pp. 466–485.

CARNAP, R.    "Modalities and Quantification," *The Journal of Symbolic Logic*, Vol. 11 (1946), pp. 33–64.

CARNAP, R.    *Meaning and Necessity*. Chicago: The University of Chicago Press, 1947.

KRIPKE, S. A.    "A Completeness Theorem in Modal Logic," *The Journal of Symbolic Logic*, Vol. 24 (1959), pp. 1–14.

PRIOR, A. N.    *Time and Modality*. Oxford: Oxford University Press, 1957.

QUINE, W. V. O.    "Three Grades of Modal Involvement," *The Ways of Paradox*, New York: Random House, Inc., 1966, pp. 156–174.

SMULLYAN, A. F.    "Modality and Description," *The Journal of Symbolic Logic*, Vol. 13 (1948), pp. 31–37.

VON WRIGHT, G. H.    *An Essay in Modal Logic*. Amsterdam: North-Holland Publishing Co., 1951.

*Part*

# 8 DEONTIC LOGIC

## *Introduction*

It has long been noticed that norms or imperatives can stand to each other in relations analogous to those in which propositions or statements do. Thus, one imperative may "entail" another, or two or more commands may be "inconsistent." Among various attempts to work out a "logic" of norms comparable to the familiar propositional logic, von Wright's "Deontic Logic" published in 1951 has attracted most attention. In it the familiar symbolism of the propositional calculus is augmented to provide a calculus for *acts*, in terms of their being "permitted," "forbidden," or "obligatory."

In a supplementary note published five years later, von Wright discusses some criticisms that had been directed against his system, and suggests a new alternative formulation to avoid what have been called "The Paradoxes of Derived Obligation."

In their essay Anderson and Moore review the development of deontic logic and consider how imperatives can be connected with the rewards and punishments that sanction them. They make some suggestions for further investigation of more comprehensive deontic systems and describe some alternative systems already constructed.

# DEONTIC LOGIC*

Georg Henrik von Wright (1916–    ), Fellow of the
Academy of Finland, has been Professor of Philosophy at
Cambridge University in England and at Helsingfors University
in Finland. He has written extensively on logic. His books
include *Logical Studies, The Logic of Preference,* and
*Norm and Action.*

1. So called modal concepts might conveniently be divided into
three or four main groups. There are the alethic modes or modes of truth.
These are concepts such as the necessary (the necessarily true), the possible
(the possibly true), and the contingent (the contingently true). There are
the epistemic modes or modes of knowing. These are concepts such as
the verified (that which is known to be true), the undecided, and the
falsified (that which is known to be false). There are the deontic [1] modes
or modes of obligation. These are concepts such as the obligatory (that
which we ought to do), the permitted (that which we are allowed to do),
and the forbidden (that which we must not do). As a fourth main group
of modal categories one might add the existential modes or modes of
existence. These are concepts such as universality, existence, and emptiness
(of properties or classes).

There are essential similarities but also characteristic differences between
the various groups of modalities. They all deserve, therefore, a special treatment. The treatment of the existential modes is usually known as quantification theory. The treatment of the alethic modes covers most of what is
traditionally known as modal logic. The epistemic modes have not to any
great extent and the deontic modes hardly at all been treated by logicians.

In the present paper an elementary formal logic of the deontic modalities
will be outlined.

2. First a preliminary question must be settled. What are the "things"
which are pronounced obligatory, permitted, forbidden, etc.?

We shall call these "things" acts.

The word "act," however, is used ambiguously in ordinary language. It
is sometimes used for what might be called act-qualifying properties, *e.g.,*
theft. But it is also used for the individual cases which fall under these
properties, *e.g.,* the individual thefts.

The use of the word for individual cases is perhaps more appropriate than

---

*Reprinted by kind permission of the author, Routledge and Kegan Paul, Ltd., and
The Humanities Press, Inc., from *Logical Studies* (New York: The Humanities Press,
Inc., 1957), pp. 58–74.
[1] For the term "deontic" I am indebted to Professor C. D. Broad.

its use for properties. For the sake of verbal convenience, however, we shall in this paper use "act" for properties and not for individuals. We shall say that theft, murder, smoking, etc. are acts. The individual cases that fall under theft, murder, smoking, etc. we shall call act-individuals. It is of acts and not of act-individuals that deontic words are predicated.

The performance or non-performance of a certain act (by an agent) we shall call performance-values (for that agent). An act will be called a performance-function of certain other acts, if its performance-value for any given agent uniquely depends upon the performance-values of those other acts for the same agent.

The concept of a performance-function is strictly analogous to the concept of a truth-function in propositional logic.

Particular performance-functions can be defined in strict correspondence to the particular truth-functions.

Thus by the negation (-act) of a given act we understand that act which is performed by an agent, if and only if he does not perform the given act. For example: the negation of the act of repaying a loan is the act of not repaying it. If $A$ denotes (is the name of) an act, $\sim A$ will be used as a name of its negation (-act).

Similarly, we can define the conjunction-, disjunction-, implication-, and equivalence-act of two given acts. (The implication-act, *e.g.*, of two given acts is the act which is performed by an agent, if and only if it is not the case that the first act is performed and the second act is not performed by the agent in question.) If $A$ and $B$ denote acts, $A \& B$ will be used as a name of their conjunction, $A \vee B$ as a name of their disjunction, $A \rightarrow B$ as a name of their implication, and $A \longleftrightarrow B$ as a name of their equivalence.

Finally, we can define the tautology- and contradiction (-act) of $n$ given acts. The first is the act which is performed and the second the act which is not performed by an agent, whatever be the performance-values of the $n$ given acts for the agent in question.

We shall call $\sim A$ the negation-name of $A$, and $A \& B$ the conjunction-, $A \vee B$ the disjunction-, $A \rightarrow B$ the implication-, and $A \longleftrightarrow B$ the equivalence-name of $A$ and $B$.

A name of an act which is neither the negation-name of another name of an act, nor the conjunction-, disjunction-, implication-, or equivalence-name of two other names of acts shall call an atomic name.

By a molecular complex of $n$ names of acts we understand:

(i)    Any one of the $n$ names themselves and any one of their negation-names.

(ii)   The conjunction-, disjunction-, implication-, and equivalence-name of any two of the $n$ names.

(iii)  The negation-name of any molecular complex of the $n$ names, and the conjunction-, disjunction-, implication-, and equivalence-name of any two molecular complexes of the $n$ names.

The *n* names are called constituents of their molecular complexes. If they are atomic names, they are called atomic constituents.

As to the use of brackets we adopt the convention that the symbol & has a stronger combining force than v, →, and ←→; the symbol v than → and ←→; and the symbol → than ←→. Thus, *e.g.*, we write for $(((A \& B)$ v $C) \to D) \longleftrightarrow E$ simply $A \& B$ v $C \to D \longleftrightarrow E$.

The symbols ∼, &, v, →, and ←→ will be used for truth-functions as well as for performance-functions. This ambiguity does not easily lead to confusion and is, therefore, to be preferred to the introduction of two special sets of symbols.

3. As an undefined deontic category we introduce the concept of permission. It is the only undefined deontic category which we need.

If an act is not permitted, it is called forbidden. For instance: Theft is not permitted, hence it is forbidden. We are *not allowed to* steal, hence we *must not* steal.[2]

If the negation of an act is forbidden, the act itself is called obligatory. For instance: it is forbidden to disobey the law, hence it is obligatory to obey the law. We *ought to* do that which we are *not allowed not to* do.

If an act and its negation are both permitted, the act is called (morally) indifferent. For instance: in a smoking compartment we may smoke, but we may also not smoke. Hence smoking is here a morally indifferent form of behaviour.

It should be observed that indifference is thus a narrower category than permission. Everything indifferent is permitted, but everything permitted is not indifferent. For, what is obligatory is also permitted, but not indifferent.

(The difference between the permitted and the indifferent among the deontic modes is analogous to the difference between the possible and the contingent among the alethic modes.)

The above deontic concepts apply to a single act (or performance-function of acts). There are also deontic concepts which apply to pairs of acts.

Two acts are morally incompatible, if their conjunction is forbidden (and compatible if it is permitted). For instance: giving a promise and not keeping it are (*morally*) incompatible acts.

Doing one act commits us to do another act, if the implication of the two acts is obligatory. For instance: giving a promise commits us to keep it.

The proposition that the act named by A is permitted will be expressed in symbols by $P\,A$.

The proposition that the act named by A is forbidden, is the negation of the proposition that it is permitted. It can thus be symbolized by $\sim (P\,A)$.

The proposition that the act named by A is obligatory, is the negation of the proposition that the negation of the act is permitted. It can thus be symbolized by $\sim (P \sim A)$. We shall also use the shorter expression $O\,A$.

---

[2] It need hardly be stressed that the question of validity of various deontic propositions (other than those which are true on formal grounds) does not concern us in this paper.

The proposition that the act named by $A$ is (morally) indifferent can be symbolized by $(P\,A)\;\&\;(P \sim A)$.

The proposition that the acts named by $A$ and by $B$ are (morally) incompatible can be symbolized by $\sim (P\,A\,\&\,B)$.

The proposition that the performance of the act named by $A$ commits us to perform the act named by $B$ can be symbolized by $O\,A \rightarrow B$. But $O\,A \rightarrow B$ means the same as $\sim (P \sim (A \rightarrow B))$, and this means the same as $\sim (P\,A\,\&\sim B)$. Commitment can thus be explained in terms of compatibility.

$P$ and $O$ are called the deontic operators. Sentences of the type "$P\quad$", where a name of an act (or a molecular complex of names of acts) has to be inserted in the blank, we shall call $P$-sentences. Similarly, we shall call sentences of the type "$O\quad$" $O$-sentences.

As to the use of brackets it should be remarked that $P$- and $O$-sentences as constituents of molecular complexes of sentences should be enclosed within brackets in order to avoid confusion. It should further be observed that a deontic operator before a molecular complex of names of acts refers to the whole complex and not to its first constituent only. Thus, *e.g.*, $P\,A \vee B$ means that the act named by $A \vee B$ is permitted.

The system of Deontic Logic, which we are outlining in this paper, studies propositions (and truth-functions of propositions) about the obligatory, permitted, forbidden, and other (derivative) deontic characters of acts (and performance-functions of acts).

We shall call the propositions which are the object of study deontic propositions. The sentences, in which they are expressed in our system, are $P$- and $O$-sentences or molecular complexes of such sentences.

4. A task of particular importance which Deontic Logic sets itself is to develop a technique for deciding, whether the propositions it studies are logically true or not. (The decision problem.)

Sometimes molecular complexes of $P$- and $O$-sentences express truths of logic for reasons which have nothing to do with the specific character of deontic concepts. For instance: If $A$ is permitted, if $B$ is permitted, then $B$ is forbidden, if $A$ is forbidden. In symbols: $((P\,B) \rightarrow (P\,A)) \rightarrow (\sim (P\,A) \rightarrow \sim (P\,B))$. This is a truth of logic. It is an application of a variant of the so called *modus tollens* which is valid for any sentences, whether deontic or not. It is, therefore, a trivial truth from the point of view of our Deontic Logic.

Sometimes, however, molecular complexes of $P$- and $O$-sentences express truths of logic for reasons which depend upon the specific (logical) character of deontic concepts. For instance: If $A$ is obligatory and if doing $A$ commits us to do $B$, then $B$ is obligatory too. In symbols: $(O\,A)\;\&\;(O\,A \rightarrow B) \rightarrow (O\,B)$. It is intuitively obvious that this is a truth of logic, *i.e.*, something which is valid on purely formal grounds. It is, however, not an application of any scheme which is valid for *any* sentences, whether deontic or not. The existence of logical truths which are peculiar to deontic concepts is what makes the study of Deontic Logic interesting.

If a molecular complex of P- and O-sentences expresses logical truth for reasons which are independent of the specific nature of deontic concepts, then its truth can be established or proved in a truth-table of propositional logic.

If, however, a molecular complex of P- and O-sentences expresses logical truth for reasons which depend on the specific nature of deontic concepts, then its truth cannot be established by the means of propositional logic alone. The question therefore arises: What is the necessary and sufficient criterion which a molecular complex of P- and/or O-sentences must satisfy in order to express a logically true proposition?

5. Let us call "permitted" and "forbidden" the two deontic values.

An act will be called a deontic function of certain other acts, if the deontic value of the former uniquely depends upon the deontic values of the latter.

It is easy to see that not any act which is a performance-function of certain other acts is also a deontic function of them. (Otherwise the logic of deontic concepts would be trivial.)

Consider first the negation of a given act. From the fact that A is performed, we can conclude to the fact that $\sim A$ is not performed. But from the fact that A is permitted, we can conclude nothing as to the permitted or forbidden character of $\sim A$. Sometimes $\sim A$ is permitted, sometimes not. If A is what we have called indifferent, then $\sim A$ is also permitted, but if A happened to be obligatory as well as permitted, then $\sim A$ would be forbidden. In the smoking compartment, e.g., not-smoking is permitted and also smoking. But in the non-smoking compartment, not-smoking is permitted and smoking forbidden.

Consider next the conjunction of two acts. From the fact that A and B are both performed, it follows that A & B is performed. But from the fact that A and B are both permitted, it does not follow that A & B is permitted. Sometimes A & B is permitted, sometimes not. For, A and B may both be permitted, but doing either of them may commit us not to do the other. I may be free to promise and also not to promise to give a certain thing to a person, and free to give and also not to give this thing to him, but forbidden to promise to give and yet not give it.

Consider, finally, the disjunction of two acts. From the fact that at least one of the two acts A and B is performed, it follows that A v B is performed, and from the fact that none of the two acts A and B is performed, it follows that A v B is not performed. Similarly, from the fact that at least one of the acts is permitted, it follows that their disjunction is permitted, and from the fact that both acts are forbidden, it follows that their disjunction is forbidden. In other words: the disjunction of two acts is permitted, if and only if at least one of the acts is permitted. Speaking loud or smoking is permitted in the reading-room, if and only if speaking loud is permitted or smoking is permitted.[3]

Thus deontic functions are similar to performance-functions (and truth-functions) in regard to disjunction, but not similar in regard to negation and conjunction. The similarity can be laid down as a Principle of Deontic Distribution:

*If an act is the disjunction of two other acts, then the proposition that the disjunction is permitted is the disjunction of the proposition that the first act is permitted and the proposition that the second act is permitted.*

(This principle can, naturally, be extended to disjunctions with any number $n$ of members.)

In virtue of familiar principles of formal logic, any molecular complex of $n$ names of acts has what we propose to call a perfect disjunctive normal form. This is a 0-, 1-, or more-than-1-termed disjunction-name of $n$-termed conjunction-names. Each of the $n$ original names or its negation-name occurs in every one of the conjunction-names.

In virtue of the above Principle of Deontic Distribution, any molecular complex of $n$ names of acts denotes a deontic function of the acts denoted by the conjunction-names in its perfect disjunctive normal form.

Consider now a $P$-sentence $P\ c$, where $c$ stands for (an atomic name of an act or) a molecular complex of names of acts. Let $c_1, \ldots, c_k$ stand for the conjunction-names in the perfect disjunctive normal form of $c$. The sentences $P\ c_1, \ldots, P\ c_k$ we shall call the $P$-constituents of $P\ c$.

Since, in virtue of the Principle of Deontic Distribution, $c$ denotes a deontic function of the acts named by $c_1, \ldots, c_k$, it follows that $P\ c$ expresses a truth-function of the propositions expressed by $P\ c_1, \ldots, P\ c_k$. Generally speaking: a $P$-sentence expresses a truth-function of the propositions expressed by its $P$-constituents.

Consider $n$ names of acts $A_1, \ldots, A_n$. There are in all $2^n$ conjunction-names which can be formed by selecting $m$ ($0 \leqq m \leqq n$) out of the $n$ names and taking the negation-names of the remaining $n$-$m$ names. (The order of the names in a conjunction-name is irrelevant.) By the deontic units in the deontic realm of the acts named by $A_1, \ldots, A_n$ we shall understand the propositions that the respective acts named by those $2^n$ conjunction-names are permitted. By the deontic realm itself we shall understand the disjunction of all the deontic units.

Thus, *e.g.*, the deontic units of the deontic realm of the sole act named

[3] The meaning of "or" in ordinary language is not quite settled. When we say that we are permitted to do A *or* B, we sometimes mean, by implication, that we are allowed to do both. Sometimes, however, we mean that we are allowed to do one and one only of the two acts. Which meaning the "or" conveys by implication depends upon the material nature of the individual case, in which it is used. It ought to be stressed that our use of "or" in this paper is neutral with regard to such material differences in the individual situations. That we are permitted to do A *or* B means here that we are permitted to do at least one of the two acts, and neither excludes nor includes, by implication, the permission to do both.

by A are the propositions expressed by $P\,A$ and $P \sim A$. The deontic realm itself is the proposition expressed by $(P\ A)\ v\ (P \sim A)$. The deontic units of the deontic realm of the acts named by A and B are the propositions expressed by $P\ A\ \&\ B$ and $P\ A\ \&\ \sim B$ and $P \sim A\ \&\ B$ and $P \sim A\ \&\ \sim B$. Etc.

The deontic units of the deontic realm of given acts are logically independent of one another, meaning that they can be true or false in any combination of truth-values. There is, however, one point at which this independence might be questioned. Could *all* the deontic units be false?

Let A be the name of an act. That all (both) the deontic units in the deontic realm of this act are false means that the act itself and its negation are both forbidden. In symbols: $\sim (P\,A)\ \&\ \sim (P \sim A)$. Since the act *or* its negation is performed by any agent whenever he acts, the falsehood of all the deontic units means that we are forbidden to act in any way whatsoever.

Is such a prohibition illogical? Its counterpart in the logic of the alethic modalities would be the case, when a proposition and its negation are both impossible, and its counterpart in the logic of the epistemic modalities would be the case, when a proposition and its negation are both known to be false. *These* cases are obviously logical impossibilities. On the other hand, in the logic of the existential modalities the corresponding case is, when a property and its negation are both empty. *This* is not an impossibility, since the Universe of Discourse may have no members. The question, therefore is, whether the deontic modes at this point resemble the alethic and the epistemic modes or whether they resemble the existential modes.

Ordinary language and our common sense logical intuitions seem at first not to provide us with a clear answer. A simple logical transformation, however, will help us to make up our minds.

That the negation of an act is forbidden means that the act itself is obligatory. Thus we can for $\sim (P \sim A)$ write $O\ A$. That an act and its negation are both forbidden means the same as that the act itself is both obligatory and forbidden.

At this point an appeal to ordinary language will, I think, be decisive. We seem prepared to reject a use of the words, according to which one and the same act could be truly called both obligatory and forbidden.[4] If, however, we reject this use, we must also reject the idea that all the units in a deontic realm could be false.

Thus, on the point at issue, the deontic modalities appear to resemble the alethic and the epistemic modalities rather than the existential ones.

The restriction on the logical independence of the deontic units, which we are forced to accept, can be laid down as a Principle of Permission:

*Any given act is either itself permitted or its negation is permitted.*

There are alternative formulations of the principle. We might also have

[4] For the "relativity" of deontic propositions cf. below, p. 315.

said: If the negation of an act is forbidden, then the act itself is permitted. And this again is equivalent to saying: If an act is obligatory, then it is permitted.

6. Which truth-function of its P-constituents a P-sentence expresses can be investigated and decided in truth-tables.

We shall here construct a truth-table for the following P-sentences: $P A$ and $P \sim A$ and $P A \& B$ and $P A \lor B$ and $P A \to B$ and $P A \longleftrightarrow B$ and $P A \lor \sim A$. The perfect disjunctive normal form of $A$ (in terms of $A$ and $B$) is $A \& B \lor A \& \sim B$. The normal form of $\sim A$ is $\sim A \& B \lor \sim A \& \sim B$. The table looks as follows (see p. 311):

The normal form of $A \& B$ is $A \& B$. The normal form of $A \lor B$ is $A \& B \lor A \& \sim B \lor \sim A \& B$. The normal form of $A \to B$ is $A \& B \lor A \& B \lor \sim A \& \sim B$. The normal form of $A \longleftrightarrow B$ is $A \& B \lor \sim A \& \sim B$. The normal form of $A \lor \sim A$ is $A \& B \lor A \& \sim B \lor \sim A \& B \lor \sim A \& \sim B$. Thus the seven P-sentences have in all four P-constituents, viz. $P A \& B$ and $P A \& \sim B$ and $P \sim A \& B$ and $P \sim A \& \sim B$. They express the deontic units of the deontic realm of the two acts named by $A$ and by $B$.

In distributing truth-values over the deontic units (or the P-constituents) we have to observe the restriction imposed by the Principle of Permission. The subsequent calculation of truth-values for the seven deontic propositions (or the seven P-sentences) depends only on the Principle of Deontic Distribution.

What is the truth-table for $P A \& \sim A$? The perfect disjunctive normal form of $A \& \sim A$ is "empty," i.e., a 0-termed disjunction. Thus $P A \& \sim A$ too is a 0-termed disjunction of P-constituents. It might be argued that a disjunction is true, if and only if at least one of its members is true, and that a 0-termed disjunction, since it has no members, is never true (always false). If, however, $P A \& \sim A$ is always false, its negation $\sim (P A \& \sim A)$ is always true. But $\sim (P A \& \sim A)$ means the same as $O A \lor \sim A$. Thus, on the above criterion for the truth of a 0-termed disjunction, it follows that $O A \lor \sim A$ is a deontic tautology.

It might, however, be questioned whether it can be regarded as a truth of logic that a tautologous act is obligatory (and a contradictory act forbidden). The corresponding proposition in the logic of the alethic modalities is that a tautologous proposition is necessary (and a contradictory proposition impossible), and the corresponding proposition in the logic of the existential modalities is that a tautologous property is universal (and a contradictory property empty). These corresponding cases are obviously logical truths. On the other hand, the corresponding propositions in the logic of the epistemic modalities is that a tautologous proposition is verified (and a contradictory proposition falsified). This is not a logical truth. For, a proposition may be tautologous (contradictory) without our knowing it. The question therefore is, whether the deontic modes at this point resemble the alethic and the existential modes, or whether they resemble the epistemic modes.

| $PAv{\sim}A$ | $PA{\leftrightarrow}B$ | $PA{\rightarrow}B$ | $PAvB$ | $PA\&B$ | $P{\sim}A$ | $PA$ | $P{\sim}A\&{\sim}B$ | $P{\sim}A\&B$ | $PA\&{\sim}B$ | $PA\&B$ |
|---|---|---|---|---|---|---|---|---|---|---|
| T | T | T | T | T | T | T | T | T | T | T |
| T | T | T | T | T | T | T | F | T | T | T |
| T | T | T | T | T | T | T | T | F | T | T |
| T | T | T | T | T | F | T | F | F | F | T |
| T | T | T | T | T | T | T | F | T | F | T |
| T | T | T | T | T | T | T | F | F | F | T |
| T | T | T | T | F | T | T | F | F | F | F |
| T | T | T | T | F | F | T | F | T | T | F |
| T | F | T | T | F | T | T | T | T | T | F |
| T | T | T | T | F | T | T | F | F | T | F |
| T | F | F | T | F | F | F | F | F | T | F |
| T | T | T | T | F | T | F | F | T | F | F |
| T | F | T | F | F | T | F | T | F | F | F |

Ordinary language and our common sense logical intuitions seem not to provide us with any clear answer. It appears, moreover, that no further logical considerations can help us to decide on the issue. It may be thought "awkward" to permit contradictory actions [5] but it is difficult to conceive of any logical argument against this permission. From the point of view of logic, therefore, the most plausible course seems to be to regard $P A \& \sim A$ and $O A v \sim A$ as expressing contingent propositions which can be either true or false.

Thus, on the point at issue, the deontic modalities appear to resemble the epistemic rather than the alethic and the existential modalities.

We suggest the following Principle of Deontic Contingency:

*A tautologous act is not necessarily obligatory, and a contradictory act is not necessarily forbidden.*

7. Let us consider a molecular complex of $P$- and/or $O$-sentences. $O$-sentences can be regarded as abbreviations for negation-sentences of certain $P$-sentences. (Cf. above, p. 309.) If the molecular complex happened to contain $O$-sentences, we replace them by negation-sentences of $P$-sentences. Thus we get a new molecular complex, all the constituents of which are $P$-sentences.

We now turn our attention to the (molecular complexes of) names of acts which follow after the modal operators in this new molecular complex of $P$-sentences. We make an inclusive list of all atomic names which are constituents of at least one of the molecular complexes of) names of acts in question. Thereupon we transform these (molecular complexes of) names of acts into their perfect disjunctive normal forms in terms of all atomic names which occur in our list. The respective conjunction-names in these normal forms preceded by the deontic operator $P$ we shall call the $P$-constituents of the initially given molecular complex of $P$- and/or $O$-sentences.( Cf. the example given below).

We know already that any $P$-sentence expresses a truth-function of the propositions expressed by its $P$-constituents. Since any molecular complex of $P$- and/or $O$-sentences expresses a truth-function of the propositions expressed by the $P$- and/or $O$-sentences themselves, it follows that any molecular complex of $P$- and/or $O$-sentences expresses a truth-function of the propositions expressed by its $P$-constituents.

Which truth-function of the propositions expressed by its $P$-constituents a molecular complex of $P$- and/or $O$-sentences expresses can be investigated and decided in a truth-table. This fact constitutes a solution of the decision problem for the system of Deontic Logic which we are outlining in this paper.

The technique of constructing truth-tables in Deontic Logic will be illustrated by an example.

[5] Contradictory acts should not be confused with (morally) indifferent acts. The former are acts which, by definition, are never performed by an agent. The latter are acts which we are permitted to perform, but also not to perform.

Let the molecular complex be (O A) & (O A → B) → (O B). (Cf. above, p. 306.)

O A is an abbreviation for ∼ (P ∼ A), O A → B for ∼ (P A & ∼ B), and O B for ∼ (P ∼ B). By replacing O-sentences by P-sentences in our initial complex, we get the new complex ∼ (P ∼ A) & ∼ (P A & ∼ B) → ∼ (P ∼ B).

The atomic names of acts which are constituents of (at least one of) the molecular complexes "inside" the operator P are A and B. The perfect disjunctive normal form of ∼ A in terms of A and B is ∼ A & B v ∼ A & ∼ B. The normal form of A & ∼ B is A & ∼ B. The normal form of ∼B is A & ∼ B v ∼ A & ∼ B. The P-constituents of the initially given molecular complex, therefore, are P ∼ A & B and P A & ∼ B and P ∼ A & ∼B.

Since the P-constituents do not represent all the deontic units of the deontic realm of the acts named by A and by B (cf. above, p. 310) the Principle of Permission does not here impose any restrictions upon the combinations of truth-values. The calculation of truth-values depends only upon the Principle of Deontic Distribution (and principles of propositional logic). The table looks as follows:

| P A & ∼ B | P ∼ A & B | P ∼ A & ∼ B | O A | O A→B | (O A) & (O A→B) | O B | → |
|:---:|:---:|:---:|:---:|:---:|:---:|:---:|:---:|
| T | T | T | F | F | F | F | T |
| T | T | F | F | F | F | F | T |
| T | F | T | F | F | F | F | T |
| T | F | F | T | F | F | F | T |
| F | T | T | F | T | F | F | T |
| F | T | F | F | T | F | T | T |
| F | F | T | F | T | F | F | T |
| F | F | F | T | T | T | T | T |

It is seen that the molecular complex which we are investigating (indicated by "→" in the column to the extreme right) expresses the tautology of the propositions expressed by its P-constituents.

8. A molecular complex of P- and/or O-sentences which expresses the tautology of the propositions expressed by its P-constituents, is said to express a truth of Deontic Logic or a deontic tautology.

A (true) proposition to the effect that a certain molecular complex of P- and/or O-sentences expresses a deontic tautology will be called a law of Deontic Logic.

We mention below some examples of such laws. When we call two molecular complexes of P- and/or O-sentences identical, we mean that their equivalence-sentence expresses a deontic tautology. When we say that (the proposition expressed by) one molecular complex of P- and/or O-sentences entails (the proposition expressed by) another, we mean that their implication-sentence expresses a deontic tautology. The propositions expressed by the molecular complexes of sentences given below (or by the equivalence- or implication-sentences in question) are easily shown by truth-tables to be tautologies.

(i) Two laws on the relation of permission to obligation and *vice versa*:

*a P A* is identical with $\sim (O \sim A)$, *i.e.* $(P\ A) \longleftrightarrow \sim (O \sim A)$ expresses a deontic tautology.

*b O A* entails *P A, i.e.* $(O\ A) \to (P\ A)$ expresses a deontic tautology.

The second of these laws should not be confused with the above (alternative formulation of the) Principle of Permission (p. 309). In the proof of (i)*b* this principle is already assumed.

(ii) Four laws for the "dissolution" of deontic operators:

*a O A & B* is identical with $(O\ A)\ \&\ (O\ B)$.

*b P A v B* is identical with $(P\ A)\ v\ (P\ B)$.

*c* $(O\ A)\ v\ (O\ B)$ entails *O A v B*.

*d P A & B* entails $(P\ A)\ \&\ (P\ B)$.

The second of these laws should not be confused with the Principle of Deontic Distribution (p. 308). In the proof of (ii)*b* this principle is already assumed.

(iii) Six laws on "commitment":

*a* $(O\ A)\ \&\ (O\ A \to B)$ entails *O B*. If doing what we ought to do commits us to do something else, then this new act is also something which we ought to do. (This was the example of a deontic tautology which we discussed above.)

*b* $(P\ A)\ \&\ (O\ A \to B)$ entails *P B*. If doing what we are free to do commits us to do something else, then this new act is also something which we are free to do. In other words: doing the permitted can never commit us to do the forbidden.

*c* $\sim (P\ B)\ \&\ (O\ A \to B)$ entails $\sim (P\ A)$. This is but a new version of the previous law. If doing something commits us to do the forbidden, then we are forbidden to do the first thing. For instance: if it is obligatory to keep one's promises and if we promise to do something which is forbidden, then the act of promising this thing is itself forbidden.

*d* $(O\ A \to B\ v\ C)\ \&\ \sim (P\ B)\ \&\ \sim (P\ C)$ entails $\sim (P\ A)$. This is a further version of the two previous laws. An act which commits us to a choice between forbidden alternatives is forbidden.

*e* $\sim ((O\ A\ v\ B)\ \&\ \sim (P\ A)\ \&\ \sim (P\ B))$. It is logically impossible to be obliged to choose between forbidden alternatives.[6]

*f* $(O\ A)\ \&\ (O\ A\ \&\ B \to C)$ entails $O\ B \to C$. If doing two things, the

---

[6] Aquinas several times refers to the laws *d* and *e*. He distinguishes between a man's being *perplexus simpliciter* and his being *perplexus secundum quid*. The former is the case, if he is, as such, obliged to choose between forbidden alternatives. The latter is the case, if he by a previous wrong act commits himself to a choice between forbidden alternatives. Aquinas rightly denies that a man could be *perplexus simpliciter* (*e*) and affirms that a man might be *perplexus secundum quid* (*d*). Cf. *De Veritate*, Q. 17, art. 4; *Summa Theologica*, jajjar, Q. 19, art. 6; *Summa Theologica*, iii, Q. 64, art. 6. For these observations I am indebted to Mr. P. Geach.

first of which we ought to do, commits us to do a third thing, then doing the second thing alone commits us to do the third thing. "Our commitments are not affected by our (other) obligations."

g O ∼ A → A entails O A. If failure to perform an act commits us to perform it, then this act is obligatory.

The truth of all these laws follows from our intuitive notions of obligation and permission. Not all of the laws themselves, however, are intuitively obvious. In the case of some of the laws, moreover, it is not intuitively clear whether their truth is a matter of logic or a matter of moral code. This proves that the decision procedure of Deontic Logic which we have outlined is not void of philosophical interest.

Any molecular complex of *P*- and/or *O*-sentences has what we propose to call an absolutely perfect disjunctive normal form. This we get by replacing every one of the *P*- and/or *O*-sentences by a disjunction-sentence of *P*-constituents of the complex and transforming the molecular complex of *P*-sentences thus obtained into its perfect disjunctive normal form. If the normal form contains the conjunction of the negation of all *P*-constituents, we omit it from the normal form.

The absolutely perfect disjunctive normal form shows with which ones of the possible combinations of truth-values in its *P*-constituents the molecular complex in question expresses agreement and with which ones it expresses disagreement. If it agrees with all possibilities, it expresses a deontic tautology, *i.e.*, is a truth of Deontic Logic.

9. There is one relevant respect, in which the deontic modalities differ from the alethic, epistemic, and existential modalities. It can be illustrated as follows: If a proposition is true, then it is possible, and if a proposition is true, then it is not falsified, and if a property is true of a thing, then the property exists. But if an act is performed (or not performed), then nothing follows as regards its obligatory, permitted or forbidden character. There is thus an important sense in which the deontic modalities unlike the alethic, epistemic, and existential ones have no logical connexions with matters of fact (truth and falsehood). This is a point about deontic categories which has often been stressed by moral philosophers.

10. In this paper deontic propositions have been treated as "absolute." They can, however, be made "relative" in several ways.

First of all, it might be argued that deontic propositions are sometimes, or perhaps always, relative to some so-called moral code. What is obligatory within one moral code, may be forbidden within another.

Secondly, instead of simply considering whether an act is obligatory, permitted or forbidden, we may consider propositions of the following type: *x* is permitted to do A, or *x* permits *y* to do A. Introducing quantifiers we then get propositions of the type: somebody is permitted to do A, or somebody permits everybody to do A, etc. The logical systems which we get by such extensions are of considerable complexity. Their decision-problem can be solved for many interesting cases, but not for all cases.

# A NOTE ON DEONTIC LOGIC AND DERIVED OBLIGATION*

Georg Henrik von Wright (1916–    ). See page 303.

1. Mr. R. N. McLaughlin, in a note in Mind, July 1955, has made some critical comments on my article "Deontic Logic" (Mind, January 1951). He contends that not all the principles of my system of a deontic logic agree with our "intuitions" concerning the logical properties of obligation-concepts. He gives two examples which are supposed to show this. In the first example, I simply fail to see any disagreement between "intuition" and "logic." In the second example, an instance of disagreement with "intuition" is certainly produced, but only because McLaughlin makes himself guilty of a logical blunder.

McLaughlin's first example is this: $O(A)$ & $O(A \to B) \to O(B)$ is a law of deontic logic. It means: If it is obligatory to do A and obligatory to neglect A or do B, then it is also obligatory to do B. Thus, to use McLaughlin's example, if it is obligatory to walk in a public place and obligatory to abstain from walking in a public place or wear clothes, then it is obligatory to wear clothes. Does it follow, McLaughlin asks, "that it is obligatory to wear clothes even though we do not walk in a public place"? I think the answer is yes—and that, the premisses of the problem being taken into due consideration, this is in good accord with our intuitions. For, if walking in a public place really is obligatory, then to neglect this action is forbidden, and the only way in which we are allowed to fulfil the obligation imposed in the second premiss (viz. not to walk in a public place or be dressed) is by being dressed. So that here the two acts of walking in a public place and wearing clothes are both obligatory.

The only explanation which I can suggest of the fact that McLaughlin is inclined to see a clash here between my deontic logic and his intuitions, is that the example he chooses is "practically absurd." Walking in a public place is not the sort of act that can reasonably be unconditionally imposed on people as being their duty. Suppose, however, that it were a derived obligation in the sense, e.g., that no-one were allowed to go to bed without first taking a walk in a public place. And suppose that, as above, walking in a public place commits us to wearing clothes. Then it would not follow that wearing clothes is obligatory even though we do not walk in a public place,—and the agent may safely undress when going to bed without risking to break the laws of deontic logic.

* Reprinted by kind permission of the author and publisher from Mind, Vol. 65, 1956, pp. 507–509.

McLaughlin's second example is this: $P(A\&B) \rightarrow P(A)$ is a law of deontic logic. It means: If it is permitted to do both A and B, then it is permitted to do A. Thus, to use McLaughlin's example, if walking in a public place and wearing clothes is permitted, then walking in a public place is permitted. "But," McLaughlin asks, "is walking in a public place permitted if clothes are not worn?" He seems to think that this consequence follows from the above formula. But this is by no means the case; for which reason we need not worry about the fact that, *if* the said consequence followed, *then* there certainly would be a conflict with our logical intuitions. The alleged consequence, which worries McLaughlin, is, in symbols, $P(A\& \sim B)$. And $P(A\& \sim B)$ does *not* follow from $P(A\&B)$.

The following analogy from the logic of the quantifiers may be helpful: Let it be established that there are cats (A) with a tail (B). From this it logically follows that there are cats (A). But it does *not* follow that there are tailless cats $(A\& \sim B)$. This, incidentally, is not a loose illustration only, but a strict isomorphy. The system of deontic logic developed in my paper is structurally identical with a fragment of the logic of the quantifiers.

The fact that an act is permitted does not mean that doing it in conjunction with anything were permitted. Indeed, if A is permitted and $\sim$ B forbidden, then we can *prove*—in deontic logic that $A\& \sim B$ is forbidden too (and A&B permitted).

I think that the above remarks will dispose of McLaughlin's objections.

2. Of a more serious kind is an objection brought forward by Mr. A. N. Prior in *Mind*, July 1951. It can be restated as follows:

$\sim P(A) \rightarrow O(A \rightarrow B)$ is a law of deontic logic. It means: If the act A is forbidden, then it is obligatory to neglect A or do another, arbitrary act B. This, in itself, is quite unobjectionable, and trivial. But if, as I did in my paper on deontic logic, it is suggested that $O(A \rightarrow B)$ expresses what we mean by saying that doing A *commits* us (morally) to do B, then a "paradox" instantly arises. For then we should have to say that a forbidden act commits us to any other act (whether obligatory, permitted, or forbidden). And this obviously, conflicts with our "intuitions" in the matter.

The "paradox" under consideration is an analogue to a well-known Paradox of Strict Implication in modal logic. The notion of a strict implication was originally introduced as a proposed "formalization" of the idea of logical consequence or entailment. The resultant paradox is, that then an impossible proposition would *entail* any arbitrary proposition.

Some authors have defended the formalization of entailment by means of strict implication on the ground that the resulting "paradox" is harmless. One may attempt a similar defence for $O(A \rightarrow B)$ as a proposed formalization of moral commitment. But my own opinion is that this would only be to shut one's eyes to a real difficulty (both in the case of entailment and in that of moral commitment).

I think that the proper conclusion to be drawn from Prior's objection is that $O(A \rightarrow B)$ *is not* (contrary to my earlier opinion) an adequate expression in symbolic terms of the notion of commitment (or derived obligation). My belief is, moreover, that a formalization of this notion *cannot* be accomplished at all within the system developed in my paper. (Just as I think that classical modal logic is unable to formalize the notion of entailment.)

3. Let us introduce a symbol $P(p/c.)$. It may be read: p is permitted under conditions $c . \sim P(p/c)$ means: p is forbidden under conditions $c . \sim P(\sim p/c)$ means: neglecting p is forbidden under conditions c or : p is obligatory under conditions c.

We introduce the following two axioms:

A1. $P(p/c) \vee P(\sim p/c)$.
A2. $P(p\&q/c) \longleftrightarrow P(p/c) \& P(q/c\&p)$.

The first axiom says that, under given conditions c, one is permitted to do or permitted to neglect any arbitrary act p; in other words, that *both* doing p *and* not doing p could under no circumstances be forbidden. The second axiom says that the joint performing of two acts, p and q, is permitted under conditions c, if and only if, p is permitted under those conditions, and q is likewise permitted, supposing that p has already been done. The "self-evidence" of these principles can hardly be disputed.

On the basis of these two axioms (and familiar principles of formal logic) one can develop a system of "relative" permission, prohibition, and obligation. This system may be said to *include* the old system of "absolute" permission, prohibition, and obligation by virtue of the fact that the laws, which hold in the old system, appear in the new system in the form of laws for permission, prohibition, and obligation *under tautologous conditions* $(c \vee \sim c)$.

The conditions, under which an act is obligatory, forbidden or permitted, may of course themselves be acts. A necessary condition for saying that doing q commits us to p is that p is obligatory under conditions q.

It is a theorem of the new deontic logic that $O(p/q)$ entails $O(q \rightarrow p/c \vee \sim c)$, where p and q are acts and c an arbitrary condition (which may or may not itself be an act). In other words: If doing q commits us to do p, then either neglecting p or doing q is "absolutely" obligatory. But the converse does not necessarily hold. This seems in good accord with common sense and "intuition".

It may also be shown that neither $\sim P(p/c \vee \sim c) \rightarrow O(q/p)$ nor $O(q/c \vee \sim c) \rightarrow O(q/p)$ are theorems of the new deontic logic. It thus neither follows that an "absolutely" forbidden act commits us to any other act nor that any act commits us to an "absolutely" obligatory act. Thus what Prior called The Paradoxes of Derived Obligation do not arise in this system.

# THE FORMAL ANALYSIS OF
# NORMATIVE CONCEPTS*

ALAN ROSS ANDERSON (1925–    ) of The University of
Pittsburgh has written extensively on logic, philosophy of
science, and philosophy of mind.

OMAR KHAYYAM MOORE (1920–    ) of Yale University has
worked and written in the areas of experimental sociology
and institutional analysis.

Although mathematical logic has been applied in several empirical disciplines,[1] logicians have only recently begun to develop formal systems that are likely to be of special interest to sociologists. From the point
of view of modern logic, indefinitely many systems can be constructed; but
whether such tools are to be of use to sociologists depends in part on the
amount of interchange across disciplinary boundaries. This article is written
in the hope of enlisting the support and interest of investigators treating
problems to which such notions as *rule, norm, obligation*, etc., are central.

Concepts of this kind are of obvious importance for sociological theory;
almost all sociologists make use, in one way or another, of such notions.
But in spite of the widespread use of normative concepts, very little is
known of their logic. For the most part logicians have restricted their attention to descriptive discourse (variously called "informative," "factual,"
"cognitive," etc.), as opposed to prescriptive discourse (or "emotive,"
"normative," "expressive," etc.). Powerful technical tools have been developed for the analysis of the former, but there have been only a few attempts
to provide analogous machinery for the latter. Whatever the reasons for the
neglect of the prescriptive may be, this situation seems unfortunate. We
all do, as a matter of fact, draw conclusions from a variety of statements
that may, broadly speaking, be called "normative." We reason from moral
precepts, from imperatives, from commands, from statements of legal responsibility and obligation, and from sets of rules for games like chess,
bridge, and football.

These facts suggest that there are grounds for optimism concerning the

---

* Reprinted by kind permission of the authors and the publisher from *The American
Sociological Review*, Vol. 22: no. 1, 1957, pp. 9–17.
    [1] See for example the references given in Omar Khayyam Moore and Scarvia B. Ander-
son, "Modern Logic and Tasks for Experiments on Problem Solving Behavior," *The
Journal of Psychology*, 38 (July, 1954), pp. 151–160.

possibility of developing a formal logic for norms.[2] There have been many informal discussions of normative discourse, centering usually around imperatives; but there have been very few attempts to give a rigorous and formal characterization of the logical structure of the family of related notions consisting of legal or moral obligations, prescriptions, sets of directions, recipes, fiats, technological commands, and the like. Among these are Mally,[3] Menger,[4] Hofstadter and McKinsey,[5] von Wright,[6] Feys [7] and Prior.[8] Space does not permit a general review of these systems, though each of them merits consideration. We have selected for initial discussion a system which is particularly relevant to sociology, namely von Wright's *Deontic Logic*.[9] But before discussing this formalism, it may be helpful to outline informally a problem typical of those on which the logical analysis might be expected to throw light.

Some sociological theorists have maintained that under certain circumstances there is a "strain of consistency," and under other circumstances a tendency toward inconsistency, among the norms of a given social order. An empirical test of such a thesis presupposes a reasonable explication of the concept of "consistency" as used in such analyses. In many instances it is difficult to see precisely what is meant by "consistency" as applied to sets of norms.[10] Despite the vagueness and ambiguity of the term "consistency," however, we would expect to find some uniformity in its application by sociologists. Consider, as illustrations, the following three cases.

---

[2] It should be emphasized that the chief value of formalizing a logic of norms, or indeed any logic at all, does *not* lie simply in the use of shorthand notational devices, though an economical symbolism can be helpful. The idea is not to "translate" from one language into another, but rather to express propositions in a language the logical structure of which is explicit and definite. An adequate formalization makes it possible to check in a detailed and rigorous way just what follows from what, and such rigorous checking is an obvious prerequisite for the use of the axiomatic approach. For an especially clear discussion of the sense in which systems of formal logic (including mathematics) are "languages," see Alonzo Church, *Introduction to Mathematical Logic*, Volume I, Princeton: Princeton University Press, 1955, pp. 47–68, especially footnotes 111 and 116.

[3] E. Mally, *Grundgesetze des Sollens*, Graz: Leuschner and Lubensky, 1926.

[4] Karl Menger, "A Logic of the Doubtful. On Optative and Imperative Logic," *Reports of a Mathematical Colloquium*, 2nd series, No. 1, Notre Dame: University Press, 1939, pp. 53–64.

[5] A. Hofstadter and J. C. C. McKinsey, "On the Logic of Imperatives," *Philosophy of Science*, 6 (October, 1939), pp. 446–457.

[6] G. H. von Wright, "Deontic Logic," *Mind*, 60 (January, 1951), pp. 1–15.

[7] Robert Feys, "Expression modale du 'devoir-être,'" *The Journal of Symbolic Logic*, 20 (March, 1955), pp. 91–92.

[8] A. N. Prior, *Time and Modality*, Oxford: The Clarendon Press, 1956.

[9] "Deontic" logic is the logic of the modes of obligation. Expositions of von Wright's system may be found in von Wright, *loc. cit.*; or in G. H. von Wright, *An Essay in Modal Logic*, Amsterdam: North-Holland Publishing Company, 1951; or in A. N. Prior, *Formal Logic*, Oxford: The Clarendon Press, 1955.

[10] It should be emphasized that "consistency," in such contexts, frequently has only a vague analogical resemblance to "consistency" in the various logical senses. For the latter see Alonzo Church, *op. cit.*, pp. 108–109.

I.  If a set of norms both obligates and forbids an agent to execute a given act under the same circumstances, the set of norms would no doubt be regarded as inconsistent.

II. If a set of norms (1) makes it obligatory to do act B if act A is done, (2) permits act A, but (3) forbids act B, then again the set would no doubt be held to be inconsistent. It might be maintained, that is, that doing the permitted never commits an agent to doing the forbidden, within a consistent set of norms.

III. Consider a set of norms which (1) makes act B or act C obligatory if act A is done, (2) permits act A, but (3) forbids both act B and act C. To say that such a set of norms is inconsistent amounts to saying that an act which commits an agent to forbidden alternatives would itself be forbidden by a consistent set of norms.

For such simple cases, it seems that common sense suffices to decide whether normative systems are consistent (though of course we are all familiar, from recent developments in science, with the fact that common sense may well be inadequate even for problems which appear to be easily resolved). But in any event it is clear that common sense does not take us very far. The following case, although undoubtedly much simpler than many situations which actually arise, will provide an illustration.

IV. Consider a set of norms from which it follows that (1) it is obligatory that if act D be done then act B not be done, (2) it is forbidden that if act A is done then act C is done, (3) it is obligatory that if act A is done then either act B or else both act C and act D be done, and (4) it is permitted that act D be done. Should (1)–(4) be taken as evidence that the set of norms is inconsistent or not? Even if it is clear to the reader how this question should be answered, it is obvious that realistic cases of much greater complexity might arise. Moreover, it would be valuable to have a clear statement of principles in accordance with which any case, simple or complex, could be decided.

But complexity is not the only problem. Some apparently simple questions may be puzzling and difficult to resolve, in part, because they are rarely raised. For example, suppose that a set of norms obligated an agent to perform some act which is impossible for causal or perhaps even logical reasons. Should such a set of norms be regarded as consistent? If not, then what should be said about logically impossible acts? Are they to be forbidden? Or should we treat them as permitted? Or should they perhaps be regarded as indifferent? Or should we say that, inasmuch as contradictory acts are vacuous in the sense that they cannot be performed in any case,[11]

---

[11] An example of a contradictory act, one that cannot be performed, is smoking-and-not-smoking (at the same time by the same person). This sort of contradictory act is not to be confused with, e.g., smoking in defiance of a "No Smoking" sign, or with sometimes smoking and sometimes not smoking.

none of the terms "obligatory," "permitted," "forbidden," are applicable to them?

Evidently what is required is a system of concepts that will handle not only the easier problems, but will also enable us to deal effectively with complex and/or unfamiliar cases. The system of deontic logic proposed by von Wright provides, among other things, a tool for treating just such questions as have been outlined above.

## FORMAL DEONTIC LOGIC

Von Wright's system assumes a universe of discourse consisting of "acts," or perhaps better, "act-types." The word "embezzlement," for example, refers to a *kind* of incident, or a class of incidents, rather than to any particular occasion on which something is embezzled. As variables for "act-types" (for brevity, now, simply "acts") he uses "A," "B," "C,". . . . In addition to the atomic acts over which the variables range, there are various combinations of acts:

Corresponding to any act A there is a *negation-act* of A, symbolized ~A. ~A is that act which is performed by an agent if and only if he does not perform A; to use von Wright's example, "The negation of the act of repaying a loan is not repaying it."

The *conjunction-act* symbolized (A & B), is that act which is performed by an agent if and only if he performs both act A and act B.

The *disjunction- act* (A v B) is that act which is performed by an agent if and only if he performs either act A or act B (or both).

The *implication-act* (A → B) is that act which is performed by an agent if and only if it is not the case that A is performed and B is not.

The *equivalence-act* (A ⟷ B) is that act which is performed by an agent if and only if he performs both A and B, or neither A nor B.

The only primitive deontic concept is "permission"; the others (i.e., obligatory, indifferent, forbidden) are defined in terms of this primitive concept. "Permission" is symbolized by "P," and the result of applying "P" to the name of an act is a formula of the system. That is, "PA" is to be interpreted as expressing the proposition that acts of kind A are permitted. (The notion of permission is, of course, always to be understood as relative to some set of norms.) Similarly, "P~A" is to be understood as saying that it is permitted not to do A; etc.

"P" together with the act-types thus provide a collection of deontic propositions. As was remarked previously, there is available adequate technical machinery for manipulating propositions, and von Wright brings to bear on the deontic propositions the classical two-valued propositional calculus. This calculus contains analogues of the operations just described for the calculus of acts.[12] The other deontic concepts may then be defined in terms of the concept of permission as follows:

Def. 1.    OA = df ~P~A
Def. 2.    FA = df ~PA
Def. 3.    IA = df (PA) & (P~A).

Definition 1 says that an act A is obligatory ("O") if and only if it is not permitted not to do A; definition 2 says that an act A is forbidden ("F") if and only if A is not permitted; and definition 3 says that an act A is indifferent ("I")[13] if and only if it is permitted to do A and also permitted to do ~A (i.e., not to do A). As von Wright remarks, indifference is a narrower concept than permission. Everything indifferent is permitted, but not conversely; obligatory acts, e.g., are permitted but not indifferent.

The definitions above make use of connectives drawn from the propositional calculus as well as from the calculus of acts. And the application of the propositional calculus to the deontic propositions yields many formulae which are theorems in virtue of their propositional structure alone. For example, (PA → PA), i.e., if A is permitted then A is permitted. However, the interesting theorems from the sociological point of view are those that depend for their status as theorems on the deontic concepts, and on the two principles governing them, which we quote from von Wright:

> I. The Principle of Deontic Distribution. If an act is the disjunction of two other acts, then the proposition that the disjunction is permitted is the disjunction of the proposition that the first act is permitted and the proposition that the second act is permitted.[14]
> II. The Principle of Permission. Any given act is either itself permitted or its negation is permitted.[15]

The formal analogue of Principle I is

$$P(A \vee B) \longleftrightarrow [(PA) \vee (PB)],$$

[12] That is, corresponding to any proposition $p$ there is a denial $\sim p$ which is true if and only if $p$ is false, and for any two propositions $p$ and $q$ there is a conjunction $(p \& q)$ (which is true if and only if both $p$ and $q$ are true), a disjunction $(p \vee q)$ (which is true if and only if at least one of $p$ and $q$ is true), an implication $(p \rightarrow q)$ (which is true if and only if it is not the case that $p$ is true and $q$ is false), and an equivalence $(p \leftrightarrow q)$ (which is true if and only if $p$ and $q$ are both true or both false). Expositions of this calculus may be found in any standard textbook in symbolic logic. Of course the symbols "$\sim$", "&", etc., are here used in a different sense, but no ambiguity need arise since, for example, "$\sim$" applied to an act-name always yields an act-name, whereas negation (symbolized the same way) applied to a proposition always yields a proposition.
[13] Von Wright discusses this concept, but does not specify notation for it; we introduce a special symbol for "indifference." For expository purposes, trivial changes and occasional departures from extreme rigor will be found here and elsewhere.
[14] Von Wright, "Deontic Logic," *op. cit.*, p. 7.
[15] *Ibid.*, p. 9.

that is, if it is permitted to do A or B (i.e., if it is permitted to execute the disjunction-act: A or B), then either it is permitted to do A or it is permitted to do B; and conversely. The formal analogue of Principle II is

$$(PA) \vee (P{\sim}A),$$

that is, either it is permitted to do A, or it is permitted to do $\sim$A.

With the aid of the three definitions and the two principles, von Wright develops a decision procedure [16] as a method of determining which formulae are theorems. The system therefore shares with axiomatic formulations the property of providing a rigorous (and in this case effective) method of testing expressions for "logical truth." The illustrative examples mentioned earlier can easily be tested by von Wright's method, and it develops that in each of the cases, (I), (II) and (III), the formal results accord with the presumed common sense solution. In case (IV), von Wright's decision procedure shows that the set of norms is inconsistent.[17]

As regards the puzzling questions concerning the deontic status of impossible acts, it appears that several alternatives are available. Von Wright discusses this question, and proposes a principle of deontic contingency: "A tautologous act is not necessarily obligatory, and a contradictory act is not necessarily forbidden." [18] This principle is consistent with the other two principles mentioned above, but it is not the only way to resolve the problem. In a system to be mentioned below, for example, application of the deontic categories is limited to contingent states of affairs (i.e., those which are neither necessary nor impossible).

It is not feasible to discuss the alternatives available in detail without giving a complete and rigorous formulation of the systems. Since it lies beyond the scope of this paper to present these systems *qua* formal systems, we will content ourselves with mentioning two more general considerations relevant to von Wright's logic.

In the first place, leaving aside for the moment the fact that certain expressions are provable as theorems, the formalism provides a clear ex-

[16] There are in general two ways of specifying the set of theorems of formal systems, either by means of an axiomatization, or a decision procedure. An axiomatization consists of a list of axioms, together with one or more principles of inference that lead to theorems. A decision procedure is an effective method for determining whether or not an arbitrarily given expression of the system is a theorem. Although for some systems there are both axiomatizations and decision procedures, the two techniques are in general independent; some systems have axiomatizations and no decision procedures, others have decision procedures and no axiomatizations. The decision procedure for von Wright's system consists roughly of a truth-table analysis of expressions in disjunctive normal form. There is as yet no axiomatization of the system in print, though it would be a simple exercise to produce one.

[17] A complete truth-table analysis of example (IV), carried out in the manner proposed by von Wright, would involve initially a two-valued truth-table with $2^{16}$ rows (some of which would be deleted). The amount of labor involved in testing such expressions can be vastly reduced by adapting methods of Alan Ross Anderson, "Improved Decision Procedures for Lewis's Calculus S4 and von Wright's Calculus M," *The Journal of Symbolic Logic*, 19 (September, 1954), pp. 201–214.

[18] Von Wright, "Deontic Logic," *op cit.*, p. 11.

plication of a number of normative concepts. In this respect it may be compared with the Hohfeldian analysis of such notions as duty, demand-right, power, immunity, etc.[19] That analysis at this level is not without value may be seen from Hoebel's application of the Hohfeldian concepts to primitive law.[20]

In the second place, the deontic concepts of von Wright's system have close formal connections with other logical concepts, a fact first pointed out in recent literature by von Wright himself. In fact it was the observation of formal similarities between the notions "obligatory," "permitted," "indifferent," "forbidden," and the extensively studied concepts "necessary," "possible," "contingent," "impossible," which led von Wright to formalize a deontic logic. The formal similarities extend to other concepts as well, as summarized in the table of modal categories. (See Table 1.)

TABLE 1.  MODAL CATEGORIES *

|    | Alethic | Existential | Epistemic | Deontic |
|----|---------|-------------|-----------|---------|
| a. | necessary | universal | verified | obligatory |
| b. | possible | existing | unfalsified | permitted |
| c. | contingent | partial | undecided | indifferent |
| d. | impossible | empty | falsified | forbidden |

* This classification appears in G. H. von Wright, *An Essay in Modal Logic*, Amsterdam: North-Holland Publishing Company, 1951, p. 2. We have again made slight changes for expository reasons. In particular, von Wright did not supply terms to designate two of the modes, on the grounds that no suitable English words were available. We have inserted "partial" and "unfalsified," by fiat. So far as we know, this use of "partial" is new.

The *alethic* modes are predicated of propositions, in such contexts as "It is necessary that $p$," and "It is impossible that $p$,"—$p$ being any proposition. These modes have been treated in the systems of Strict Implication due originally to Lewis,[21] and further studied by McKinsey,[22] von Wright,[23] and others. The *existential* modes are regarded, in many important contexts, as properties of classes. For example, the statement that there are no rich professors can be construed as saying that the class of rich professors is empty. The existential modes are handled in the theory of quantification, for which one *locus classicus* is *Principia Mathematica*.[24] The *epistemic*

[19] W. N. Hohfeld, *Fundamental Legal Conceptions as Applied in Judicial Reasoning and Other Essays*, edited by W. W. Cook, New Haven: Yale University Press, 1923.

[20] E. Adamson Hoebel, *The Law of Primitive Man*, Cambridge: Harvard University Press, 1954.

[21] C. I. Lewis, *A Survey of Symbolic Logic*, Berkeley: University of California Press, 1918.

[22] J. C. C. McKinsey, "A Solution of the Decision Problem for the Lewis Systems S2 and S4, with an Application to Topology," *The Journal of Symbolic Logic*, 6 (December, 1941), pp. 117–134.

[23] Von Wright, *An Essay in Modal Logic, op. cit.*

[24] A. N. Whitehead and Bertrand Russell, *Principia Mathematica*, Cambridge: Cambridge University Press, 1910, 1912, 1913.

and *deontic* modes were first investigated formally by von Wright. It is clear that the epistemic modes, like the alethic, apply to propositions. Von Wright, as previously noted, takes the deontic modes as applying to acts, though other alternatives are available, one of which will be discussed in the next section.

Among the formal similarities noted by von Wright are the following (where the letters refer to entries in the table): whatever is *a* is *b*, whatever is *b* is not *d*, and whatever is *c* is neither *a* nor *d*. To put the last relation more concretely: a *contingent* proposition is neither *necessary* nor *impossible*; a *partial* class is neither *universal* nor *empty*; an *undecided* proposition is neither *verified* nor *falsified*; and an *indifferent* act is neither *obligatory* nor *forbidden*. Of course these examples by no means exhaust the relations among modes in a given category. Moreover, there are systems of logic, some of which von Wright discusses, which combine concepts from two or more categories. In our opinion, a more adequate conceptual scheme for the analysis of normative concepts would involve a combination of the modal categories listed above.

## FURTHER DEVELOPMENTS

Given a social group with an empirically specified normative structure, von Wright's logic would clearly facilitate the analysis of relations among the norms. However, these relations by no means exhaust the interesting and important aspects of normative systems. Two crucial aspects of such systems are the following. (1) There is a need for a method of relating norms to the system of social sanctions or penalties that support them. (2) It is important to relate both norms and sanctions to possibilities for action.

1. It is, of course, customary to couch discussion of norms in terms of the consequences of conforming to, and deviating from, their demands. The lack of such consideration is not to be regarded as a defect in von Wright's approach; it is in fact common in logical studies to isolate concepts and consider only some of their formal properties. Von Wright's system simply exhibits the methodological principle of dividing difficulties in order to conquer them individually, a practice characteristic of twentieth century studies in mathematics and logic. But this lacuna does point to the need for an expansion or elaboration of von Wright's system so as to take adequate account of sanctions.

Although it is clear that the notions of sanction must somehow be got into relation with the deontic logic, methods of effecting this rapprochement have not yet been extensively explored. However, some work has been done toward analyzing the relation between commands (rather than norms) and sanctions.

In an article primarily concerned with commands and imperatives,

Bohnert suggested a formal analysis of the role of "penalties" in imperative discourse.[25] In brief, he recommends that commands be treated as ellipses for disjunctive propositions, one part of which is ordinarily unverbalized, but nevertheless understood in the context of utterance of the command. The locution "Do A," for example, is to be understood as elliptical for the declarative proposition "Either you will do A, or else S," where "S" is understood as referring to a penalty or sanction that the recipient of the command will presumably attempt to avoid. Alternatively "Do A" might, depending on the context, be understood as an ellipsis for "Either you will not do A, or else R," where now "R" refers to a reward which the recipient of the command will presumably attempt to attain.

Bohnert's suggestions have not been axiomatized, but they show at least one way in which commands can be related to penalties so as to yield propositions. This feature of Bohnert's analysis is a distinct advantage, since it makes possible the application of the usual logic of propositions to commands.[26] Other ways of relating commands to propositions have been proposed,[27] but Bohnert seems to have been the first to formulate such a relation in a way that brings in penalties and rewards explicitly.

It would not be difficult to treat Bohnert's suggestion axiomatically,[28] and the resulting "logic of sanctions," as we might call it, would constitute a rigorous formal theory on a par with von Wright's *deontic logic*. The obvious next step would be to construct a formal theory that encompasses both these systems so as to bring out the relations between obligations, the imperative sentences which express these obligations, and the sanctions associated with them.

2. It is clear that the possibilities of human action can be studied without regard either to particular realizations of these possibilities, or to the consequences of acting in any particular way. As an illustration of this point we may take the theory of games.[29] The analysis of any game begins with a complete characterization of all possible ways of playing, these possibilities being circumscribed only by the (non-normative) rules of the game, and not by their chances of success or failure. From among these possibilities, certain strategies are selected as, roughly speaking, most likely to win.

[25] H. G. Bohnert, "The Semiotic Status of Commands," *Philosophy of Science*, 12 (July, 1945), pp. 302–315. We have made inessential changes in his notation to facilitate subsequent discussion.

[26] Traditionally, commands have not been regarded as propositions, primarily on the grounds that we are not inclined to ask of a command such as "Mail this letter" whether it is true or false. Certain writers have evinced an extreme reluctance, for philosophical and grammatical reasons, to admit any very close relation between propositions and commands. In our opinion this is an open question, to be decided by constructing logical systems whose utility can be tested in scientific practice.

[27] See for example R. M. Hare, *The Language of Morals*, Oxford: The Clarendon Press, 1952.

[28] In formalizing Bohnert's proposal, care would be required to avoid, if possible such counterintuitive results as those mentioned by Menger, *loc. cit.*, p. 60.

[29] John von Neumann and Oskar Morgenstern, *Theory of Games and Economic Behavior*, Princeton: Princeton University Press, 1947.

The case seems to us to be similar in analyzing normative systems. If we think of possibilities for action as being bounded by non-normative "rules" consisting of "laws of nature," then the social norms stipulate that certain of these possibilities will, if actualized, lead to rewards or penalties.

There are extensively studied formal systems suitable for the analysis of possibilities (and the other alethic modes). Pioneer work on this subject was done by Lewis in 1918,[30] and since then the systems S1 to S5,[31] S6,[32] S7 and S8,[33] M,[34] and T,[35] to mention only a few, have been constructed and discussed extensively. These modal systems provide alternative explications of the concepts of possibility, necessity, contingency, etc., and this kind of analysis is required for the clarification of the vague notion of "possibilities for human action."

Just as deontic logic makes a contribution to the analysis of normative systems, and the "logic of sanctions" could also contribute to this end, so the logic of "possibility," taken together with the foregoing, may shed light on the problem. What is wanted is a formal frame of reference rich enough to incorporate at least these three facets of normative systems.[36] From the formal point of view, (1) and (2) above motivated the construction of systems more comprehensive than von Wright's upon which we will comment briefly.

The system O'M· [37] has the following features. In addition to the usual primitive notions of alethic modal logic,[38] O'M· takes only the notion "sanction" symbolized "S," as primitive. The basic deontic modes are defined with the help of this notion in such a way that von Wright's sys-

---

[30] Lewis, op.cit.

[31] C. I. Lewis and C. H. Langford, Symbolic Logic, New York: The Century Company, 1932.

[32] M. J. Alban, "Independence of the Primitive Symbols of Lewis's Calculi of Propositions," The Journal of Symbolic Logic, 8 (March, 1943), pp. 25–26.

[33] Sören Halldén, "Results Concerning the Decision Problem of Lewis's Calculi S3 and S6," The Journal of Symbolic Logic, 14 (January, 1950), pp. 230–236.

[34] Von Wright, An Essay in Modal Logic, op. cit.

[35] Robert Feys, "Les Logiques Nouvelles des Modalités," Revue Neo-scholastique de Philosophie, 40 (November, 1937), pp. 517–553, and 41 (May, 1938), pp. 217–252.

[36] Of course there are other important aspects of normative systems; there are, for example subtle problems concerning the relations between possibilities for action, and beliefs about these possibilities. There are a number of ways in which the systems we are discussing might be extended so as to cover such questions. Epistemic modal operators may prove of value in this connection, and one obvious and important way in which these systems should be extended is by adding quantification theory (a generalization of the existential modes).

[37] This system is closely related to a group of new systems described and elaborated in Alan Ross Anderson, The Formal Analysis of Normative Systems, Technical Report No. 2, Contract No. SAR/Nonr-609(16), Office of Naval Research, Group Psychology Branch, 1956.

[38] The underlying alethic system of O'M· is in fact von Wright's system M (shown to be equivalent to Fey's system T by Boleslaw Sobocinski, "Note on a Modal System of Feys-von Wright," The Journal of Computing Systems, 1 (January, 1953), pp. 171–178). Choice of alternative alethic logics yields systems somewhat different from O'M·. The exposition here of O'M· does not reflect various "reductions" effected for the family of systems OM of Anderson ibid.

tem (with appropriate qualifications) emerges as a subsystem of OM′·. The only axiom mentioning the sanction states that the sanction is contingent; i.e., it is possible to behave in such a way that the penalty or sanction will occur, and also in such a way that it will not occur. The deontic modes are construed as applying only to contingent propositions; that is, (1) propositions $p$, $q$, $r$, . . . rather than acts, are the elements of the universe of discourse,[39] and (2) the question of what to do with contradictory and tautologous propositions is answered by limiting the range of deontic modes to propositions that are contingent.

It is beyond the scope of this paper to present O′M · in detail, but it may be of interest to mention the way in which the deontic modes are defined. We use the letter "M" to represent "possibility"; that is, "Mp" is read "it is possible that $p$."

Def. 4.[40]    $O'p = df [(Mp) \& (M{\sim}p)] \& {\sim}M ({\sim}p \& {\sim}S)$.

In this definition of obligation "O′," the first clause, $[(Mp) \& (M{\sim}p)]$, says that $p$ is contingent, i.e., possibly true and possibly false. That is, it is possible to act in such a way as to make $p$ true, and also in such a way as to make it false. The last clause ${\sim}M ({\sim}p \& {\sim}S)$ says that it is impossible that $p$ and the sanction should *both* be false; thus if $p$ is false, then the sanction S is true. This amounts to saying that $p$ is obligatory if and only if it is contingent, and failure to do what is required to make $p$ true would lead to the sanction.

Similarly, we define:

Def. 5.    $F'p = df [(Mp) \& (M{\sim}p)] \& {\sim}M (p \& {\sim}S)$.

That is, $p$ is forbidden if (as before) $p$ is contingent, and moreover, it is impossible that $p$ should be true and S false. In other words, it is impossible to act in such a way as to make $p$ true without incurring the sanction.

Def. 6.    $I'p = df M (p \& {\sim}S) \& M ({\sim}p \& {\sim}S)$.

That is, $p$ is indifferent if it is possible that $p$ should be true and S false, and it is also possible that $p$ should be false and S false. I.e., it is possible to act so as to make $p$ true, without incurring the sanction, and also possible to act so as to make $p$ false, without incurring the sanction. (The con-

---

[39] The letter "$p$," for example, is a variable ranging over propositions. In this context, the propositions may be about "acts," in von Wright's sense.

This point should not be construed as meaning that "acts" are unimportant, or have somehow been done away with; taking propositions as elements of the universe of discourse, is simply *an* alternative interpretation, worth investigating. There may well be others, e.g., propositional functions.

[40] Definitions 4–6 are arranged to facilitate comparison with definitions 1–3. We here use "O′" instead of "O", etc., to distinguish these notions from those of von Wright. An analogue of von Wright's primitive notion of permission is defined in O′M· as follows: $P'p = df M {\sim} p \& M (p \& {\sim} S)$.

tingency of an indifferent $p$ is a logical consequence of the definition of indifference, and hence need not be explicitly stated.)

With these definitions the relations expressed in Def. 1–3 all become provable as theorems of O'M·; moreover, the two principles enunciated by von Wright are also theorems of O'M·.[41] This means that von Wright's system is a subsystem of O'M·; and that some account is also taken of Bohnert's suggestions. It would be pointless to try to characterize O'M· further in such a brief compass; formal systems always require intensive study if their explanatory power is to be fully appreciated.

If the "explanatory power" of such constructs seems highly abstract or remote, the situation should be compared with contemporary physical theories, where mathematical theories much more recondite than those presented here have a direct and immediate bearing on empirical research. And just as many mathematical developments were initiated by empirical problems, so the development of O'M· was motivated by the hope of throwing light on some empirical problems in small-group research. More specifically, in experiments currently being conducted in the Yale Inter-action Laboratory, opportunities are available for studying, under well-controlled conditions, small groups in the process of developing normative structures. A clear and accurate account of these interactional processes calls for a precise and rigorous conceptual framework within which to characterize the behavior of the group.

Small-groups research is of course only one, and not necessarily the most important, area of application of such formal systems. It is hoped that the foregoing discussion will have suggestive value for workers in other socio-logical fields, and will stimulate interest in current research in mathematical logic, especially modal logic. This research is not remote from the daily affairs of sociologists. For instance, whenever instructions are given for filling out a questionnaire, commands expressing obligations are involved. More generally, any adequate sociological theory must encompass, in our opinion, the concepts *norm, obligation,* etc. It is therefore a matter of im-portance to develop sound techniques for analyzing norms and systems of norms.

## SUMMARY

The development of an adequate theoretical structure for sociology will in all likelihood require interdisciplinary co-operation between sociologists and those working in the formal sciences if it is to proceed in a maximally fruitful way. The purpose of this article is to bring to the attention of soci-ologists recent work in mathematical logic which has direct relevance for their research. Von Wright's deontic logic offers promising leads for the

[41] As applied to contingent propositions, that is; this qualification applies elsewhere as well.

analysis of normative structures; the family of systems of which O'M· is a member provides a more comprehensive framework, taking account of the role of penalties and possibilities for action *vis-a-vis* norms.

## SUGGESTIONS FOR FURTHER READING ON DEONTIC LOGIC

ANDERSON, A. R.   "A Reduction of Deontic Logic to Alethic Modal Logic," *Mind*, Vol. 67 (1958), pp. 100–103.

ÅQVIST, L.   "Postulate Sets and Decision Procedures for Some Systems of Deontic Logic," *Theoria*, Vol. 29 (1963), pp. 154–175.

————. "Interpretations of Deontic Logic," *Mind*, Vol. 73 (1964), pp. 246–253.

DAWSON, E. E.   "A Model for Deontic Logic," *Analysis*, Vol. 19 (1959), pp. 73–78.

FISHER, M.   "A Three-Valued Calculus for Deontic Logic," *Theoria*, Vol. 27 (1961), pp. 107–118.

————. "A System of Deontic-Alethic Logic," *Mind*, Vol. 71 (1962), pp. 231–236.

FITCH, F. B.   "A Logical Analysis of Some Value Concepts," *The Journal of Symbolic Logic*, Vol. 28 (1963), pp. 135–142.

RESCHER, N.   "An Axiom System for Deontic Logic," *Philosophical Studies*, Vol. 9 (1958), pp. 24–30 and 64.

SMILEY, T.   "Relative Necessity," *The Journal of Symbolic Logic*, Vol. 28 (1963), pp. 113–134.

VON WRIGHT, G. H.   *Norm and Action*. London: Routledge and Kegan Paul, Ltd., 1963.

# *Part*
# 9 MANY VALUED LOGICS

## *Introduction*

Logical systems of more than two truth values were developed independently by Jan Lukasiewicz in 1920 and by E. L. Post in 1921. As abstract formal systems or calculi they are not of much importance, though they have their own mathematical interest. Prior to interpretation it is even somewhat misleading to refer to them as "logical" systems. Early efforts to interpret them have been, as Rosser and Turquette point out, "definitely premature." Their existence raises fascinating philosophical questions, however. Some of these issues are discussed and debated in a remarkably stimulating manner in the following essay. It is the introduction to the authors' book on many valued logics, in which they carry the technical development of their abstract formal systems to new heights.

# MANY VALUED LOGICS*

Joнn Barkley Rosser (1907–    ) of Cornell University has written extensively in symbolic logic, the analytic theory of numbers, and rocket ballistics. He is the author of *Logic for Mathematicians*.

Atwell R. Turquette (1914–    ) of The University of Illinois has written extensively in logic and philosophy of science.

It has become a truism that every statement is either true or false. It might be supposed that this principle must be disproved before one can write a serious work on many-valued logic. This is by no means the case. In fact, the present volume will not constitute a disproof of such a principle. However, in the following chapters, systems of many-valued logic through the level of the first order predicate calculus will be constructed in such a manner that they are both consistent and complete. The tools of construction will include the logical procedures of ordinary English and those of some formalized systems of two-valued logic. Thus, in effect, we shall use the truism in constructing many-valued logics. It does not follow from this that ordinary two-valued logic is necessary for the construction of many-valued logic, but it does follow that it is sufficient for such constructions. The ability to establish such a sufficiency is certainly no more mysterious than the fact that a Harvard graduate can learn Sanskrit using his native English.

At this point, however, a word of warning is in order, for the treatment of many-valued logic which follows is concerned with the behavior of many-valued statements and not with their meaning. This indifference toward the meaning of many-valued statements indicates that we have no prejudices regarding the possible interpretations of our systems of many-valued logic. As far as our treatment is concerned, the meaning of a many-valued statement could be a linguistic entity such as a many-valued proposition [1] or a physical entity such as one of many positional contacts.[2] For that mat-

---

* Reprinted by kind permission of the authors and publisher from *Many Valued Logics* (Amsterdam: North-Holland Publishing Co., 1952), pp. 1–9.

[1] For example, see D. A. Bochvar, "Ob odnom tréhznačnom isčislénii i égo prіménénii k analizu paradoksov klassičéskogo rasšіrénnogo funkcіonal'nogo isčislénіá," *Matématičésky sbornik (Recueil mathématique)*, n. s. vol. 4 (1939), pp. 287–308, and H. Reichenbach, *Philosophical Foundations of Quantum Mechanics*, Berkeley, University of California Press, 1944.

[2] For example, see C. E. Shannon, "A Symbolic Analysis of Relay and Switching Circuits, *Transactions of the American Institute of Electrical Engineers*, Vol. 57 (1938), pp. 713–723, and V. I. Šéstakov, "Prédstavlénié haraktéristіčéskih funkcіj prédložénіj posrédstvom vyražénü, réalizuémyh réléjnokontaktnymi shémami," *Izvéstіá Akadémii Nauk SSSR, Sérіá matématіčéskaá*, Vol. 10 (1946), pp. 529–554.

ter, the meaning of a many-valued statement might be quite different from either a proposition or a positional contact. In any case, regardless of the possible interpretations of many-valued logical systems, it is our opinion that most interpretations that have so far been proposed can not be taken too seriously until the precise formal development of such systems has been carried to a level of perfection considerably beyond that which is reached even in the present work. Of course, we do not wish to deny the possibility of finding interpretations for subsystems of many-valued logic such as the statement calculus or predicate calculus of first order, but we do consider various recent proposals for interpretations of many-valued logic definitely premature.[3] Typical of such interpretations are those which concern recent physical theories that involve a theory of measurement requiring the use of numbers. Since a theory of many-valued numbers has not yet been constructed, it is not possible at present to show that the proposed interpretations actually apply for systems of many-valued logic incorporating a theory of numbers.[4] Since the present work does not complete the task of constructing many-valued logics beyond the level of the predicate calculus of first order, if one should judge our results in terms of meaning, then the most that could be claimed for them is that they take us a few steps toward the goal of formalizing many-valued logics which are at least rich enough to include a theory of numbers. In this manner we move a little closer to a decision concerning the applicability of many conjectures regarding interpretations.

As will be seen from the following chapters, the amount of complexity involved in taking our few steps toward the ultimate goal of formalizing many-valued logic is quite considerable, and this might lead the skeptic to question the wisdom of taking such steps, much less any further steps, without considerable assurance of ultimate success in terms of meaning and interpretation. Actually we are willing to take the inevitable risk associated with novel investigations, but in due regard for the skeptic we shall indicate our belief that the gamble has some chance of success. Admittedly, we can not now give conclusive proof of final success, but some favorable evidence can be presented. To this end, consider the following dialogue which might be occasioned by the meeting of certain contemporary logicians who will be referred to as Mr. TURQUER and Mr. ROSSETTE. Mr. Turquer is a spokesman for those twentieth century logicians who believe that two-valued logic embodies the absolute truth, while Mr. Rossette speaks for those who believe that two-valued logic is but a man-made instrument which can be abandoned if the desire or need arises. As might be expected with such representatives, Mr. Turquer defends his case with

---

[3] For example, see Reichenbach, *op. cit.*, and such writings by members of the Destouches group at Paris as J-L. Destouches, *Principes Fondamentaux de Physique Théorique*, Paris, Hermanet Co., 1942.

[4] For further details concerning the attitude here expressed, see B. Rosser, "On the Many-Valued Logics," *American Journal of Physics*, Vol. 9 (1941), pp. 207–212, and H. Margenau, *The Nature of Physical Reality*, New York, McGraw-Hill, 1950.

strong appeals to "truth," "precision," and "accuracy," while Mr. Rossette is an ardent defender of the "rights of men" to use language as they see fit. The entire dialogue, the highlights of which we shall now record, was initiated by only the slightest change in the weather.

MR. ROSSETTE: It is raining.

MR. TURQUER: You mean it is raining in Ithaca, New York, at 2 P.M., July 14, 1950, for you do not know whether or not it is now raining in El Paso, Texas.

MR. ROSSETTE: Would you agree then that my statement is neither true nor false?

MR.TURQUER: No, that is not my opinion, since every statement is either true or false. Hence, our only conclusion is that what you called a "statement" is really not a statement at all. Rather, it is a statement form or matrix implicitly containing free variables of time, place, etc., which must be bound in order to convert the matrix into a statement.

MR. ROSSETTE: But is this not a bit arbitrary? It seems to me that you assume that every statement is either true or false and then distinguish between statements and statement forms in order to escape being refuted. Why not assume that statements are either true or false or neither? Surely this would be just as acceptable as your distinction between statement and statement form.

MR. TURQUER: Your proposal is equally arbitrary, for it amounts to defining some alternative things which you choose to call *statements* and which are either statements or statement forms. You then argue that if *P* is a statement from the class of *statements*, then *P* is true or false according as the statement *P* is true or false, while if *P* is a statement form from the class of *statements*, then *P* is neither true nor false. This most certainly does not deny the fact that statements remain either true or false.

MR. ROSSETTE: I would prefer to say that one can not deny an interesting fact about Mr. Turquer, namely, that he is determined to distinguish between statements and statement forms. If I choose to so decide, I could argue that neither is the fact altered that *statements* are either true or false or neither.

MR. TURQUER: Well, if the situation is as arbitrary as all that, then I shall merely remark that you are voicing the early opinion of Hugh MacColl,[5] and in such arbitrary matters it is well to let history choose between the alternatives. You realize, of course, that history has not decided in favor of Mr. MacColl's views.

MR. ROSSETTE: I do not grant that the decisions of history are always sound. Only a few generations ago, the decision of history was over-

[5] For example, see H. MacColl, "The Calculus of Equivalent Statements," *Proceedings of the London Mathematical Society*, Vol. 28 (1896–97), pp. 156–183.

whelmingly in favor of the divine right of kings and a universe based on Euclidean geometry. Now both doctrines are quite in disfavor. However, for the sake of argument I will grant your distinction between statements and statement forms. Nevertheless, I believe that there are some actual statements which are possibly neither true nor false.

MR. TURQUER:    You know you are being ridiculous. I challenge you to produce such a statement.

MR. ROSSETTE:    Well, suppose that when the janitor arrives we ask him if he is in this room. No doubt, he will reply in the affirmative and with complete assurance, but if the question is repeated as he leaves and while he is passing through the door, then he will certainly be flustered and unable to give an answer.

MR. TURQUER:    Oh, that is no problem, for all we need to do is inform the janitor of the necessity of specifying some boundaries to the room which will define precisely when he is in and out of the room.

MR. ROSSETTE:    But what about *him?* Will it not also be necessary to specify the physical boundaries of the janitor's body?

MR. TURQUER:    Yes indeed, or we might just as well use the center of gravity of the janitor's body, specifying that when this is beyond a certain point, the janitor's body is out of the room. In the last analysis, all such difficulties are easily resolved by indicating the presence of certain free variables which must be bound before statement forms can become statements.

MR. ROSSETTE:    If I accept your solution, then I am forced to the conclusion that the janitor's original assurance about being in the room was completely illusory, for at that time he was as ignorant of the precise meaning of being in and out of the room as he was when we repeated the question at the time he was leaving through the door. Actually, from your point of view, he could only utter statement forms until he became versed in the use of free and bound variables. Thus, it would appear that ordinary discourse must consist entirely of statement forms. If so, it must fail completely ever to convey meaning. But after all, scientific discourse developed from ordinary language.

MR. TURQUER:    I would rather say that scientific discourse divorced itself from the vague expressions and ambiguities of ordinary language. In a nutshell, it learned the importance of distinguishing statements from statement forms and, in general, it learned the necessity of precise definition.

MR. ROSSETTE:    I doubt that the transition from ordinary common sense to scientific knowledge is as sharp as you would have it,[6] but again for the sake of argument, let us suppose that it is and further examine the question of the truth or falsity of all statements.

[6] See M. Born, *Natural Philosophy of Cause and Chance.* Oxford, Oxford University Press, 1949.

Mr. Turquer: By all means let us get on with a scientific discussion. Ordinary discourse is just so much nonsense to me.

Mr. Rossette: That is another interesting fact about you, but to be scientific let us return to the center of gravity of our janitor. We would like to specify the precise center of gravity of the janitor's body in order to be able to define exactly when he is in or out of the room. How should this be done in an acceptable scientific manner?

Mr. Turquer: Perhaps the best method would be to specify the collection of atoms which constitute the janitor's body, and using their positions calculate the exact center of gravity of this body.

Mr. Rossette: But the janitor's body is at a temperature which can be estimated, so we can estimate the thermal velocities of the atoms which compose his body. However, does not the principle of indeterminacy assert that if we have any information whatever of the velocities of atoms, then exact information concerning their positions is impossible? If so, we could not give an exact definition of the center of gravity of our poor janitor's body.

Mr. Turquer: Your point is cogent only if we fail to recognize that the statements of quantum physics are probability statements. It most certainly is possible to be exact about the numerical probability that the center of gravity of the body in question is at a certain point, and the probability will be sufficiently high to give us a location for the center of gravity which is quite accurate enough for practical purposes in the macrocosmic world of our janitor's body.

Mr. Rossette: This still leaves me in the air concerning the exact point at which the macrocosm ends and the microcosm begins, not to mention the fact that one would like an exact definition of "accurate enough for practical purposes," if your position is correct.

Mr. Turquer: Such questions as you ask can be generated without end, but like ordinary expressions, the fact that they can be framed does not guarantee that they make any sense.

Mr. Rossette: That's a neat trick of evasion.

Mr. Turquer: You know very well that it would not be difficult to definite the boundary line between the microcosm and macrocosm if we wished to take the time, and the same goes for "practical accuracy". A certain choice for a precise numerical probability would turn the trick in either case.

Mr. Rossette: I am not so sure, for a numerical statement of probability is merely a statement to the effect that if a certain kind of experiment is repeated more and more times tending toward infinity, then the frequency of a certain type of occurrence approaches a certain limit. Clearly, this is not a testable affair. Hence, we have no convincing evidence that the corresponding statement of an exact numerical probability is either true or false.

Mr. Turquer: Very well then. You have displayed a statement such that neither the laws of physics nor the laws of probability prove that the statement must be either true or false. However, there are still the laws of logic, and they assure us that the statement must indeed be either true or false.

Mr. Rossette:    Do you mean the laws of logic, or the history and tradition of logic?

Mr. Turquer:    I don't get you.

Mr. Rossette:    Let's look, then, at the more general case and put the point like this: I agree that there has developed a tradition, and a glorious one, of two-valued logic. This may have been the result of its simplicity and very considerable scientific success from at least the time of Euclid up to the present day. Your "laws of logic" are just part of this tradition.

Mr. Turquer:    Such a long and glorious history is strong evidence of the truth.

Mr. Rossette:    Am I to conclude, then, that you are a believer in the divine right of kings and in a Euclidean construction of the universe?

Mr. Turquer:    Not at all. We have learned the limitations of both kings and Euclidean geometries but not of two-valued logic.

Mr. Rossette:    But in time we may so learn.

Mr. Turquer:    I do not admit that there are any limitations of two-valued logic to be learned.

Mr. Rossette:    You *are* a stickler for tradition! Don't you believe in bold experiments, and aren't you curious about the results of experimenting with alternative logics?

Mr. Turquer:    I fear that such experiments are only the result of an idle curiosity.

Mr. Rossette:    I can not agree. After all, there are many-valued logics in which two-valued logic can be embedded [7] and surely such many-valued logics would work as well as ordinary two-valued logic.

Mr. Turquer:    You forget that the truth and simplicity go hand in hand. Why use a more complex logic when a simple logic will do as well?

Mr. Rossette:    But I question whether it will do as well. Might not the alternative between the traditional two-valued logic and many-valued logic be analogous to that between the once traditional Euclidean geometry and the now more physically acceptable non-Euclidean geometry?

Mr. Turquer:    Perhaps, but I have little confidence in arguments by analogy.

Mr. Rossette:    There is the further point that highly exact sciences

---

[7] For example, see T. Hoo, "M-valued Sub-system of $(m + m)$-valued propositional calculus," *The Journal of Symbolic Logic*, Vol. 14 (1949), pp. 177–181, and J. Slupecki, "Pełny trójwartościowy rachunik zdań," *Annales Universitatis Mariae Curie-Sklodowska*, Vol. 1 (1946), pp. 193–209.

such as modern physics have long since learned the value of having possible models with a wealth of formal structures and inter-relationships, for these greatly increase the chances of finding useable models. We already feel fairly confident that many-valued logic offers a much greater wealth of structure than the ordinary two-valued logic.

Mr. Turquer:   I will be happier about many-valued logics after the applications are found, and from all the effort which is required just to construct these logics, there would appear to be little hope for finding applications any time soon. Hence, I would prefer to spend my time sharpening well established tools.

Mr. Rossette:   Since we can find no a priori reason against it, I think I would prefer to help those who are interested in performing a bold experiment.

At this point the dialogue was ended by the entrance of the janitor whose center of gravity had proved so elusive, and who now announced that it was time to clean the room which Mr. Rossette and Mr. Turquer had been occupying during their debate. Hence, no proof which was mentioned in the dialogue was ever completed. Yet, we feel that enough evidence was presented to make it unreasonable to attempt to persuade Mr. Rossette not to undertake his bold experiment. On the other hand, we sympathize with the claim of Mr. Turquer that such an experiment is not likely to yield any definite results within the near future, and that our final evaluation of many-valued logics must rest with just those results of the distant future. However, if all men practiced the extreme caution of a Mr. Turquer, no scientific progress would be possible. No doubt it would be equally disastrous to revolt blindly against tradition as some have done, but careful self-conscious experimentation is not of the nature of a blind revolt. . . .

## SUGGESTIONS FOR FURTHER READING
## ON MANY VALUED LOGICS

Anderson, A. R. et al.   "Modal and Many-Valued Logics," *Acta Philosophica Fennica*, Fasc. 16 (1963).

Burch, G. B.   "Seven-valued Logic in Jain Philosophy," *International Philosophical Quarterly*, Vol. 4 (1964), pp. 68–93.

Chang, C. C.   "Algebraic Analysis of Many Valued Logics," *Transactions of the American Mathematical Society*, Vol. 88 (1958), pp. 467–490.

Clay, R. E.   "A Standard Form for Lukasiewicz Many-Valued Logics," *Notre Dame Journal of Formal Logic*, Vol. 4 (1963), pp. 59–66.

Hay, L. S.   "Axiomatization of the Infinite-Valued Predicate Calculus," *The Journal of Symbolic Logic*, Vol. 28 (1963), pp. 77–86.

Lewis, C. I.   "Alternative Systems of Logic," *The Monist*, Vol. 42 (1932), pp. 481–507.

McNAUGHTON, R. "A Theorem about Infinite-Valued Sentential Logic," *The Journal of Symbolic Logic*, Vol. 16 (1951), pp. 1–13.

MOSTOWSKI, A. "Axiomatizability of Some Many Valued Predicate Calculi," *Fundamenta Mathematicae*, Vol. 50 (1961), pp. 165–190.

ROSE, A. "Axiom Systems for Three-Valued Logic," *The Journal of the London Mathematical Society*, Vol. 26 (1951), pp. 50–58.

ZINOV'EV, A. A. *Philosophical Problems of Many-Valued Logic.* Edited and translated by G. Kung and D. D. Comey. Dordrecht, Holland: Reidel Publishing Co., 1963.

# Index

20 302